INJURIES OF NERVES

AND THEIR CONSEQUENCES

by

S. Weir Mitchell, M. D.

With a new Introduction by
Lawrence C. McHenry, Jr.

Dover Publications, Inc., New York

Published in Canada by General Publishing Company, Ltd., 30 Lesmill Road, Don Mills, Toronto, Ontario.
Published in the United Kingdom by Constable and Company, Ltd., 10 Orange Street, London W. C. 2.

This Dover edition, first published in 1965, is an unabridged and unaltered republication of the work first published by J. B. Lippincott & Company in 1872, to which have been added a new Preface by the Publications Advisory Committee of the American Academy of Neurology and a new Introduction by Lawrence C. McHenry, Jr.
This Dover edition is published as Volume II in the American Academy of Neurology Reprint Series.

Library of Congress Catalog Card Number: 65-?4020

Manufactured in the United States of America

Dover Publications, Inc.
180 Varick Street,
New York, N. Y. 10014

PREFACE TO THE DOVER EDITION

THE CLASSICAL period of nineteenth-century neurology was characterized by a succession of thoughtful clinical observers who delineated the distinctive features of major disorders of nervous function, related their observations to anatomic pathology, and attempted to deduce the physiological basis for the derangement of function which attended the morbid states with which they were concerned. Their ability to document the onset and evolution of disease, arrange related phenomena in an orderly sequence and express themselves with lucidity helped establish the clinical method upon which modern neurology is founded. S. Weir Mitchell was outstanding among them for his many clinical studies, but especially those related to peripheral nerve injuries. A regrettable consequence of the bayonet, gunshot and high velocity fragmentation wounds and injuries to bones and joints suffered in modern wars has been the large number of cases of injury to major nerve trunks and the distressing symptoms which follow in their train. The work of Mitchell was among the first to provide a systematic approach to this subject and define carefully the motor and sensory distribution of each peripheral nerve, and the sequence of clinical events which occurred during a recovery period which might extend over many months or years. Mitchell, unlike many of his successors, carefully documented and followed the cases which he had observed in the military hospital in Turner's Lane in Philadelphia and was thus able to issue a sequel to the original report. It is fortunate that *Injuries of Nerves* preserved so much of the vivid account of symptoms described by Mitchell, George R. Morehouse, and William W. Keen in the original report, *Gunshot Wounds and Other Injuries to Nerves*. The potential for recovery of function, the nature

v

of causalgia and the changing character of phantom symptoms
were, however, well-established by 1872. The unique character
of the second volume remains its correlation of clinical observations with what was known of anatomy, pathology and physiology, and its description of the course and evaluation of the
treatment of such injuries. It is for this reason that *Injuries of
Nerves,* rather than the earlier volume by Mitchell, Morehouse
and Keen, was selected for reproduction. His thoughtful reflec-
tion about modification of the character of the phantom limb
by painful paresthesiae, the relation of causalgia to psychic
and to cerebral function, and the effect of weather, general
health and other factors on the character of the phantom have
become even more significant with the advent of modern studies of perception and peripheral nerve function. Mitchell's task
was so well accomplished that little opportunity for fresh description remained to his successors. His recognition of the effects of penetrating nerve injury upon vasomotor function and
the introduction of the concepts of causalgia were revolutionary
in establishing a sound basis for modern approaches to peripheral nerve disorders. Each study of peripheral nerve injuries
incident upon major wars since the American Civil War has
drawn upon Mitchell's account of his own experience. None has
had the impact of Mitchell's. Each subsequent study was
presented from a particular viewpoint, e.g., surgical repair, statistical analysis, refinement of anatomical knowledge, introduction of new diagnostic features or histologic study. None has
drawn quite as had Mitchell upon a broad medical background which was centered upon the injured man himself and
considered his psychology, general health and effect of environment. Mitchell's concern was with his patients who often
needed relief from suffering before returning to productive life.

Mitchell's particular viewpoint was psychological and hu-
manistic and to this degree was a product of the time in which
he lived. It made the individual patient the focal point of
clinical interest rather than particular features which were peculiar to the injured nerve itself. This was in keeping with

Mitchell's interest in the reactions of men to their environment which he fulfilled in his poems and novels. This aspect of Mitchell's work, interest in the individual patient, assumes particular importance in the present era during which so much energy is devoted to the treatment and medical rehabilitation of patients suffering chronic neurological disorders.

The policy of the Publications Advisory Committee of the American Academy of Neurology has been to select works for reproduction which provide a model of the neurological method, establish by observations those features which distinguish clinical disorders from one another, and continue to provide inspiration and guidance for the modern neurologist. Because Mitchell so well fulfilled these criteria, the Publications Advisory Committee is pleased to recommend this volume to the American Academy of Neurology.

THE PUBLICATIONS ADVISORY COMMITTEE
OF THE AMERICAN ACADEMY OF NEUROLOGY

H. William Gillen, M.D., Chairman
Howard D. Fabing, M.D.
Simon Horenstein, M.D.
Lawrence C. McHenry, Jr., M.D.
Richard P. Schmidt, M.D.
Edwin D. Clarke, M.D., *ex-officio*

INTRODUCTION TO THE DOVER EDITION

S. WEIR MITCHELL, physiologist, neurologist, and novelist has been considered by some to be the most versatile American since Benjamin Franklin. An extraordinary man of incredible energy, he contributed significantly to both medicine and literature. Mitchell's *Injuries of Nerves* (1872), its predecessor, *Gunshot Wounds and Other Injuries of Nerves* (1864), and the follow-up volume, *Remote Consequences of Injuries to Nerves* (1895) by his son, John Kearsley Mitchell, combine to form one of the most remarkable scientific studies of nineteenth-century medicine and neurology. The definitive study, *Injuries of Nerves,* which not only describes his wartime experience, but also surveys the contemporary literature, is a classic in American neurology, and is being reprinted for this reason. That Mitchell himself may be considered the father of American neurology is reflected by his unanimous election in 1874 as the first president of the American Neurological Association. Mitchell indeed held a unique place in American neurology as the predecessor of James Jackson Putman, William G. Spiller, Charles K. Mills, Charles L. Dana, Wharton Sinkler, M. Allen Starr, Bernard Sachs and others who were the founders of neurology in this country. The various biographical sketches of Mitchell* do not give a full picture of his neurological contributions which will be included here along with the background of his experience with injuries of nerves.

*Charles K. Mills, "Silas Weir Mitchell, M.D., LL.D., His Place in Neurology," *J. Nerv. Ment. Dis.*, 41:65-74, 1914.
Anna Robeson Burr, *Weir Mitchell, His Life and Letters,* New York, Duffield & Co., 1929.
Ernest Earnest, *S. Weir Mitchell, Novelist and Physician,* Philadelphia, University of Pennsylvania Press, 1950.

Silas Weir Mitchell was born into a refined Philadelphia family on February 15, 1829. His father, Dr. John Kearsley Mitchell (1793-1858), a busy practitioner and medical writer, taught at Jefferson Medical College. Weir Mitchell became the seventh physician in three generations and himself lived eighty-four years, until the eve of World War I. After a desultory preparatory education, he attended the University of Pennsylvania for three years, leaving a year before graduation because of his father's illness. In 1848, he entered Jefferson Medical College, and following graduation in 1850, spent a year in Europe. He attended Claude Bernard's lectures in Paris, where he possibly received his first stimulus to study the nervous system, for it was at this time that Bernard was performing the experiments which culminated in his classic *Leçons sur la Physiologie et la Pathologie du Système Nerveux* (1858). Mitchell also attended the lectures in microscopy by Charles Phillippe Robin, who gave the earliest complete description of the perivascular spaces in the nervous system.

Upon his return to Philadelphia, Mitchell was unable to obtain an internship at the Pennsylvania Hospital, and served instead as a charity physician at the Southwark Dispensary. Mitchell then entered medical practice, and also began a series of experiments that were to establish his reputation as an experimental physiologist. His first reports were on uric acid and hemoglobin crystals. Most noteworthy of his earlier investigations were those on snake venom which were an extension of the work of Felice Fontana (1767). The experiments on viper poison with William A. Hammond* were the first cooperative

*It was appropriate that Mitchell dedicated this work to William Alexander Hammond (1828-1900), one of the outstanding, but little recognized, leaders in the early part of the Civil War. In 1863, Hammond at the age of 34 was appointed Surgeon General of the Army. He drastically reorganized the Army medical service to meet the tremendous demands of the war, by revamping medical supply and transportation systems, constructing hospitals, ordering the keeping of records of illnesses and wounds, etc. Hammond remained Surgeon General for nearly two years when he was caught in the wartime political web of intrigue and court-martialed. Fourteen years later Congress vindicated Hammond

efforts between these two remarkable men. Between 1852 and 1863, Mitchell published twenty-two papers, mostly on physiology, pharmacology and toxicology. The most important of these early publications dealt with comparative anatomy and physiology of respiration and circulation, and on arrow and ordeal poisons (curare and erythrophleine) and snake venom. After 1863, he published at least ten physiological and about twenty-five pharmacological papers, which included his work on plant alkaloids (quinine, morphine, atropine and mescaline). Howell has written that before the establishment of laboratories by Henry P. Bowditch and Newell Martin in the seventies, "probably the most significant name from the standpoint of physiological investigation is that of S. Weir Mitchell."†

Mitchell's contributions to neurology have been divided by Mills into four areas: (1) clinical and pathological wartime observations of injuries and diseases of the peripheral nerves; (2) the description of new clinical entities and a thorough study of symptoms and clinical combinations recognized, but not fully appreciated and expounded by others; (3) physiological investigations of the cerebellum; and (4) the therapeutics of nervous diseases, particularly his organization of the rest treatment and his addition to the knowledge and use of drugs and special methods of local treatment.

The Civil War began in 1861, but Mitchell did not enlist in the Army until October, 1862, because his father's death made it necessary for him to support his family. Mitchell enlisted as a "contract surgeon" and was appointed Acting Assistant Sur-

and placed him on the retired list as Surgeon General with the rank of Brigadier General. Following dismissal from the Army, Hammond became one of the leading neurologists in the country. In 1871, he published *A Treatise on Diseases of the Nervous System*. This work, containing his classic description of athetosis, was the first American neurology textbook and passed through nine editions. Hammond, like Mitchell, also became a novelist of some merit.

†William H. Welch, "S. Weir Mitchell, Physician and Man of Science," In: *S. Weir Mitchell, M.D., LL.D., F.R.S., 1829-1914—Memorial Addresses and Resolutions,* Philadelphia, 1914.

geon. He was assigned to one of the first wartime hospitals established in Philadelphia. The only account of this hospital in the old armory building at 16th and Filbert Streets is in Mitchell's novel *In War Time*. During his early service at Filbert Street Hospital Mitchell became interested in neurological disorders.

> I began here to take interest in cases of nervous diseases, which, at that time, nobody desired to keep for the reason that they were so little understood and so unsatisfactory in their results. I was, therefore, allowed to accept these cases from other wards, transferring in return ordinary types of disease. When this became known to the surgeon-general he was at once interested and set aside a larger ward for neural maladies. When this overflowed with cases we took over the building known as Moyamensing Hall, on Christian Street.*

On May 5, 1863, General Hammond ordered the establishment of the United States Army Hospital for Diseases of the Nervous System on Christian Street. Following the battle of Gettysburg in July where there were 27,000 wounded, the 275-bed hospital on Christian Street outgrew its facilities, but continued to function until October 29, 1864. In August, 1863, another hospital was established on the grounds of an old estate on Turner's Lane. It was at this 400-bed hospital that Mitchell and his colleagues were to perform their pioneer studies of nerve injuries. Mitchell, along with George R. Morehouse, was placed in charge of the hospital, and subsequently a resident surgeon, William W. Keen, was added. The amount of clinical material that accumulated was phenomenal. There were as many as eighty epileptics at one time in the Turner's Lane Hospital, and all kinds of nerve wounds, palsies, choreas and stump disorders were represented there. After each battle cases would flow into the crowded wards, and finally a separate

---

*S. Weir Mitchell, "Some Personal Recollections of the Civil War," *Transactions of the College of Physicians,* Philadelphia, 27:87-94, 1905.

ward was set aside for "wounds and other injuries of nerves."
In the introduction to his *Gunshot Wounds*,* Mitchell wrote:

> No sooner did this class of patients begin to fill our wards,
> than we perceived that a new and interesting field of observa-
> tion was here opened to view. Before long, so many of these
> cases were collected that, for a time, they were the majority
> of our patients. Among them were representatives of every
> conceivable form of nerve injury, from shot and shell, from
> sabre cuts, contusions, and dislocations. So complete was the
> field of study, that it was not uncommon to find at one time
> in the wards four or five cases of gunshot injuries of any
> single large nerve. It thus happened that phenomena which
> one day seemed rare and curious, were seen anew in other
> cases the next day, and grew commonplace as our patients
> became numerous.

Mitchell, Morehouse and Keen realized the opportunity for
clinical investigation was "indeed unique," and "thousands of
pages of notes were taken." Often they "worked on note-taking
as late as 12 or 1 at night, and when we got through, walked
home, talking over our cases." Mitchell's original notes from
at least eighty of these cases are in the Library of the College
of Physicians of Philadelphia. Written in Mitchell's clear ex-
pository style, a single case may take up five to nine pages of
foolscap. For each case there was specific information, including name, place of birth, general health, circumstances and
geographic place of wounding, description of the wound, length
of time before treatment and the nature of treatment and the
extent of recovery of sensation and motion. In addition to those
on nerve injuries, extensive notes were taken on cases of
epilepsy, which were to be written up by Morehouse. Morehouse, however, delayed writing these up and they were destroyed when his library burned. Fifty years later Mitchell
related that, "to this day I cannot think of it without regret,"

---

*S. Weir Mitchell, George R. Morehouse and William W. Keen, Jr.,
Gunshot Wounds and Other Injuries to Nerves, Philadelphia, J.B. Lippincott, 1864.

for in the lost notes were records of types of cases of epilepsy that Mitchell never saw again.

As a consequence of their first fifteen months experience with nerve injuries, Mitchell and his colleagues published two works, *Gunshot Wounds and Other Injuries of Nerves* (1864), and *Reflex Paralysis*.* The latter was published on March 10, 1864, as Circular No. 6 from the Surgeon General's Office. In this article the authors describe cases of paralysis resulting from wounds in remote regions of the body. They describe and differentiate what is now termed primary and secondary shock. The syndrome of secondary or traumatic shock is clearly recognized and was later referred to by Walter Cannon in his *Traumatic Shock* (1923). They also describe the phenomenon of collapse from being in the proximity of an explosion without any sign of external injury. In this pamphlet "Mitchell clearly recognized the presence of motor centers in the forebrain and that they controlled musculature on the opposite side of the body."† Fulton considers this work, along with *Gunshot Wounds*, as one of the great milestones of American neurology and clinical medicine.

In Mitchell, Morehouse and Keen's *Gunshot Wounds*, forty-three cases of wounds of large nerves are described in vivid clinical histories taken verbatim from the initial notes. Although this work does not, like its successors, emphasize anatomical distribution of nerves, it is of greater historical value than the enlarged *Injuries of Nerves*, for as Mitchell himself points out, "never before in medical history has there been collected for study and treatment so remarkable a series of nerve injuries." In the previous works on military medicine wounds of the nerves were related "rather as curiosities and as

*S. Weir Mitchell, Geo. R. Morehouse, and W.W. Keen, Jr., *Reflex Paralysis*, Circular No. 6, Surgeon General's Office, March 10, 1864. This was reprinted with an introductory note by John F. Fulton in 1941, Historical Library, Yale University School of Medicine.
†*Ibid.*

matters for despair, than with any view to their full clinical study and systematic treatment."

Injuries of Nerves, published eight years later, was an elaboration and expansion of the general subject that included a survey of the current knowledge of anatomy and physiology of the peripheral nerve. In the earlier work and this revision, Mitchell describes causalgia, ascending neuritis, the effects of various types of pressure on nerves, trophic changes from nerve injury, recurrent sensibility and referred sensation and the psychological effects of amputation, as well as other clinical and physiological phenomena. Of particular importance was the development of the treatment of nerve injuries by splinting, the use of electricity, massage, cold, drugs and other means. Of this work Welch wrote:

> The study and description of peripheral nerve phenomena, especially those resulting from injury, constitute the largest, most original, distinctive, and important contribution of Weir Mitchell to neurology, and in this narrower field his work is comparable to that of Duchenne and of Charcot upon diseases of the spinal cord.

Mitchell's work became a standard text in the last quarter of the nineteenth century. It was translated into French by A. F. Dastre in 1874, with a preface by E.F.A. Vulpian, and was used as a textbook by the French during World War I.*

Twenty-three years after Mitchell had published *Injuries of Nerves,* his son, John Kearsley Mitchell, added a follow-up, *Remote Consequences of Injuries of Nerves* (1895).†

> The present little volume is the result of a desire to examine into the very late consequences of such wounds and injuries . . . It happened sometimes in the course of service at

---

*S. Weir Mitchell, *Des Lésions des Nerfs et de Leurs Conséquences,* Traduit et annoté avec l'autorisation de l'auteur par Dastre et précédé d'une préface par Vulpian, Paris, Masson, 1874.

†John K. Mitchell, *Remote Consequences of Injuries of Nerves and Their Treatment,* Philadelphia, Lea Brothers & Co., 1895.

the Orthopedic Hospital and Infirmary for Nervous Diseases
that men who had been in the charge of Drs. Mitchell, Morehouse, and Keen during the Civil War applied for treatment
of conditions resulting from their former wounds, and this
suggested the study of as many as could be reached of the old
cases.

J. K. Mitchell found twenty of the original cases that were
wounded in 1863-1864, and examined them over a period of
two years beginning in the spring of 1890. He had thus made
a twenty-seven to twenty-eight year follow-up of the original
cases of nerve injuries. This work and those of his father that
preceded it combine to make one of the most extensive and
unique investigations of this type in the history of medicine.

Although other works on nerve injuries appeared in the late
nineteenth century, such as those by Beaugrand (1864), Brown-
Séquard (1870), Clarke (1870), Larue (1871) and Bowlby
(1890), they were not comparable to Mitchell's monographs of
1864 and 1872, and his son's sequel of 1895; indeed, no comparable study of nerve injuries appeared until 1905, when
Henry Head and James Sherren published "The Consequence
of Injury to the Peripheral Nerves in Man," in *Brain*. This
extensive and detailed study was based on accident cases from
the London hospitals, injuries from the South African War and
Horsley's patients in whom he had divided the posterior roots.
In this work Head gives credit to Mitchell and his colleagues
for their definitive elucidation of the phenomena of causalgia,
"To Weir Mitchell, Morehouse and Keen is due the credit for
a complete description of a series of cases illustrating this condition."

Mitchell's work, a product of the Civil War, has often been
compared to other works on nerve injuries which followed
World War I. After World War I, several monographs on nerve
injuries appeared, including works by Spielmeyer (1915), Tinel
(1916), Athanassio-Benistry (1916), Oppenheim (1917), Pur-
ves-Stewart and Evans (1919) and Foerster (1929). In the
work of Tinel, probably the most valuable of these contribu-

tions, there are several direct quotations from Weir Mitchell's *Gunshot Wounds.* Tinel* writes:

> In 1864, after the War of Secession, S. Weir Mitchell described under the name of causalgia a particular neuralgic syndrome, characterized by its intensity, its long duration, its special pains and its habitual resistance to every therapeutic measure.

This short paragraph of Tinel's summarizes Mitchell's greatest single contribution to neurology. Although causalgia symptoms had been described by Paget (1864), Mitchell's more complete report has withstood the test of time and is still referred to in contemporary neurological texts.

Following World War II again there appeared several further studies of nerve injuries, probably the most notable being the United States Veterans Administration follow-up study of 3,656 cases of peripheral nerve injuries.† In this report and the many others following both World Wars there have been remarkable advances in knowledge of peripheral nerve anatomy, physiology and pathology, but the style of these works is rather routine, mundane and technical. The contributions of both Mitchells and their colleagues, however, were pioneer investigations that convey the excitement of the Civil War along with the self-assured formality of the nineteenth century, while at the same time maintaining a certain scientific status that gives them a worthy niche in the history of medicine.

To clinical neurology itself, Mitchell made a variety of original and significant contributions that were published in over one hundred papers, books and reports. He gave the first description of erythomelalgia (1872), which subsequently became known as "Weir Mitchell's disease." Although Erb and

---

*J. Tinel, *Nerve Wounds, Symptomatclogy of Peripheral Nerve Lesions Caused by War Wounds,* trans. by R. Rothwell, revised and edited by C.A. Joll, London, Tindall and Cox, 1918.
†B. Woodall and G. W. Beebe, *Peripheral Nerve Regeneration; a Follow-up Study of 3,656 World War II Injuries,* Washington, D.C., U.S. Government Printing Office, 1957.

Westphal independently described the deep-tendon reflexes in 1875, Mitchell (1886, 1888) was one of the first to utilize the tendon reflexes as a general part of the clinical examination. With Morris J. Lewis, he demonstrated that the knee jerk can be reinforced by sensory stimuli (1886). Papers on the cremasteric reflex (1879) and on ankle clonus (1902) were also published. In 1874, he reported eight cases of a variety of posthemiplegic movements which he termed "hemichorea" or postparalytic chorea. Mitchell contributed other papers on a variety of neurological subjects, including epilepsy (1912), facial tic (1887), eyestrain as a cause of headache (1876) and visual scotoma with headache (1887). In 1889, he reported a case of bitemporal hemianopsia from an aneurysm of an anomalous artery that caused posterior displacement of the optic chiasm. This also included a review of the literature on anomalies of the circle of Willis. In 1873, Mitchell reported on the use of the ophthalmoscope in the diagnosis of intracranial disease. In addition to these scientific papers, Mitchell often presented in the case-report sections of the *Medical and Surgical Journal* and other medical journals a wide variety of clinical neurological patients that were seen in his clinic at the Philadelphia Orthopedic Hospital and Infirmary for Nervous Diseases.

In his studies of nerve injuries, Mitchell was the first to clearly elucidate the effects of meteorological changes on traumatic neuralgias, especially old amputation stumps (1877). In 1874, he outlined the overlapping of cutaneous innervation a generation before the definitive work of Head, Foerster, Sherrington and others. Mitchell froze his own ulnar nerve and described the anesthesia distribution, an experiment similar to one Head would repeat with his own radial nerve. Mitchell's wartime investigations on causalgia, head and nerve injuries, primary and secondary shock, hysteria and malingering have all been notable contributions to clinical neurology and psychiatry. Many of his contributions were summarized in his *Clinical Lessons on Nervous Diseases* (1897), which also included chapters on post-hemiplegic pain and disorders of sleep. These lectures enjoyed wide popularity and filled the need that today is met by postgraduate refresher courses.

When Mitchell carried out his experiments on the cerebellum, it was generally held, based on Rolando's studies, that the cerebellum augments and reinforces movements initiated by the cerebrum. Mitchell was familiar with other early work on the cerebellum by Flourens, Magendie, Brown-Séquard and others. His experiments, carried out over a period of six years from 1863 to 1869, were performed on pigeons, rabbits and guinea pigs. They consisted of partial or complete ablations, freezing or the injection of mercury globules into various parts of the cerebellum. Mitchell summarized his findings in the *American Journal of the Medical Sciences* in 1869. His views anticipated to a certain degree the classical studies of Luigi Luciani of the effects of irritation of the cerebellum. Mitchell clearly recognized the phonomenon of compensation by other parts of the nervous system for the losses caused by lesions elsewhere in the body.

Besides his studies on hysteria and malingering, Mitchell introduced to psychiatry the "rest cure" as a treatment of functional disorders by prolonged rest in bed. The "Weir Mitchell treatment" also included sedation, isolation, physical therapy and optimal feeding. The indications for and applications of the rest cure were summarized in two monographs, *Wear and Tear* (1873) and *Fat and Blood* (1877). The latter passed through eight editions and was translated into German, French, Russian, Spanish and Italian. Mitchell also published a monograph of *Lectures on the Diseases of the Nervous System, Especially in Women* (1881). Concerning this work and his *Fat and Blood* there is a letter* extant from Sir William Gowers to Mitchell's son:

*Reproduced, with permission, from the original in the library of the College of Physicians of Philadelphia.

Apr 30

Dear Dr. John Mitchell,

You will be prepared before this for the absence of promptness in my replies to write an acknowledgement of books and realise that this involves no imperfection in my estimation of their value.

This indeed, "goes without saying," of necessity and obviousness in the case of such a book as "Fat & Blood," to which, we are all more indebted than we know, and *that* is much.

I put before this, in personal regard, the little book on Diseases of Women which appeared almost at the same time. I doubt whether a letter to your father was posted in which, a few years ago, I mentioned to him the remarkable service the *style* of this book was to me, in serving me as a model which to frame my own style of medical description, as far as concerns its use for clinical lectures.

Sincerely yours,
W.R. Gowers.

It appears from this letter that Mitchell's *Lectures* served as a guide for Gowers in the preparation of his various *Lectures* on diseases of the nervous system that were published in 1885, 1904 and 1907.

Mitchell's scientific achievements were largely accomplished in the first half of his life; the second period was devoted to his literary career. At twenty he had sent to a Boston publisher a volume of verse that was seen by Oliver Wendell Holmes, who suggested that the author make his medical calling before launching into general literature. So he did, and at fifty published the first of his nineteen novels, *Hephzibah Guinness* (1880). In addition, he wrote seven books of poetry, a scholarly and controversial biography of Washington, a children's story, *Kris Kringle,* and translated a fourteenth-century poem into modern verse. His poem *Ode on a Lycian Tomb* was compared to Keats' *Ode on a Grecian Urn,* and contains this noteworthy fourth stanza:

> Thou who has wept for many, weep for me,
> For surely I, who deepest grief have known,
> Share thy stilled sadness, which must ever be
> Too changeless, and unending like my own,
> Since thine is woe that knows not time's release,
> And sorrow that can never compass peace.

His novels were largely historical studies of the neurotic personality of the nineteenth century, including elements of autobiography and stereotyped romances. The historical aspects of his novels, however, are centered to a great extent, like his scientific work, on his personal experiences during the Civil War. *In War Time* (1884) opens with the arrival of the ambulances with the wounded from the field at Gettysburg, which Mitchell had personally visited the third day of the battle. His last novel, *Westways* (1913), written thirty years later, painted the grim horror of this battle. *Roland Blake* (1886) deals with Grant's Wilderness Campaign, and *Constance Trescot* (1905) with Reconstruction in the South. His most famous novel, *Hugh Wynne, Free Quaker* (1896), is meticulous in historical detail of the Revolutionary War, and sold over 500,000 copies. Concerning this work, George Meredith wrote to Mitchell, "I am assured that whatever you put your hand to write will have the stamp of noble on it." This appealed to Mitchell's great vanity, for some of his contemporaries believed him to be a genius, and he himself had come to share their belief. Garrison wrote that in the world of letters, as poet and novelist, Mitchell has a place near Goldsmith and Holmes, and not far below Scott and Lamb.

To the history of medicine Mitchell contributed several memorials on William Harvey, including two unpublished letters, a dissertation, *The History of Instrumental Precision in Medicine* (1892), and a report, *Historical Notes of Benjamin Rush* (1903). He also donated several items and numerous books to the Historical Collections of the College of Physicians of Philadelphia.

Mitchell's friends included many of the great men of the

period, but one of his outstanding colleagues was William Osler. In 1884, Osler came to Philadelphia as Professor of Clinical Medicine at the University of Pennsylvania. Osler said that Mitchell was partially responsible for his coming to Philadelphia. Mitchell had been commissioned by the trustees of the University to "look over" Osler as a possible successor to William Pepper. In London, Mitchell arranged to meet Osler for the first time at dinner at the Limmer Hotel on Conduit Street, and had been so impressed that the next morning he cabled the trustees, "All right! Elect Osler."

Osler, Mitchell and his son, J. K. Mitchell, served as physicians at the Philadelphia Orthopedic Hospital and Infirmary for Nervous Diseases. It was here that Osler gathered his material for a series of lectures which were published in 1889 as *The Cerebral Palsies of Children.* Osler dedicated this work to Mitchell "in recognition of his work in scientific medicine and in grateful acknowledgement of innumerable acts of friendly service." In his other neurological monograph, *On Chorea and Choreiform Affections* (1894), Osler mentions Mitchell and his contributions.

In his obituary of Mitchell, Osler said we have to go to other centuries to find a parallel in his career, "not, it is true, in his professional work, for others have done more, but in the combination of a life devoted to the best interests of science with literary and social distinction." Mitchell reminded Osler of Richard Mead, "who filled so large a place in public and professional life of the early part of the eighteenth century." Of Mitchell, Osler continues, Samuel Johnson's remark of Mead is equally true, "No man ever lived more in the sunshine of life." Osler believed, too, a much closer parallel might be with the great seventeenth-century naturalist, Francesco Redi, in the triple combination of devotion to scientific study and to *belles lettres* and in the position which he enjoyed in public esteem.

May, 1965
Philadelphia, Pa.   Lawrence C. McHenry, Jr., M.D.

INJURIES OF NERVES

AND THEIR CONSEQUENCES

TO

WM. A. HAMMOND, M.D.,

PROFESSOR OF DISEASES OF THE MIND AND NERVOUS SYSTEM

AND OF

CLINICAL MEDICINE

IN THE

BELLEVUE HOSPITAL MEDICAL COLLEGE, NEW YORK;

Whose liberal views created the special hospital which furnished the chief
experience of this volume; with admiration of his high qualities
as physician and scholar, and with grateful memories of
a long and constant friendship, I dedicate the
following pages.

"I hold every man a debtor to his profession; from the which as men of course do seek to receive countenance and profit, so ought they of duty to endeavor themselves, by way of amends, to be a help and ornament thereunto."—FRANCIS BACON.

PREFACE.

In the following pages I have endeavored to present in as concise a form as possible the history of lesions of nerve trunks and their consequences. While I have not hesitated to use the observations of others, the work is chiefly based upon my own experience.

I am largely indebted for assistance to Drs. George Morehouse and W. W. Keen, my former colleagues at the U. S. A. Hospital for Injuries and Diseases of the Nervous System, and I am also under many obligations to Dr. Tyson.

S. WEIR MITCHELL.

1332 Walnut Street, Philadelphia,
February, 1872.

CONTENTS.

CHAPTER I.

ENGLISH medical literature contains no complete treatise on injuries of nerves and the diseases consequent upon them. In fact, few persons have at any time in medical history been so situated as to command the peculiar opportunity which has fallen to the lot of the writer of these pages, and which alone he feels may justify him in adding another to the numerous monographs which to-day claim the attention of the profession.

In May, 1863, Dr. Wm. A. Hammond, then Surgeon-General of the U. S. Army, requested me to share with Dr. George Morehouse the medical charge of an army hospital for nervous diseases, the foundation of which I had suggested to the medical bureau, over which at that time Dr. Hammond presided with such ability as has caused his name to be inseparably associated with the medical and surgical history of the late civil war.*

---

* When this hospital was organized, I urged upon the Surgeon-General the necessity of freeing its medical staff from the usual administrative duties which take up so much of the time of our military hospital surgeons. Arrangements were therefore made which permitted us to devote to our cases all available time, and left the government of the house in charge of a competent surgeon-in-chief. I may be permitted to add, that when Dr. Hammond left office he had established special wards or hospitals for diseases of the eye, for syphilis, for stumps, for

This hospital promised very early to surpass in usefulness the fondest expectations of its founder and of the
staff, to which, at my request, Dr. W. W. Keen was added,
as resident surgeon.

It was finally enlarged to 400 beds, and removed
from Christian Street, Philadelphia, to Turner's Lane,
in the suburbs of the city, where, for the first time, its
capacity enabled us to classify in distinct wards the
numerous cases which fell under our care. Never has
such an opportunity for the study of nerve lesions and
their results presented itself. A multitude of cases, re-
presenting almost every conceivable type of obscure
nervous disease, was sent to us from this department
and that of Washington, by surgeons who felt conscious that these forms of disease were rarely amenable
to treatment in wards crowded with grave wounds,
constantly demanding all the time and care of over-
worked attendants. The medical inspectors, and especially Dr. John Le Conte, were active in selecting and
forwarding such instances of disease as seemed to them
suited to our service; so that we received and treated
during two years an enormous number of cases of diseases and injuries of the nervous system.

Among these was a vast collection of wounds and
contusions of nerves, including all the rarest forms of
nerve lesion of almost every great nerve in the human
body. Nor was this mass of material neglected in any
point of view. New modes of treatment were devised,
and gymnastic classes instituted, under the care of intelligent sergeants of the invalid corps; electricity was
constantly employed, and hypodermic medication — at

---

diseases of the heart and lungs, and was maturing a plan for the further
extension of this system, with such arrangements as must have resulted
in vast advantages to scientific medicine and surgery.

that time somewhat novel—was habitually resorted to, and its effects carefully studied.

The Surgeon-General and the hospital staff equally felt that besides the benefit to the sick soldiers, in thus aggregating cases alike in character, and therefore fitted to produce the special experience so useful in their treatment, this opportunity of study entailed upon us certain obligations to the profession. The responsibility which was involved in the possession of such rare experience we endeavored conscientiously to meet. Careful notes were taken by the surgeon or the resident of every case, and were methodically continued until the time at which the patient left us; while in many instances the utmost care has been taken to collect, in the interval which has elapsed since the war, such details of later history as were needed to clear up or complete the story of symptoms or prognosis.

The experience thus acquired during the war led to the publication of a number of communications on various subjects. One of these was a small volume on gunshot wounds and injuries of nerves,* which has been long out of print. I supplemented it, a year ago, by a paper on "The Diseases of Nerves resulting from Injury," which was published in the medical volume of the Reports of the U. S. Sanitary Commission; but as this volume is bulky and costly, and as neither it nor the monograph before mentioned at all cover the ground which I propose to occupy in the following pages, I still feel that there is room for my present work.

The study of the natural history of any class of diseases so constantly relates itself to the healthy workings of the

* Gunshot Wounds and other Injuries of Nerves, by S. Weir Mitchell, M.D., Geo. R. Morehouse, M.D., and Wm. W. Keen, M.D. J. B. Lippincott, & Co., Philadelphia, 1864, pp. 164.

organs involved, that I need scarcely apologize for following many good examples in the introduction of preliminary chapters upon the anatomy and physiology of nerve trunks. Since, however, these are subjects more or less familiar to all physicians, I have omitted much that is to be found in the physiology of nerves which has no near relation to the practical wants of my subject.

CHAPTER II.

Structure of nerves.—The nervous system consists essentially of receptive or controlling ganglionic centres, and of the nerves which connect these with one another and with the skin, muscles, and viscera. Nerves are usually divided into those known as cerebro-spinal and those belonging to the great sympathetic system. The former chiefly concern us at present, since, indeed, the latter are rarely injured, and since their diseases have only of late begun to claim attention. The former, often known as nerves of animal life, are such as emerge from the encephalon or from the spinal axis, and carry to every part of the body excitations originating in the great centres, or in turn bring to these the numberless impressions arising from without, or having birth within the tissues themselves. Yet, varied as seems to be the character of the messages with which they are charged, an astonishing sameness of structure marks the organization of all these fibres.

The encephalic nerves have certain peculiarities of origin and of exit which we may have further occasion to mention in connection with the forms of injury to which these trunks are liable.

The spinal nerves arise from either side of the medulla by two roots, distinguished as anterior and posterior, each having a number of rootlets. Those which form the posterior root pass through a small ganglionic enlargement; those of the anterior stem unite without passing into a ganglion; and both sets of fibres on coming together constitute one spinal nerve. The anterior root is motor in function; the posterior, sensory: the former carries messages from, and the latter to, the nerve centres. Thus constituted, the compound nerve passes outward until its fibres, separating anew into their physiological constituents, enter the muscles on the one part, or are distributed to the surfaces upon the other.

The nerve so made up has, at an early part of its course, certain relations to the chain of sympathetic ganglia, with which there is probably a mutual interchange of filaments. Besides the various fibres devoted to forms of sensation and to motion, whether vasal or muscular, each nerve is by some authors supposed to possess nutritive or trophic filaments, which may be derived either from the spinal centres or from the sympathetic system,—a point as yet undetermined.

The trunk of each of the spinal nerves is surrounded by a neurilemma, or general sheath, which has the same relation to the nerves as the myolemma has to the muscles. It has been best described by Robin, in 1854, and still further by Sappey,* in 1868. This sheath surrounds the nerve at its escape from the cord, sends out prolongations which pass in between the separate bundles and fibres, and dividing and subdividing, as the branches become smaller, follows them through their multiplied divisions until it envelops with a delicate membrane the primitive fibres themselves, and is lost to view just before these end in the muscles or the sensitive surfaces. The portion which covers the ultimate tubules has certain peculiarities of structure to which I shall presently refer. The sheath of the main nerve trunk, and of its lesser divisions, is composed of fibrous tissue, the strands of

---

* Journ. de l'Anat. et de Phys., 1868, t. v. p. 48.

which, running in every direction, and crossing each other
at all imaginable angles, leave between them minute
areolæ of irregular form. Within, upon, and about the
fibrous sheath, a considerable amount of fine adipose tissue exists in the primary, and even in the secondary, divisions of the nerve. It is met with in the most emaciated,
and follows chiefly the track of the neural blood-vessels,
or is found collected here and there in small masses.

Contrary to the common opinion, Sappey has found that
the vascularity of the nerve sheaths is greater than that of
ligaments, tendons, or aponeuroses, and approaches in this
respect the spinal or cerebral pia mater.

The arteries are exceedingly numerous, and lie chiefly
between the walls of the fibrous partitions in the spaces
formed by their juxtaposition. The veins, sometimes
single, at others double, form, like the arteries, an intricate plexus, but neither are met with in the sheath of the
ultimate nerve fibre.

The nerve sheaths also possess nerves which follow the
path of the vessels, and are less and less numerous as the
nerve branches, until, on the smaller divisions, they are
said to be absent. Sappey has described them as nervi
nervorum, a phrase to which there is no objection, unless
we attribute to the words too large a physiological significance, since, in reality, these fibres are rather nerves of
the sheath than of the nerves themselves. They in all
respects resemble other neural fibres, except that they are
unusually minute. Each nerve, as we follow it with the
naked eye, surrounded and protected by its neurilemma
of connective tissue, is capable of being further resolved
by the microscope into rodlets or fasciculi, known as the
primitive fibres or tubules. Around each collection of
these is the delicate sheath which Robin has admirably
described as the perineurium. The structure of this covering is very simple. It is composed of an almost homo-

geneous, yet at places longitudinally striated, substance, dotted more or less with nuclei and with minute gray molecular granules.

When the primitive bundles of nerve fibres exchange filaments with others, as in a plexus, their peculiar sheaths accompany them until the single nerve tubules approach a free termination, when the sheath ceases to be visible. Should the tube end, however, in a corpuscle of Pacini, the sheath is continuous with that which covers these bodies. Neither nerves nor vessels have, in man at least, been traced into these ultimate sheaths.

Within this covering pass the ultimate nerve tubules, the structure of which has been the subject of numerous investigations. According to the latest authoritative observers, the nerve tubule consists of four distinct parts:

1st. The sheath of Schwann, or tubular membrane.

2d. The medullary matter, or white substance of Schwann.

3d. The axis cylinder.

4th. The elements of the axis cylinder, which may be one or many fibrils.

This complex structure only becomes visible in consequence of post-mortem changes or the action of reagents, so that the fresh nerve fibre looks like a pellucid rod. The sheath of Schwann is described as a thin, delicate membrane, only perceptible when torn or treated by reagents, or when excessive atrophy has removed its contents. Within this envelope is found the medullary matter, which is transparent, semi-fluid, and of a high refracting power, which gives to it the appearance of possessing a double contour or outline. In chemical composition it is undoubtedly fatty. It is this substance which gives to the nerves a white hue, and the absence of which causes them to look translucent or gray. It is wanting in certain nerves.

The cylinder axis is a flexible rod of azotized matter which fills the tube formed by the white medullary tissue around it. When the nerve is torn, the axis cylinder can sometimes be seen projecting, button-like, from the torn end of the tubular membrane and medullary substance. Numerous conjectures have been formed as to the ultimate structure of this portion of the nerve tubule; some having described it as composed of minute longitudinal fibres, while others regard it as made up of laminæ placed one upon another. Every physiological reason would teach us, however, to accept with Schultze, in Stricker's "Hand-buch," the belief that the ultimate anatomical neural element is what he terms the primitive fibril,—of which a number, great or small, is needed to make an axis cylin-der,—so that the primitive fibril is the essential nerve element around which, or around groups of which, may be the medullary sheath and the sheath of Schwann,—although of the modifications in physiological function which these impress upon it we know absolutely nothing.

Fromman, and more recently Grandry,* by exposing the nerves to a peculiar treatment with nitrate of silver, reached the conclusion that the cylinder axis is composed of disks superimposed and isolated by a substance differ-ing from them in composition. I have verified these observations on the sciatic nerve of the rabbit with prep-arations made by Dr. Keen, and obtained the same result, so that it seems difficult, considering the regularity of the structure thus brought out, to reach any other conclusion than that the axis is probably less simple in construction than has been believed. If we admit with Schultze† and Stricker that this substance also possesses longitudinal striæ, the likeness to the anatomical disposition of the

---

* Journ. de l'Anat. et Phys., 1869, p. 289.
† Disc. Acad. Bonn, Aug. 1868.

muscle would be remarkable,—a likeness, I may add, for which there may also be some physiological foundation.

The mode in which the nerve tubule relates itself to the centres and to the exterior organs is full of interest. It appears now to be pretty generally admitted that the tubule may finally be traced into the cells of the ganglia composing the spinal medulla and the brain, and that before joining these cells it loses its sheath and white covering, becoming thus reduced to the single element of the axis cylinder. It has been inferred from this that the latter part is the essential portion of the ultimate tubule, and that the exterior portions are merely meant to serve for protection or for insulation.

Observers are also well agreed that a similar loss of the external medulla and sheath, and a like thinning of the axis cylinder, is usually observable in the peripheral extremities of nerve tubules; but the most extreme diversity of opinion is held as regards the manner in which they terminate and as to the relation they bear to muscle, on the one hand, and to the sensitive surfaces on the other.

Perhaps no questions in micrology have been less distinctly answered than these. The mass of observers agree that the *sensitive* nerves may be traced for the most part to a plexiform series of loops which underlie the skin and other sentient surfaces. According to Beale and some others, these plexiform series constitute the true peripheral termination of many sensitive nerves, which, returning again to their central cell connections, form, as it were, a neural circuit. On the extreme outer loops, Dr. Beale located little masses of germinal matter, which he presumes to have an office connected with the incessant maintenance and increase of these ultimate loops,—a view which has been much controverted.

The appearances so described have of late been otherwise interpreted by Langerhaus.* He considers "that processes of non-medullated nerve fibres from the cutis penetrate between the cells of the rete Malpighii, exactly in the way described by Hager and Cohnheim as the mode of termination of nerves in the cornea. These nerve fibrils pass again into small cells lying between the deeper cells of the rete mucosum, whence fine fibrous outrunners enter the upper layers, to terminate finally in slightly clubbed extremities just beneath the horny layer." These have no relation to tact corpuscles, and the research of Langerhaus, in which Stricker seems to have faith, tends to weaken the belief in terminal peripheral nerve loops for which also physiological ground is wanting.

On the other hand, while it is as yet uncertain whether the sensitive fibres end externally in loops or in absolutely free ends, it is generally held that a vast number are externally related in some way to the little bodies known as the corpuscles of Meissner, of Vater, or Pacini (Vater, Pacinische Körperchen), and of Krause. The latter are found chiefly on mucous surfaces, those of Pacini in the submucous cellular tissue, the mesentery, the muscles, and the papillæ of the derm. These bodies are most numerous in the regions possessed of great tactile sensibility, such as the cushions of the fingers,—M. Meissner having counted eight hundred in a square line of the palmar face of the last phalanx of the index finger.

The structure of these corpuscles does not differ so essentially as to induce the belief that they must have different physiological functions, were it not for their varying anatomical relations to tissues.

The tactile corpuscles of Meissner, for instance, consist of "oblong oval bodies tolerably distinct from the remainder of the digital papillæ in which they lie. They

---

* Stricker's Comp. Histol., p. 187; New Sydenham Soc. edition.

are generally rounded off at the upper and lower ends, and do not exhibit the longitudinal striation as do the Pacinian bodies, but, on the contrary, transverse nuclei."* Two nerves can be usually traced to these bodies, but their after-relation to them is less clear. In some cases the nerve seems to envelop the corpuscle spirally, in others, to be lost in the centre of the mass. I have very little doubt that in some instances of local nervous disease the starting-point lies in the dermal nerve papillæ. In a case to which I shall have to refer, the corpuscles of Pacini were certainly both too large and too numerous, and in one which I myself have seen, there was some probability that a neuroma of the thumb was merely an overgrown tact corpuscle.

The corpuscles of Pacini consist of many concentrically arranged layers of connective tissue, always becoming more closely packed towards the centre, and surrounding a cavity filled with soft, abundantly nucleated and easily alterable material, which coagulates after death, and into the interior of which the nerve fibres penetrate. These, after they have lost the medullary sheath and the sheath of Schwann,—which latter becomes continuous with the laminated sheath of connective tissue investing the corpuscle,—consist only of the axis cylinder, which terminates in a little bulb.

The nerve corpuscles of Krause, described and depicted by him as existing in the conjunctiva, genitals, and other mucous surfaces, differ from the Pacinian corpuscles *only by the absence* of a thick, laminated investment.†

Most authors have held that these little bodies are apparatuses of reinforcement (Vulpian) for the impressions

---

* Virchow, Cellular Pathology, translated by Dr. Chance, p. 277. New York, 1861.

† Schultze, in Stricker's Histology, New Syd. Soc. Transactions, p. 168.

to which the sensitive nerves are submitted, or that each corpuscle is a centre of ganglionic matter, without which certain impressions cannot originate,—a view sustained, to some extent, by the analogy of some of the special senses, but contradicted by a host of pathological phenomena. Their function may possibly be protective, as regards the nerve ends, but that they have some relation to general sensibility, or to touch, seems alone clear. Rauber—who has stated the number of the deep-seated corpuscles of Pacini at 2142, too small a number for large relations to sensation—believes them to be the sensory organs as to the muscles. Vulpian states very justly that except as to the well-known mesenteric connection between certain Pacinian bodies and the sympathetic nerve, we have no clear information as to the peripheral distribution of this nerve system, nor are we much better instructed in the mode in which nerves terminate on vessel walls, a subject of daily increasing interest.*

Since the researches of M. Rouget and their general confirmation by Krause and Kühne, there is less difference of sentiment as to the motor termination of nerves. The nerve fibre undergoes division, and each branch on entering the sarcolemma loses its sheath of Schwann, which becomes continuous with the sarcolemma. The axis cylinder alone enters, the medullary matter as in other cases having previously disappeared. The cylinder axis of the nerve spreads out over the muscle substance in a granular mass, which is slightly prominent, and as to the true nature of which observers have disagreed. According to Trinchese, and to Rouget's latest researches, the granular cone, now known as the motor plate, conceals a delicate set of fine loops or plexuses, which are the true terminations of the motor nerve. Dr. Beale, however, believes that

---

* See Duchenne, translated by H. Tibbits, M.D. London, 1871, p. 153.

the terminal nerve fibre of motor nerves does not perforate this sarcolemma, but forms a network on its surface. This view, Kühne contends, is due to imperfect observation, though we confess that Dr. Beale's drawings, if correct, scarcely admit any other interpretation than that which he places on them.

Before passing to the consideration of the laws which control the passage of impressions over nerve fibres, there are a few points to be considered which concern the general or rational anatomy of nerves, and derive importance from their connection with disease or wounds of these parts.

Protection of nerves, owing to their physical peculiarities.— The fibrous character of the grosser nerve sheath, and the fact of each nerve being composed of a multitude of fibres, give to the nerves far more strength or power of resistance than might be supposed to belong to it, if we considered only the delicate structure of the neural substance itself. Dr. P. Tillaux* has examined this subject with the following results : The sciatic nerves of two fresh bodies were laid bare at the level of the popliteal space, then all the other parts of the member having been cut across so that the limb remained attached to the body by the nerve trunk alone, traction was made upon the limb in the direction of the nerve. A power equal to 54 to 58 kilogrammes—108 to 116 lbs.—was found to be necessary in order to rupture the nerve. To break the median or ulnar, under similar circumstances, a force of 40 to 50 lbs. was requisite. In practice it has been observed that when a limb is torn off, the nerve frequently gives way at a point above that at which the other parts are torn. Thus the sciatic may be broken off at the level of the buttocks, owing to the external and posterior portions of

---

* Tillaux, Aff. chir. des Nerfs, p. 11.

the leg having been dragged off, while the tissue of the
thigh, save for the nerve rupture, remained intact. Actual
experiment on the dead body showed, according to Tillaux, a like tendency on the part of the greater nerves to
tear apart at some point usually near or at a joint. Thus
the sciatic gives way where it runs under the pyramidal
muscle, at the line of the sciatic notch, and the median
and ulnar part at the bend of the elbow, when traction
has been made on a lower portion of their trunks. These
facts may, in rare instances, be of value to the surgeon,
and might possibly determine, in certain cases of torn
limbs, the point for amputation.

The toughness and elasticity of nerves are also shown
in some cases of disease and injury. Romberg and the
author just quoted remark upon the extent to which they
will stretch without breaking. Thus the median or ulnar
will gain 15 to 20 centimetres in length before parting.
I have also noticed many times, as other observers must
have done, the same physical quality in nerves; but it has
seemed to me far more important to know how far this
extension may go without loss of physiological properties
in the portion stretched. We have all had occasion to
watch the slow lengthening of nerves pushed aside by
morbid growths, but in these cases it is probable that a
constant process of repair in the interstices of the nerve
accompanies the extension and limits the mischief. A
healthy nerve will bear an amount of pressure and handling, which both in surgical and physiological operations
has occasioned me much surprise. Several years ago I
endeavored to estimate the limits of this capacity to endure extension by a series of experiments on the sciatic
nerve of the rabbit.

I give a single experiment to illustrate these remarks.
The sciatic nerve of a rabbit was separated from the point
of exit down to the knee; it was then cut across at the

highest level and attached to a string, which passed over
a little roller and carried a pan on which weights were
placed. The nerve was then tested by mechanical and
electrical irritation, and having been found to respond,
weights were placed on the scale-pan, and these, with the
amount of stretching of the nerve, were noted. In this,
and in other experiments on frogs, it seemed to me that
the nerve bore best a slow addition of a weight, which,
suddenly added, caused abrupt loss of physiological properties. As the extension was increased, the muscles were
thrown into a state of irregular convulsive activity, which
did not cease altogether when the nerve was for a time
allowed to relax. Slight mechanical injuries ceased to
cause reaction when the nerve had elongated to the extent
of one-fifth, but electricity still produced muscular contraction until the lengthening was equal to ¾ of an inch in
three inches. It is very probable that much less stretching will be found competent to destroy the perfect control
of the will over the muscles, or to interfere with the conveyance of delicate sensory impressions to the centres.
I have seen a curious illustration of the degree to which
a nerve may be meddled with before losing its power to
carry impressions. In a case of hospital gangrene of
the thigh, resulting in an enormous cavity, the sciatic
nerve was left intact. During one of the dressings, this
large trunk was at first quite roughly drawn out of the
wound, and afterwards pushed down to the bottom or
side of the cavity by the dressing employed. Some pain
resulted, as may be supposed, but the sense of touch
was scarcely disturbed. I witnessed the removal of
the dressings. The nerve must have been pushed fully
four or five inches out of its path, and very much
elongated.

The fibrous nature of the coarser nerve sheaths serves to
protect the fibres from the ravages of disease, of which fact

the case I have just mentioned is a fair illustration, although few surgeons are without similar experiences.

Besides this insurance against certain forms of disease, the structure of the nerve fibre, and its vascular relationships, also contribute to its safety, for as each nerve fibre has its sheath, the essential axis cylinder is well protected; while also the absence, in man at least, of blood-vessels within the delicate covering described by Robin, serves to prevent, to some extent, the access of inflammation. Thus it is that the nerves are able to traverse, uninjured, parts in divers states of degeneration or inflammation. It is also this sheathing by a non-vascular envelope that limits to a degree the changes caused by neuritis, and enables the non-vascular fibres to recover rapidly and thoroughly from such disease, because during inflammation the nerve fibres suffer principally from pressure, owing to effusion in and about the vascular portions of the nerve.

The toughness and general elasticity of nerve trunks sometimes serve a useful purpose in cases of ball wound, and I have repeatedly seen nerves escape total destruction from missiles simply because they were thrust aside, instead of being divided. Some of these escapes, which can be explained in no other way, are very interesting. They are most apt to occur where a missile has passed through a limb midway between two joints. On the other hand, injuries of nerves in connection with bone or near to joints are likely to be severe and lasting, because at these points and in these positions the nerve trunk is more firmly anchored than elsewhere, and shares in every injury which directly affects parts in its near neighborhood.

When a spinal nerve emerges from the intervertebral canal it is motor and sensory, by the union of the anterior and posterior roots, which represent motion and sensation respectively. Whether or not these fibres become at once scattered so that every part of the area of the nerve contains an equal share of the nerve tubes, both of sense and motion, is not at present very clear. Such, however, is the popular medical belief, though there is a good deal of reason to think that the nerve filaments of either function remain in bundles; because, as we shall see later, it is very common to find that a nerve trunk, injured by a missile, has suffered in its sensory or motor functions alone, which could scarcely be accounted for upon any other supposition than that last mentioned. Any other explanation must presuppose some greater susceptibility to injury in one set of fibres than in another.

In passing from the centre to the periphery, the nerves give off branches which, as a rule, leave the main stem at an acute angle, and more rarely at a right angle. Nerves in certain positions are liable during movement of limbs to be acutely bent, as happens at the elbow; and although such flexion is harmless when not prolonged, it is liable to cause loss of function when continued for some time, as may be felt by retaining the arm in a position of extreme flexion for ten or fifteen minutes.*

In their branchings nerves come into relation with other nerves, and give or get fibres; but the function of these is not altered thereby, nor do the nerve tubes in man anastomose in the sense in which vessels do.

A considerable number of nerve fibres appear to form loops, for the most part having their convexity towards

---

* It would appear, however, from the following instance, that recovery from this may occur when a limb remains bent for long periods. I saw lately, at the Hospital for Deformities and Nervous Diseases, a girl whose left arm had been bent at a most acute angle for years, owing to the cicatricial contraction following a burn. Although at first there was some loss of tactile power, at present there is absolutely perfect sensation throughout the limb, and the intrinsic finger movements are well preserved.

the periphery, from which in many cases filaments emerge; while in other instances these loops are merely recurrent communicating branches. Hyrtl has given numerous instances of these. Some of the more familiar are the loops of the hypoglossal, the return upwards of the recurrent laryngeal, and the palmar or plantar arcades. The chiasm of nerves on opposite sides of the body is more rare. That of the optic nerves in man seems to be in him the sole instance of a true physiological chiasm, since Vulpian* thinks he has proved that in the case of the intercommunication of the right and left hypoglossals pointed out by Hyrtl, there is no transmission of power from side to side; and, indeed, if I correctly understand the passage, he would seem to have some doubt as to whether there is really an interchange of fibres.

In man the cerebro-spinal nerves, at least, seem to be physiologically limited to their own side of the body, a proposition which becomes of some importance in the recognition and limitation of paralytic affections. I have once or twice felt doubtful as to the strict truth of this law as applied to certain traumatic palsies of the face, where in rare cases the motor fibres of the upper lip have appeared to me to cross over, so that irritation of the nerve on the sound side seemed to cause slight muscular contractions on the diseased side.

In the lower animals, the existence of any true physiological chiasm, other than that of the optic nerves, was first demonstrated by the author, and his friend Dr. Morehouse, in the case of the chelonians, all of which have a chiasm between the two superior laryngeal nerves, so that irritation of the left nerve acts on both the left and right lips of the larynx, and *vice versa*. Guided by this discovery, my friend Prof. Wyman found similar chiasms in

---

* Vulpian, Leçons sur la Phys. Comp., etc., p. 160.

reptiles and birds. He has also discovered that in frogs the nerves of the skin cross the central line of the body. I have recently examined frogs to learn whether this anatomical crossing involves physiological consequences. To test this, the skin of the frog's back or belly was divided longitudinally at varying distances from the middle line, and then irritants, as biliary and stronger acids, were applied to the skin between the central raphé and the line of section; no response was obtained to such irritations, even in frogs which had been previously rendered excitable by strychnia. The purpose, therefore, of such interchange of nerves must still be considered doubtful.

During their distribution, the nerves from more or less remote parts of the nervous system in some localities run together, and then separate to reunite and part anew, thus forming, by the free communication between neighboring branches, a plexus or network, from which emerge finally the nerve trunks which are to be distributed to a particular member. This intricate interlacing seems to be merely an arrangement for the interchange of fibres, since those which enter the plexus acquire in it no physiological properties which they did not previously possess.

A knowledge of these networks is essential to the study of nerve wounds, because injuries of the plexuses, especially that of the neck, are very common in war, and their arrangements enable us to explain in many cases the transmission of disease from one nerve to another, which is closely related to it in the plexus, or as its parent stem. After leaving the plexus, the limb nerves are usually distributed with great regularity, anomalies being rather uncommon.

While in most men we may take for granted that nerves obey the normal law, it is still important to remember that in the arm especially, peculiar and exceptional arrangements may occur in the way of unusual interchanges of nerve fibres.

Chassaignac, and, more recently, Mr. Hilton, in his thoughtful book on " Pain and Rest," have pointed out, as one of the elements of protection to nerves, the fact that in most instances the motor nerves enter their respective muscles on the under side, so that the whole thickness of the muscle is interposed between the nerve and the exterior sources of injury. We may add that on their first entrance to a limb, the larger nerves lie in the leg at the back, or in the arm, upon the inside, where they are singularly secure from harm.

CHAPTER III.

NEURO-PHYSIOLOGY.

Varieties of nerves.—The nerves which connect a limb with the centres fulfill the following functions: They convey outwardly motor impressions, resulting in voluntary or involuntary motion, as the case may be. They carry centripetally the myriads of impressions which constitute sensations, or which, unfelt as sensations, are excito-motory in purpose. Lastly, a system of nerves, known as sympathetic, exercises control over the flow of blood to the tissues. Section of these nerves paralytically dilates the vessels; galvanization contracts them. This system originates in the spinal cord, but there is also evidence that certain spinal nerves, unrelated to the sympathetic, possess the power to cause directly enlargement of arterioles and increase of vasal supply.

Through this compound group of nerves occur such nutritive changes as depend on increased or lessened flow of blood, but these are insufficient to account for all the trophic changes which we witness from disease or injury; and hence has arisen the belief that there are also trophic nerves proper, which, apart from variable blood supplies, or in connection with these, bring about in the tissues alterations, examples of which I shall have to point out from time to time.

In connection with nerve wounds and their consequences, we have to deal with alterations due to the destruction or irritation of the various fibres of nerves

(30)

which minister to pain, touch, the thermal sense, motion, calorification, and nutrition.

I do not think it desirable to enter as largely into these subjects as they would be dealt with in a physiological treatise, but I cannot avoid some reference to such portions of their physiology as either aid us to comprehend and relieve nerve wounds, or as are set in new or clearer light by the phenomena of these accidents.

Trophic nerves.—The question which most often presents itself for answer to the neuro-pathologist is as to the existence or non-existence of nerves directly affecting the nutrition of the tissues, apart from the changes induced in them by the section or irritation of vaso-motor nerve fibres. Without attempting to treat fully of this matter, for which, indeed, the physiological groundwork is still deficient, I shall content myself with stating the impressions in this direction which a large experience of nerve wounds has left upon my mind.

When the physiology of the vaso-motor nervous system was first elucidated by the labors of Bernard, Brown-Séquard, Schiff, and others, it was supposed that it would enable us readily to explain the many obscure phenomena which arise out of nerve wounds; but despite the able arguments of Handfield Jones* and some other observers, this hope has gradually faded away, and it is now generally admitted that we must seek elsewhere for a satisfactory explanation of the facts in question.

The effects of injuries or sections of these nerves can be only to cause either contraction or dilatation of vessels, or to put a stop to the pulsatile movements which have been seen in minute vessels in many parts of the animal economy. These alterations, with the consequent changes in blood supply which they bring about, may be direct

---

* St. George's Hospital Reports, 1868, p. 89 et seq.

results of nerve lesions, or may be caused after partial
nerve lesions by reflex influences originating in the wound.
No matter how caused, they are limited to too large or
too small a supply of blood, or to alternations of these
conditions.

To test the probability of the competency of vaso-motor
changes to cause the multiplied lesions which follow wounds
of the nerves of the limbs, we naturally turn to the simpler case of injuries of the sympathetic in the neck.

Section of this nerve merely increases the amount of
blood which flows in any given time through the tissues
in which it is distributed, and also causes a rise in their
temperature.   But these changes are not permanent, and
neither do we find that the face, for example, is then
subject to spontaneous inflammations or to other trophic
alterations unless the animal be in bad health.   Thus, in
rabbits long kept confined, I have frequently seen inflammation of the conjunctiva and cornea follow such sections,
but not in their more vigorous companions, and such was
also Bernard's experience.   Moreover, artificial lesions in
the latter class appear to heal with unusual celerity.

Like Weber, I have made many attempts to bring about
trophic changes in the face by irritating and partially
wounding the sympathetic, but my efforts have uniformly
failed ; nor have like experiments, such as Lister's, upon
the sympathetic nerves in the limbs of the frog, been any
more fortunate.

Of course, section of these nerves in their course through
the compound nerves of the limbs of man is not without
indirect influences on the life of the tissues, but unhappily
we need as yet early thermometric observations after
nerve wounds of the extremities to complete their history.

In speaking of the effect of nerve wounds on temperature, I shall again approach this subject.   At present it is
only necessary to say that at remote periods after total

sections of nerves in a limb, there are usually lowered temperature and a condition of passive congestion, while the still more remote future affords some evidence of greatly lessened blood supply; the reasons for which changes are not very difficult to trace. Under these circumstances the life of the limb is lowered and exposed parts are easily injured; but repair, though sometimes slow, still occurs, and may even be unusually rapid.

I have watched many such cases of complete separation of a limb, or parts of a limb, from all neural influence, and have failed to see any inevitable consequence except general atrophy, with usually muscular contractions, and a sallow, unhealthy look of the skin, which is apt to become scaly and rough. The nails grow as usual, perhaps a little more slowly, and the hair is commonly unchanged.

Now and then I met with one of these cases in which whitlows occurred, or ulcers formed on parts which either were or were not exposed to mechanical injury. In most instances these ulcers healed easily, in some cases with unusual facility. We can only conclude from these facts that a certain individuality of cell-life controls the results, and that the cell-life of one man so differs from that of another as thus to present us with varied phenomena under what seems to be equality of conditions. At all events, here, if in any case, we have total vaso-motor palsy, and for a long while, at least, probably an excessive blood supply, but no constant symptom save atrophy, and in no case hypertrophy. But atrophy may, and does, take place from nerve injury without notable changes of temperature, so that we are by no means justified in considering this the only constant result of total nerve section, as due to vaso-motor palsy.

After partial nerve wounds there may be contraction of vessels from direct irritation, or reflectively produced dilatations or contractions. I believe that I have seen each of these conditions in limbs, or portions of limbs, and have watched in vain for their results in the way of nutritive mischief.

The best cases are those in which prolonged spasm of the vasal muscles of one limb has been caused by wound of another. In such rare cases the temperature may be remarkably lowered for weeks, thus showing lessened blood supply without the appearance of any remarkable nutritive changes.

If the vaso-motor nerves were alone responsible for the existence of all the lesions which follow nerve wounds, it would be reasonable to expect always to meet with some rise or fall in temperature. Such, however, is not the case, and I have frequently met with profound trophic changes unattended by thermal perturbations; and the same remark has been made by other neuro-pathologists.

It is also difficult to explain, on the theory of changes in vasal supply, the completeness of some of the trophic conditions attendant upon nerve wounds, or central disease, for it seems scarcely possible to conceive that without the least apparent change in the appearance or color of the related part there could be, from lack of blood, or its excess, that absolute arrest of growth which I have shown to occur for a time in the nails after certain cerebral palsies.

For such reasons, then, I am unwilling to admit that vaso-motor nerve lesions have any other share in the production of the tissue changes which may follow nerve wounds than merely to prepare the ground for their production by other more direct agencies.

In 1858, Brown-Séquard first distinctly expressed the opinion that "the nervous system determines an increase of the attraction exerted upon the blood by the living tissues, and, in this case, the phenomenon is attended by dilatation of blood-vessels. The nervous system acts directly and originally upon the parenchyma of the tissues." In 1860, Samuel,* resting upon facts such as I have urged in regard to the vaso-motor nerves, rejected them as the sole causes of nutritive changes, and declared his theory of trophic nerves as distinct fibres concerned in governing the nutritive conditions of the tissues.

This observer conceived that the trophic nerves have their centres in the intervertebral spinal ganglia, or in cerebral ganglia having like physiological powers. He distinguished them as centripetal nerves, receiving and conveying inward impressions connected with trophic changes; and centrifugal nerves which, when palsied, give rise to atrophies, and, when irritated, to inflammations.

Thus, while he regards nutritive activity as the result of a force inherent in the molecules or cells of the tissues, he looks upon the trophic nerves as the means of regulating their changes, increasing, retarding, or enfeebling them, as the case may be.

The experiments on which he chiefly bases this hypothesis have failed in the hands of other observers, and as yet there is no absolute physiological proof of the existence of such nerves. The anatomical demonstration of these fibres is equally wanting, so that at present the justification for their existence lies in an apparent necessity for their presence which so impressed Duchenne as to cause him to remark that "if we had no knowledge of such nerves, we should be forced to invent them."

If, in fact, we exclude vaso-motor influence as capable alone of explaining the pathological changes which follow nerve wounds, we are forced to fall back upon the nerves of motion and sensation, or to believe in a system of independent trophic nerves. The discovery by Bärensprung of inflammation of the intervertebral ganglia of

---

* Trophischen Nerven. Leipzig, 1860.

nerves, in the track of which in the skin were developed herpetic eruptions with neuralgia, appeared to be a valuable confirmation of Samuel's views; but the attendant neuralgia, showing an affection of sensory fibres, weakens the evidence which would have been perfect if there had been a painless herpes with some disease of the ganglia.

The phenomena of nerve wounds, as I have seen them, lend no conclusive support to the theory, and there are in them, as in many other pathological facts, certain arguments in favor of the possibility of disorders of nutrition being capable of production by the irritation of ordinary nerves of sensation, and, indeed, of motion.

Among these are the grave changes which sometimes occur in tissues affected with neuralgias, and also the phenomena of muscular atrophies. It is, moreover, to be remembered that the functional activities of skin and muscle have some distinct and close relations to the preservation of their nutritive life, and that pathological irritations do not traverse nerves of motion or sensation in one direction only, but disturb them really from end to end, and may thus, in any case, come to influence abnormally the tissues in which lie their ultimate filaments. At present it seems alone clear that while neural and central irritations alike are competent to pathologically disturb the status of nutritive health, we are without absolute proof of the existence of true trophic nerves, devoted solely to regulating nutrition, and are equally without just reasons for asserting that the nerves of sense and motion may not be largely concerned in propagating to the tissues irritative and other influences quite competent to occasion disease.

There exist, in fact, certain observations of Vulpian and Phillipeaux which make it probable that the nutritive integrity of tissues depends chiefly upon that of the nerves concerned in their several functions, and that to destroy a sensitive nerve is to affect injuriously the skin and its appendages, while section of a motor nerve is equally certain to bring about atrophy in the muscle.

Thus, when the lingual sensory nerve was cut, the mucous surface of the tongue and the papillæ became wasted, without muscular changes, while these alone followed division of the hypoglossal nerve. Since, say these observers, the hypoglossal possesses also a few sympathetic and sensory filaments, it is still possible that some of these may be concerned in the result, so that direct experiments on this nerve do not decisively settle the question. It has been found possible, however, by lesions of the floor of the fourth ventricle, to paralyze the hypoglossal at its origin without involving any other nerves. Yet, under these circumstances, the atrophy follows as is usual after peripheral sections, and leaves us with the fair presumption that the nutritive life of the muscles depends chiefly upon their motor nerves.

There is at present in the Pennsylvania Hospital a rare case which corroborates these views. A small pistol-ball traversed the neck, and, without causing any graver lesion, cut the left hypoglossal nerve. This accident resulted in motor palsy of one-half of the organ, with atrophy of the muscles, but left undisturbed the senses of touch and taste, as well as the nutrition of the mucous surface.

The mechanism by which neural irritations or palsies give rise to inflammations, eruptions, and the like, is made more clear by the attendant facts in regard to the secretions of the skin. These, as I shall show, are sometimes lessened or annihilated, sometimes increased, and more often altered so as to become excessively acid and offensive. It is quite conceivable that the products of disintegration in the deeper tissues are similarly affected, so as to be sometimes either excessive or deficient, and sometimes abnormal in character; meanwhile the irregular and retarded circulation fails to remove these products with even the normal rapidity, and their accumulation may come to act as local poisons to limited regions of tissue, and so be efficient in bringing about the diseased conditions of which I have spoken.

The most interesting generalizations as to trophic changes consequent upon lesions of nerve trunks are these :

Total section of the main nerves of a limb results invariably in atrophy, but not necessarily in any inflammatory conditions. It does not, however, forbid these, nor is repair always interfered with to any great extent.

Partial wounds of nerves, and especially gunshot lesions, are apt to give rise to a large number of trophic changes in the skin, hair, nails, areolar tissue, and muscles. Except the entire arrest, for a time, of nail growth, every trophic alteration capable of arising from injuries or diseases of the centres is also to be met with as a consequence of wounds of the nerves.

Section of muscle nerves causes atrophy and contraction of the related muscles. Partial wounds occasion various degrees of wasting, with more or less loss of muscular sensation, and impairment or loss of power to respond to electric, galvanic, or mechanical irritation.

Exceptional cases exist of atrophy without defect of excitability under stimulation.

Trophic changes in the skin, hair, and nails are never present after nerve wounds without some affection of sensation, such as dysæsthesia, anæsthesia, or hyperæsthesia; but any of these latter states may exist without the nutritive alterations in question.

Trophic changes are most prone to follow wounds of nerves which are distributed to the hands and feet, and more rarely occur when the injury has involved only the nerve branches which supply the upper portions of a limb.

Nerves of pain.—There is a good deal of doubt as to whether or not the various forms of sensory impressions, such as heat, cold, tickling, etc., affect the sensorium through distinct sets of fibres, or whether they travel on a common track with impressions of touch and pain. These latter are, certainly, in a manner distinct; but, although it has been made clear that one or more of the varied forms of sensory expressions may disappear without any other being lost, this is no absolute proof that separate fibres are needed for their conveyance to the centres. Brown-Séquard is disposed to admit the existence of a number of such sets of nerve tubes; but while there is a good deal in general nervous pathology to make it probable that the distinction of sensations depends upon their central discrimination alone, the phenomena of nerve injuries tend to discredit by negative proof the theory of the existence of numerous sets of sensory nerve fibres, as I shall have future occasion to point out.

Of the exact nature of the affection of nerve matter which produces pain we know but little. In general, for the causing of pain we must have mechanical impressions far more severe than those which excite the nerves of tact and temperature; while it would also seem that neural excitation attaining the grade of pain is possible, as in many neuralgias, without the least evidence of visible organic alteration of tissue.

In the normal condition, the sense of pain is very unequally distributed as regards the skin surfaces, and bears no definite proportion to the acuteness of the tact sense. Indeed, there are certain portions of the tissues in which it is extremely deficient, as the back and a limited space over the tibia. As a rule, the thigh is less sensitive than the arm, the leg than the forearm; but as no complete

study of this sense has been made, it is impossible to carry
such comparisons further. In the lower animals the dorsal skin seems, in some cases, to possess little or no feeling,
so that I have actually made incisions through this part
in dogs and rabbits without seeming to produce any pain
whatsoever. The interior organs are variably provided,
as to the pain sense, some of them appearing to have little
or none of this form of sensibility; yet in all, even in the
bones and intestines, lie remote capacities for torture
which seem capable of development in the presence of
diseased states.

Are we to suppose that there exist always in these
organs pain nerves, and that only once, perhaps, in a lifetime these filaments are to be aroused into activity? Or,
as regards the skin, how shall we deal with the like difficulty if we choose to believe that everywhere are peculiar
nerve fibres devoted only to transmitting painful sensations? The skin, in this view of the case, must have a
set of nerves so rarely used that it is difficult to comprehend how they can sustain their organic life uninjured,
and ready to awaken into functional activity at long and
irregular intervals.

I am unwilling, in view of these facts, to look upon pain
as a distinct sense with afferent tracks peculiar to itself;
and when we consider also how sensory impressions made
on nerves purely of special sense may rise to the height
of being painful, it becomes more and more probable that
pain is the central expression of a certain grade of irritation in any centripetal nerve.

There is, indeed, every probability that the sensory
nerves are competent to carry inward a variety of impressions, which, owing to the peculiar nature of the excitations they cause in the nerve, are capable of appreciation
only by the separate centres devoted to their perception,
so that pain, touch, and thermal excitations may need, in

the peripheral nerves, no different channels for their passage.

It is as if through a single tube were spoken various languages which could be only understood when, at its farther end, they reached the ear of the hearer native to each form of speech. There is in physical science a good deal in favor of the view I have so briefly urged, and, clinically, something may be said for it.

We now know that motor-excitations may be made to pass over sensory nerves, and *vice versa*, while in most of the instances of loss of pain without loss of tact the lesion has been plainly central. In the rare cases of peripheral analgesia without anæsthesia, it is quite possible that such modifications may have taken place in the nerves as to have destroyed the power of the nerve tissues to transmit particular forms of excitation.

Recurrent sensibility.—Although we admit the general proposition that the anterier roots of spinal nerves are motor, and the posterior are sensory, there is an apparent exception to this which has generally been admitted of late years.

When we divide the posterior root of a spinal nerve, all sensation is lost to the terminal branches of the mixed nerve of which it makes a part. So also is motion utterly lost by dividing the anterior root. If, however, the spine has been opened with certain precautions, and the nerve roots, after exposure, have been left at rest for a certain time, it will be found that distinct evidences of sensibility may be evoked by irritating the anterior root. Should we then divide this trunk, the central end will be found to possess no sensibility such as will exist in the peripheral extremity, and section of the posterior root will abolish altogether these evidences of feeling; so that it becomes clear that the fibres communicating sensation to the anterior root must depend upon the posterior root.

The experiments of Bernard, especially upon the recurrent sensibility of the cranial nerves, seem to prove that the sensitive fibres turn backward at different points in the nerve route to accompany the motor fibres all the way to their proper root, and even into the spine itself. The author named conceives that the most of these recurrent branches are derived from terminal anastomoses of the sensitive and motor nerves. Concerning this point, there is still some doubt, but the existence of this peculiar sensibility of the anterior nerve roots is now regarded as an accepted fact in science.

Gubler and Brown-Séquard have both suggested different and ingenious explanations of the so-called recurrent sensibility, but neither are satisfactory; so that no one, as yet, has offered any competent explanation of the physiological necessity for the arrangement in question. The difficulty of so doing is not lessened by the fact that recurrent sensibility does not exist in fishes, and that Vulpian failed to detect it in the pigeon. I repeated some years ago Bernard's experiments, and reached the same conclusions as he has done. I failed, however, to discover recurrent sensibility in the duck and the chicken, notwithstanding every precaution to insure success, nor was I more fortunate in our large chelonians (Chelonura serpentina), which are admirably fitted to be the subjects of such experiments.

Neurility and neural excitants.—Every stimulus capable of acting on a nerve causes in it the development of the nervous force, the true nature of which is extremely problematical. For a long time there has been a decided tendency to regard this force as some form or manifestation of electricity; but just in proportion as we have come to know more of the true relations of the latter force to nerve tissue has the probability of the identity of nerve force and electric force diminished.

Beyond a doubt, certain electrical phenomena exist in connection with all nerves and in the presence of all nerve action; but so far from these facts showing that nerve force is electricity, their whole bearing is to prove quite the contrary.

There seems, indeed, to be every likelihood that the electric states which arise during nerve disturbance are merely manifestations related to the states of nervous activity, and passively dependent, directly or indirectly, on nutritive changes or upon molecular alterations, themselves connected with the altered polarity of the nerve during its conditions of rest or excitation.* More probably nerve force depends, like magnetism, upon peculiar conditions of certain matter for its manifestations, so that only where these exist can it be studied, while, as regards its kinship to electricity, we can only surmise that they are correlated, and that the one may give rise, under certain conditions, to the production of the other. Besides the common arguments against their identity, such as the fact that crushing the nerve destroys its power to convey impressions, while it may still conduct electricity, there are certain other objections to the conception of their oneness which appear to me to present insurmountable obstacles to any such belief. The most formidable of these is the difference in the speed with which the galvanic and the nerve currents are propagated. Thus, in the frog's nerves, at a temperature of 52° F. up to 70° F., nerve force moves at a rate of from 81 to 126 feet per second. In man it is estimated to travel on motor nerves at a speed of 200 feet a second. In sensory nerves the rate at which impressions move is about 110 feet per second, with some variation for the different nerves. It has also been shown by Munk that the speed is not uniform for all parts of a given nerve. If

---

* Vulpian, p. 104.

now we remember that electricity travels at a rate of 462,000,000 feet per second, we shall see how difficult it is to assimilate these two modes of motion. As regards reflex impressions, the difficulty is still greater, because most of these move slower than the excitations which cause voluntary motions, and are often so much retarded as to be capable of estimate by far coarser means than those employed by Helmholtz and Donders.

I shall elsewhere have occasion to point out, when studying nerve injuries, how this question of the rate at which nerve force moves may come to possess practical value in determining the possible seat of the originating lesion. Just now, the matter has only thus much of interest. In certain pathological spinal conditions the speed of nerve force is so strikingly lessened as to be capable of rough estimate by a metronome beating quarter seconds. In some instances, this slowing reaches at least five seconds,—a degree of retardation which no alteration of conductors will enable us to realize as regards electrical currents. So that if we had only this fact as to relative speed, it alone would oblige us to believe that these two forces are absolutely distinct, and that they possess only such relationships as exist among the other natural forces.

The conclusions thus reached are sustained by the later researches of Marey, who, however, puts the rate of nerve force at about half of that assigned to it by Helmholtz.

He also sees in these facts an argument against the unity of nerve and electric force, but remarks that Gaugain has shown that electricity in passing through moistened threads has so low a rate of movement as to make him still hesitate concerning the question of possible identity. In another place I have pointed out the need for some such experiments on bad conductors with electricity of low tension; but the problem can only be definitely settled by a careful determination of the rate at which the nerves themselves act as electrical conductors. At present the weight of evidence, as I have said, is opposed to the idea of the oneness of these two modes of motion.

The property of being excited, which, following Lewes, Vulpian calls *neurility*, is common to all nerves. Sensitive, motor, reflex, nutritive, or sympathetic filaments, all alike have one and the same property, with no greater difference than exists between the physiological properties of different muscular tissues.

There seems, indeed, to be every probability that however aroused and whenever, in sensitive or motor nerves the vis nervosa does not vary in its nature. As regards the nerve fibres themselves, it is likely that their anatomical similarity, which is very great, whatever be their function, represents a greater likeness in physiological effects than would at first sight seem possible. We are well aware that the sensitive and afferent nerves when irritated or normally stimulated seem to carry messages only in a centripetal direction, while of motor nerves the reverse holds true. There are, however, many facts which tend to show that irritation of any portion of either a motor or sensory nerve is propagated alike in both directions, central and peripheral, so that the nerves only appear to carry messages in one direction, because only at one end is either set provided with organs which have the power to announce the reception of an impression. It is probable, therefore, that if in any nerve of mixed function we could suddenly connect the sensitive fibres with the motor centres at one end and the muscles at the other, that we should still have these latter effectively called into play, while of the motor fibres a like statement would hold equally good.

This view, which might for a long while back have been sustained on theoretical grounds, has received positive evidence in its favor through the recent experiments of Vulpian and others.

To settle the question, MM. Vulpian and Phillipeaux cut across the hypoglossal (motor nerve of the tongue); the central portion was then plucked out with its bulbous roots, next the pneumogastric was in like manner divided, and a long piece of the peripheral end excised, after which its central end was brought by suture in contact with the peripheral end of the cut hypoglossal.

A post-mortem inspection after four months showed complete union and restoration of the neural integrity; but, previous to this examination, pinching of the central parts of the pneumogastric caused free movements of the tongue; there was, therefore, perfect communication of excitations from the central end of the pneumogastric to the peripheral end of the hypoglossal. The effect was the same when the pneumogastric had been divided a little way above the line of union; what remained of the nerve was still able to conduct impressions to the muscles of the tongue, and under this modification of the experiment all possibility of deception through reflex action was cut off.

In like manner, when to the peripheral end of the pneumogastric is united the central end of the hypoglossal, irritations of this latter nerve influence the heart's movements. In these instances it is clear that the impressions passed in directions exactly the reverse of those which they would usually follow, if the original function of the nerve determined and limited the direction possible to nerve force. Still more decisive are the cases in which the lingual nerve (sensitive) and the hypoglossal (motor) are united; for here it was possible, according to the mode of union, to excite motion through a sensitive nerve, or sensation through a motor nerve.

There is, then, as Vulpian states, no histological distinction between motor and sensory nerves.   Excitants affect either.   Their electrical condition is alike.   Toxic agents only seem to influence them differently because they act variously upon the parts, muscular or ganglionic, which lie at their extremities.   Their degenerations and regenerations present no distinct difference, and both are capable of carrying messages in either direction.*

Not less interesting and demonstrative are the cases in which M. Bert has grafted the tip of the rat's tail into the dorsal region, and after a time cut the tail off at the normal point of attachment.   A year subsequent to this operation irritations of the end of the tail were felt as pain, so that its sensitive nerves, now in union with dorsal nerves, must have carried impressions in a reverse direction.

Where the central end of the lingual and the outer end of the hypoglossal nerves are united, it is found that irritation of the lingual causes pain and tongue movements at one and the same time.   The excitation is, in this case, propagated in both directions, so that it would seem as if in all cases of nerve irritation or excitement the impression affects the nerve from end to end, precisely as happens when a stretched cord is made to vibrate throughout its length by a force applied to any portion of it.†

This remarkable fact which has now been set in the clearest light by the experiments just related, as well as by the previous results obtained by Dr. Du Bois-Reymond, is full of interest to the pathologist as well as to the phys-

---

* Vulpian, op cit., p. 286.

† We may also illustrate the case by a tube open at one end, and having a whistle at the other.   Blow into the centre of the tube and the air moves in both directions, but as it emerges it makes a sound only at the end possessing a whistle, so that a careless observer would say that the air moved only in one direction.   We pinch the trunk of a motor nerve and the muscle moves, but if at the other end of the nerve there were also a muscle, we should in like manner be able to see it brought into action.

iologist. Nor is it possible to read these proofs without
perceiving that as an irritant affects a nerve from end to
end, and excites it in both directions, important results
for nutrition may ensue if this irritation be extreme and
long continued.

Irritants applied along the track of nerves cause in the
sensory nerves sensation; in the motor nerves, motion.
Where a mixed nerve is divided, stimulation of the peripheral end occasions motion only, while the like agency
applied to the central end produces pain. Under these
circumstances, the other and varied forms of sensation
felt during health are not distinctly reproduced, pain alone
being present.

If, however, the nerve ends, having been allowed to
cicatrize without union, should be constantly irritated, as
by imprisonment in the hard tissues of stumps, or scars,
or by neuritis, a great variety of peculiar sensations are
felt, such as the feeling of being tickled, of motion in the
lost or disconnected part, heat, cold, etc. These facts,
to which I shall have occasion to return, seem at least
to prove that the physiological conception of the need for
some peculiar peripheral arrangements for the production
of touch, sense of movement, and the like, is without firm
physiological foundation.

A host of facts similar to these has led to a knowledge
of the law of the reference of sensations, by virtue of
which irritations along a nerve trunk, or of the centrally
connected end of a divided nerve, give rise to sensations
which are inevitably referred to the parts to which, in
the normal state, this nerve was distributed. A knowledge of this law, and of the anatomical arrangement of
nerves, is, of course, essential to the clear understanding
and diagnosis of neural injuries, and a want of such
knowledge has led, in certain cases, to operations as
grave as amputation, for the purpose of relieving pains

which had their true cause in the upper end of a divided nerve.

Neural stimulants.—The various forms of irritation which may affect the nerve trunks are capable of classification, and their character and mode of action are not devoid of interest to the neuro-pathologist. Laying aside the volitional stimuli, and those which result from the action of external agencies on sensory nerves, we shall find in disease another set, which may affect like those just mentioned, not alone the extremities of nerves, whether central or peripheral, but which may attack the nerves either in these localities or in their passage to and from the tissues with which they are functionally related. To this set of irritations belongs inflammation, with all its consequences of increased temperature, swelling, and defective nutrition. Disturbed mechanical relations of tissues to nerves, tumors, cicatrices, dislocations, or fractures, may all come to act as irritants to neighboring nerve trunks, as well as the near passage of missiles, the presence of foreign bodies, wounds, etc. From these varied causes result numerous sensations, such as numbness, so called, formication, burning, itching, and, most prominently of all, pain in its endless variations.

The physiologist has studied a class of nerve irritants which have, for the pathologist, only an occasional interest. These are electricity, heat or cold directly applied to nerve trunks, desiccation, excess of water and chemical agents, such as salt, sugar, bile, acid, etc.

The first of these may be set aside for future study.

Our information on these subjects is due chiefly to Eckhardt, Budge, Kölliker, Kühne, and Bernard. The first of these authors pointed out the power possessed by common salt to excite, without destruction, the nerves of motion; so that when a divided peripheral end is placed in a concentrated solution of this agent the muscles are seen to contract; no such result being attained by weak

solutions. Kühne has described like effects from the use
of glycerine; but the two reagents differ in this respect,
that salt in strong solution acts convulsively on both
nerve and muscle, but glycerine on nerves alone, except
it be diluted with water, when it influences both nerve
and muscle alike. Solutions of certain acids appear also
to possess this property, while others, or stronger prepara-
tions of the same, destroy the power of the nerve to act
further.

The most interesting of the substances thus capable of
exciting the nerves are undoubtedly the biliary acids, for
it is to these, as Budge and Kühne have proved, that we
must assign the capability of the bile itself to evoke
neuro-muscular spasms, a quality upon which some very
extraordinary hypotheses have been founded.

In all probability many of these agents act by subtract-
ing from the nerve its water, and thus, finally, abolishing
for a time one of the conditions of its active physiological
life; for, as has been repeatedly shown, the function of
the nerve may be restored by carefully allowing it to
reabsorb a supply of this essential element.

These studies have led to certain useful conclusions.
Thus, when we see a nerve preserving its conductive and
excitative abilities, despite the corrugation and apparent
injury of the medullary portions of its structure, we have
some right to infer that in the unaltered axis cylinder
alone lies the capacity to convey impressions. Vulpian
has also shown that sensitive and motor nerves are alike
acted upon by these reagents; a proof added to the rapid
accumulation of facts leading to a belief in the unity of
construction and of mode of activity of the various orders
of neural conductors.

The manner in which nerve trunks and their extremities
in the periphery are acted upon by the excess of water,
or its abstraction, is one of larger interest to the neuro-

pathologist. As concerns the individual nerve, the facts are as follows:

When a nerve is placed in a dense solution of certain salines it is at first excited, and then finally loses its functional powers, which may again be restored by placing it in water.

If a nerve be slowly and carefully desiccated to a certain degree by warmth, or mere exposure to the air, it is excited for a time so as to convulse its connected muscles, and at last ceases to be irritable until moistened anew. On the other hand, when we place nerves in distilled water, they lose their capacity to be excited, but regain it again when the balance is restored, by soaking them in weak solutions of phosphate of soda. Indeed, so delicate is the status of the nerve, so easily is it disturbed, that mere separation from the centres, or exposure short of perceptible desiccation, modifies the excitability of the fibres.

We have thus learned that every modification in the amount of water, either towards desiccation or towards excess, tends to alter, and finally to abolish, the neurility of a nerve, while a restoration of the aqueous supply, or a loss of fluid by the water-soaked nerve, will, in either case, suffice to restore its function.

As I have previously said, these are purely physiological experiments, and nothing akin to them is seen in man, except by rare opportunity in wounds exposed to improper dressings, or on the surface of ulcers. At first thought it might seem as if conditions of anæmia or hydræmia offered some analogy to that one of the conditions just now described as an oversupply of fluid to the nerve; but in hydræmia, the pathological approach to this state, there are probably more complex changes in the nutritive supplies besides those arising from a too fluid blood. The opposite condition is best represented among diseased states by cholera, where the fluids are rapidly expelled from the system by purging and vomiting, until the blood becomes thick and of almost tarlike consistency. It seems not unlikely that the terrible cramps and pains of this malady may be due to this condition of the fluids, since in the individual nerve an excitation, resulting in spasms, follows always the drying of its tissues.

Far more interesting are the neural phenomena which occur from absolute diminution or loss of blood or from the various degrees of excess of that fluid.

When from arterial emboli, or owing to the ligation of a main artery, the blood is for a time cut off from a limb, its loss is followed in many cases by excessive pain, and more rarely by cramps. As Vulpian has justly remarked, the preponderance of sensory phenomena in these cases is due to the fact that the organ of final reference for irritations, the brain, is unaltered, whilst the muscles suffer early a loss of irritability, which deprives the motor nerves of all means of expressing the excitations to which, in common with the sensitive filaments, they are subjected.

Examples of the pain produced in a limb by tying its great artery are familiar to surgeons; but I believe the phenomenon is not a constant one. In a case of ligature of the aorta by Mr. James,* the pain thus caused was terrible, nor did careful examination of the body furnish any explanation of the fact. It is at all events instructive, as concerns the causation of neuralgia, to learn that the lack of blood supply may be a condition productive of such extreme torture.

As regards emboli in main arteries, I do not think the pain a constant symptom, but it is sufficiently common, and in more than one case within my own experience, its

* Med.-Chir. Trans., vol. xvi. p. 17.

presence and severity have been the first indications which called attention to the arrest of local circulation by clot. Instances of venous occlusion differ somewhat in being less entire, and also in the increased rather than the diminished pressure which they bring about.

Undoubtedly, the nerves are excited under these circumstances, but the cause of their excitation does not seem to be very clear. Brown-Séquard attributes it to the gradual collection of carbonic acid in the tissues; but there are other elements of disintegration which may not be incompetent to disturb the nerves, and his hypothesis has found less acceptance than might have been expected from the really strong arguments which its author has adduced in its favor. Vulpian, on the other hand, is disposed to consider the absence of oxygen as more likely to occasion these excitations,—a view which certainly has less to recommend it than that of the former physiologist. Perhaps the causation may be more complicated than has been suspected, and at all events the sudden annihilation of nutritive osmoses and the novel conditions of pressure cannot be excluded from our enumeration of possible causes of pain, especially when we remember that all the neural phenomena of health are carried on in the presence of a certain varying but definitely limited pressure, alteration of which, in the brain at least, is a fertile source of mischief. How far these pressure conditions may be needed for the proper functional life of the nerve, we can hardly surmise; nor can we, in any case, separate their probable influence from that of the nutritive supply, which varies with them and ceases when they no longer exist.

That sudden alterations of pressure may alone be sufficient to painfully excite the nerves, is seen when a tourniquet is removed after having been some hours on a limb. Such a treatment was resorted to, many years ago, for the

purpose of controlling cramps or hysteroid attacks. I
have heard patients who had been subjected to it speak
of the sensations accompanying the return of blood into
the limb as agonizing.

The facts here related, as to the excitability of nerves
by acids and alkalies, with the probability that much
more dilute solutions would in man cause perceptible
sensations for the existence of which in the animal we
have no test, naturally leads us to speculate upon the
share in producing or increasing pain which may be due
to chemical alterations in diseased tissues.

In nerve injuries, as I have already pointed out, the
changes in surface secretion which give rise to over-acid
or acrid sweats, may be paralleled by like chemical disturbances in the interstitial products of the nutritive
processes, and from these may directly originate new
sources of pain and of disturbed or diminished sensation.
Probably, in this way, we are to account for the stiffness
and pain which follow intense fatigue, and which most
likely are due to accumulation in the tissues of the
material products of disintegrative change.

Influence of heat and cold.—The effect of heat upon
nerves, when these are exposed to the air, is to desiccate
them, and therefore to produce the symptoms already
mentioned as due to desiccation.

The effect of extreme cold upon the nerve centres was
studied experimentally by the author in 1866 and '67;
and the special influence of this agent upon nerves was
examined with care by Dr. Richardson, of London, in
1867, both making use of the spray producer invented
by the latter observer.

When a nerve is rapidly frozen by ether or rhigolene
spray, spasms are caused at first in its connected muscles,
but in all classes of nerves the conducting power diminishes, until finally, when absolutely frozen, it no longer

responds to volitional or electrical irritations ; and all the sensitive parts to which it is distributed become devoid of feeling. As the nerve thaws again, all of its functions gradually return. Altered vascular conditions also occur. At first the cold contracts the vessels, and almost instantly, as the part thaws, they dilate, and the part becomes the seat of a more or less intense congestion,—a circumstance of which I have made use in studying the congestions of nerves and ganglionic centres.

The best clinical study of the influence of cold on nerves was made by Dr. A. Waller,* in 1862. I shall have occasion to refer to it again.

---

* Proc. Royal Soc. London, vol. ii. 1860–62, p. 89 et seq.

CHAPTER IV.

In the different forms of mechanical injury of nerves, a certain share of functional loss depends upon the cutting, tearing, stretching, or bruising of nerve tubes which the missile or weapon occasions. To this set of incapacitating causes are soon added, in varying degrees and at more and more remote periods, congestion, inflammation, and sclerosis, so that the remote pathological consequences are very often more serious than the primary hurt. Because, in the study of symptoms and of the varieties of nerve lesion, it becomes difficult or impossible to discern what are due to mechanical interference, and what to the sequent pathological states, it is desirable to view these latter separately, and also to study the process by which an isolated nerve alters (degeneration), and that by which in time it is repaired (regeneration). For whatever so affects the nerve tubes as to annihilate their power to carry impressions, whether this be mechanical, as a wound, or a pathological state, such as inflammation or sclerosis, inevitably dooms them to a gradual change, which results first, in their partial destruction, and possibly, after a time, in their more or less complete repair.

Congestion of nerves.—Our clinical knowledge as to the congestion of nerve trunks is so very limited that were we asked to define the symptoms which indicate its existence, few pathologists would be ready with an answer. Yet there can be little doubt that such a condition does often exist, and that upon this pathological state, which

(56)

disappears with death, may depend some of the neural maladies which we are as yet forced to style functional. Any effort to lessen our ignorance on this subject should be indulgently received, and I have, therefore, felt justified in setting forth the following observations, incomplete though they be.

When by any method we freeze or even chill the living tissues, the act of thawing is followed by more or less congestion. The nervous tissues are no exception to this law, and whether in brain, spine, or nerve trunk, congestion is sure to follow the return of warmth, and to occasion symptoms which vary with the neural region attacked. The changes of tissue, immediately due to the process of congelation, have probably but little to do with these sequent conditions, because the symptoms in question hold a relation in time and severity to the amount of visible congestion, and arising with it are most intense when it is at its height. By means, therefore, of chilling and thawing a nerve, I have been able, as I believe, to produce congestion with great certainty, and thus to study in man its associated symptoms, and in animals the pathological traces which it leaves upon the nervous tissues.

The sciatic, the pneumogastric, and the sympathetic of the neck were, in animals, the nerves chosen for the purpose of pathological study. To effect congestion, no form of cold is so well fitted as that which, profiting by Dr. Richardson's atomizer, I have myself introduced among the methods of physiological and pathological research. When a jet of ether spray, or of rhigolene, which Dr. H. J. Bigelow first employed, and which I greatly prefer, is thrown upon the skin, as the part thaws the vessels become paralyzed, and a spot of deep congestion is left, which lasts, in my own case, for twenty-four hours or longer. The effect is still more striking when the membranes and tissue of the spinal cord are attacked. The

visible vessels then abruptly enlarge, new ones come into
view, and the part obviously darkens.*

Precisely the same effects follow when we freeze a nerve,
and this is the case whether we protect its tissue from the
chemical influence of the rhigolene or act upon it directly.
I have usually preferred to cover it with thin rubber, or
with a layer of some neighboring tissue. In some instances the nerves were frozen once, and examined after
half an hour. In others the freezing was repeated once
or several times, at intervals of hours or days.

When a single brief freezing has been effected, there is
usually a distinct congestion, which very soon lessens, and
at all events leaves behind it no changes which can be
seen under the lens. In more prolonged freezings, or
when these had been repeatedly employed, distinct lesions
were visible, and even to the unassisted eye the nerve
looked darker, and in some cases larger, than was natural.
Sections of nerves in this condition exhibit a seeming increase in the number of vessels, as well as frequent vascular ruptures, which dot the nerve with interfibrillar
clots; while in some cases, long lines of red mark where
the escaping blood has followed the areolar interspaces
between the grosser divisions of the nerve. Cases as
grave as this are not merely congestions, but actually apo-
plexies of the neural tissue, and show their influence in
the animal used, by lameness, and sometimes by distinct
lessening of sensation in the parts to which the congested
nerve is related. Of course the minor symptoms of sensory disturbance are incapable of study in the animal.

---

* In the spine, as in the nerve trunks, sudden loss of power is the
primary result of freezing, then follows a rapidly-increasing congestion,
which is marked, in the case of the spinal cord in birds, by certain epilep-
tiform phenomena of a very instructive character.

See Am. Journ Med. Sci., Jan. 1867, and Jan. 1868, for my own researches on this subject.

When animals, the nerves of which have been subjected
to extreme congestion, are allowed to survive, the lameness usually lessens and disappears ; but if, at the close of
two weeks, the animal be sacrificed and the nerve subjected to study, it is common to find that, owing to the
pressure of the minute clots above described, or to other
causes, a certain number of the nerve fibres are undergoing the Wallerian degeneration.

If we subject the ulnar nerve of man, at the elbow, to
extreme cold, we shall have certain phenomena, due to
the suspension of nerve function, which will be followed,
as the cold is removed, by a group of symptoms which
it seems to me we have every right to look upon as caused
by the sequent congestion of the nerve, and which, indeed,
can scarcely be referred to any other cause.

I had myself made several experiments upon the symptoms which follow congelation, when I became acquainted
with Waller's admirable research. The following statement is therefore based upon his experiments and my own,
which closely agree.

I have repeatedly chilled or frozen the ulnar nerve in
myself with ice, or ice and salt. The first effect is to cause
intense aching pain, which, although most severe in the
little finger, the outside of the third finger, and the ulnar
palm, is also felt in the whole hand, and especially on the
back of the hand, at the space between the metacarpal bones
of the thumb and forefinger. The pain rather suddenly
ceases at a certain stage of freezing, and for a moment
the hand feels natural. Then the ulnar distribution in
the hand begins to be numb, and this increases until all
sensibility is lost,—touch, pain, and the thermal sense
disappearing in turn. Last of all, motility, which very
early is slightly affected, lessens by degrees, and is lost
altogether. Soon after the part grows numb the thermometer rises slowly, sense of heat is felt in the ulnar

palm, and this region, in my own case, sweats excessively.
At the same time, the ulnar nerve at the elbow grows
very excitable, and the least tap on the nerve causes slight
pain in the third and fourth fingers, and sudden flexion
of the first phalanges of all the fingers save the first, as
well as adduction of the thumb.

The average rise of the thermometer in moderate chilling, which does not annihilate sensation and leaves motion
but slightly impaired, is 2° F. In more complete freezing,
it is in my case from 3° to 4° F.

The symptoms which follow the thaw are, as I believe,
due chiefly to congestion. The nerve remains sore at the
elbow and even some distance below and above it, while
the brachial plexus may become tender (Waller), and as
the thawing occurs, the heart may be enfeebled and syncope threaten (Waller) or vertigo occur, as I have felt
in my own case. The terminal distribution of the nerve
suffers, after severe freezing, for hours or days, so that
soreness of surface, numbness, prickling, and partial loss
of power may continue, together with a certain fullness
which is felt and which makes itself visible to the eye.
Even after slight freezing, there may remain for hours
certain uncomfortable sensations which scarcely admit
of distinct description. In one instance these symptoms endured for eleven days, according to Waller, and
in my own case they usually lasted from ten to fourteen
days.

We may therefore conclude, without being thought
hasty, that numbness, hyperæsthesia, slight prickling,
formication, and more or less loss of motility are the
symptoms of congestion of a great nerve trunk. Temperature affords us no aid, as it becomes equal in all parts
of the hand soon after the freezing is over. Such a combination of symptoms in clinical experience should teach
us at once to explore the whole nerve track with care, in

order to find, if possible, a spot where the nerve is tender
on pressure, and where we would have a right to infer
that there might be a local congestion which could be
relieved by proper treatment.

Neuritis.—Neuritis is in man one of the most common
consequences of nerve wounds, and we might suppose
from this that it would be always easy to produce it in
animals by experimental interference with nerves. In
some of the lower animals, such as the dog, upon which
Dubreuihl made his observations, such inflammations
may be produced, but not with any great ease or certainty; for although in one animal a caustic or a seton occasions more or less neuritis, in others this result altogether
fails us, while it is also exceptionally rare to bring about
in these creatures any well-marked sclerosis.

In animals such as the short-eared rabbit, it is difficult
to produce neuritis by any plan of dealing with a nerve.
After numerous experiments, I succeeded but once, and
unfortunately did not see the animal again until too late
to study its neuritis in the active stage. It resulted in
the formation of a number of abscesses within the sheath
of the nerve. The nerve fibres in a degenerated state were
found passing over the outer walls of the abscesses, and
the resultant neural change passing upward had invaded
the spine, causing sclerotic alterations of the same lateral
half of the cord.

Acute neuritis. — This disease is probably of extreme
rarity as an idiopathic affection. It occasionally arises
from wounds or from the inroads of cancer. I recall a
terrible instance of the latter causation in a lady who
died after horrible agony from pelvic carcinoma. She
suffered from intense pain in the regions to which the
sciatic nerve is distributed; the pain being remittent,—
increasing at night. The sciatic nerve was exquisitely
tender, and a distinct redness of skin accompanied its

track half-way to the knee. After death I found the softened nerve lying in the pelvis behind a cancerous mass. Exterior to the pelvis it was swollen, red, and vascular to a remarkable degree.

I have seen sudden and violent neuritis set up in an unhealed nerve wound, but have had no chance of examining such cases pathologically.

Symptoms.—The symptoms of acute neuritis as it is seen to follow upon a nerve wound are these: At some time between the reception and the healing of the wound the patient is attacked with rigors, which are not usually very severe. In the only case in which I have studied the temperature, the chill came on at noon, owing to a wound of the right median nerve received a week before, and followed by exposure in an open car during a journey. At four P.M. the rigors still continued, and at this hour the right axilla* gave a temperature of $102\frac{1}{2}°$ F. Fever came on in the night, and continued with evening exacerbations for three days. With the rigor there was, in this case, a gradually increasing pain, which seemed very soon to pervade the whole limb. In four cases of which I have notes, there was slight delirium, owing as much to the horrible pain as to any other cause. In fact, some of these cases become what in a woman we should call hysterical, and by turns bewail their condition, or pitifully apologize for their want of manly endurance. The pain seemed to be worse at night, and to be aggravated by motion and by a dependent position. In three of my cases, all arm wounds, it gradually increased both in severity and in the extent of the region affected, until it seemed to influence not merely the nerve first injured, but all the cords of the parent plexus. In one man there were, on the second day, sympathetic pains in the fifth nerve of the

---

* The left was the same.

same side, and slight stiffness with severe pain in the muscles at the back of the neck. In one of my cases there was a distinct band of red overlying the nerve and running upward from the elbow, the site of the wound, into the axilla. In the remainder this symptom was absent. Two cases had been carefully examined beforehand without finding any notable tenderness; but in these as in the others, not only was the nerve tender on deep pressure or on rolling it, but the skin above its track was sore, and during the second or third day the whole limb was hyperæsthetic; while in two at least the sense of touch, already impaired, was notably diminished in acuteness by the attack.

In only one was there sudden and marked œdema within three days, and this case presented, a week later, one of the best examples of neural arthritis I have ever met with.

Terminations.—Cases of acute neuritis are said sometimes to terminate early in resolution, without mischief to the nerve; but in no case within my experience has this happened. Usually the inflammation lessens, the fever subsides, and the pain diminishes, but does not altogether disappear. At last we have the nerve passing into a state of subacute inflammation, which may last for months, or not, as it is well or ill treated.

The following histories may serve better to illustrate the clinical features of acute neuritis than any more methodical details:

Case 1.—Dubreuilh* relates a very clear case which followed upon the excision of a tumor overlying the brachial plexus. The mass was adherent to these parts, and consisted of a sac full of hydatids and serum, which were removed, and then the mass dissected out. The usual

---

* Névrite, p. 104.

antique French charpie dressing to excite suppuration
was employed. On its removal, at the fifth day, a sharp
pain began to be felt in the plexus, and, gradually increasing, became intense. There was high fever, insomnia,
and headache. The median nerve was hard, enlarged,
and exquisitely tender throughout, but especially high
up. Over it the skin was deep red. The pain, which was
constant, was made worse by movement. The forearm
was swollen, and the fingers numb and feeble. The case
was actively treated with leeches, venesection, and emol-
lients, and, after a threat of erysipelas, which proved to
be only an extension of the super-neural erythema, the
case was discharged, well, at the twenty-fourth day.
There were no after-consequences.

The following example is less striking and was also less
fortunate:

Case 2.—J. C., sergeant, consulted me on account of loss
of power in the arm, with severe neuralgia. At Gettysburg he received a ball wound in the left neck, splintering
the clavicle and emerging through the trapezius. Some
fragments of bone were lifted out of the wound, which
did well until a week later, when, on the way to Washington, he was suddenly taken with a chill, of some
severity, followed by high fever. At the same time the
whole arm began to ache, darting pains shot up and down
it, and the skin on the inside of the arm, below the axilla,
was seen to be red. The nerve tracks were extremely
tender. On the third day the whole arm was somewhat
swollen, and the darting and aching pain was only sub-
dued by frequent hypodermic injections. His first notable
relief was obtained by an application of cut cups to the
neck and shoulder, and gradually the pain lessened to
its present grade of severity. The ulnar and median were
hard, enormously enlarged, and very tender. J. C. described himself as having been made delirious by the

earlier pain of his disease; and even when seen by me
after it had abated, he showed very plainly that the mind
as well as the body had suffered,—his memory being impaired, and his temper excessively irritable. This was a
very good example of acute traumatic neuritis passing
into the chronic form.

Case 3.—L. P., a sergeant, was shot through the middle
third of the thigh in the battle of Fredericksburg, and
reached our wards within seven days. Whether the ball
wounded the sciatic nerve or not was uncertain, but it
must at least have bruised it, since there was some loss
of power and of feeling.

A small abscess in the walls of the wound of exit discharged itself with a fragment of clothing on the morning
of the eighth day, and that evening he had a slight chill
followed by fever and occasional rigors, lasting all night.
There was sharp pain in the wound, and, before next
morning, agonizing aching down the sciatic distribution,
with intense burning in the foot. All next day the man
was delirious, his face flushed, his pulse 130 and upwards,
his tongue red and dry. He begged at times to be killed,
at others, to go home; while sometimes he would lie open-
eyed, regarding ferociously the passers-by who shook his
bed as they walked, every movement seeming to add to
his torment. On the third day the fever abated and his
pulse fell. He said the pain was no better; but by this
time he was quite unmanned, and his evidence was valueless. He would at this time, however, allow me to handle
the limb, which he had, until then, refused to do. It was
slightly swollen, bathed in profuse sweat, as it had been
throughout the attack, and the nerve track was exquisitely
tender; when, indeed, an assistant rudely pressed upon it,
he shrieked with pain, and grew faint, pallid, and sick at
the stomach. I could detect no band of redness over the
nerve, but at two places, between the wound and the

foot, there were very red spots. One of these was in the popliteal space, and one over the point where the peroneal nerve dips into the muscles.

Under active treatment the pain lessened, but the foot became subject to severe burning, and it was many months before the patient recovered from the shock of this painful malady. From being a man of gay and kindly temper, known in his company as a good-natured jester, he became morose and melancholy, and complained that reading gave him vertigo, and that his memory of recent events was bad.

Diagnosis and prognosis.—I do not see how this malady can well be confounded with any other, especially when it is the result of a wound. Its future must depend, to some extent, upon how soon it is recognized, how boldly and skillfully treated. It may pass away, as I have said, doing little harm, or, what is more probable, it may occasion subacute neuritis or sclerosis, or may be the fertile parent of neuralgia, causalgia, joint disease, and local palsies.

Chronic or subacute neuritis.—This condition is a common consequence of wounds of nerves, and is apt to follow amputations, but, though rare as an idiopathic malady, it is not excessively uncommon. It is brought on by cold or rheumatism, and as a result of acute neuritis, while only once have I seen it as a consequence of syphilis.

Symptoms.—Subacute neuritis is often incapable of distinct clinical discrimination when of a mild type, and when there is an absence of traumatic cause. In its fullest development it is characterized, as I have seen it, by the following peculiarities, which are best marked after it has existed for a length of time. The affected nerve is tender over a large portion of its track, and the points of emergence, from a bone or through a fascia, are still more sensitive, while in true neuralgias it is only the points of Valleix which are easily hurt by pressure. Moreover, unlike the hyperæsthetic spots of neuralgia, the sensitive nerve tracks of neuritis are constant, and alike tender at all times. Some difficulty may arise where the neuritis is limited and lies near to a recent wound, the tenderness from which may be confounded with that of the nerve.

In many old cases of neuritis, unless the nerve is small and deep seated, it can be felt as an enlarged and hardened cord, so that it is frequently easy to distinguish even the deeply placed sciatic nerve.

The redness which may overlie an acutely inflamed nerve I have not seen in cases of chronic neuritis; but, when long continued, it is the cause of structural changes, such as atrophy of the skin, with causalgia, changes in the nails, œdema, and rarely of sclerotic thickening of the dermis. The pain of subacute neuritis is aching in character, and less distinctly follows the larger nerve tracks than does that of neuralgia. Like neuralgia, it is, however, liable to increase at night, and may even affect such returns of violence at fixed hours, although it is rather to be described as remittent than intermittent.

Whatever quickens the circulation makes it worse, and movement always lights up the torture afresh. Indeed, so surely is this the case that absolute rest is indispensable in the treatment.

Chronic neuritis has a constant tendency to pass centripetally, and thus to involve new nerves; and this is so characteristic of neuritis and of sclerosis, whether the latter be of inflammatory origin or not, that in any traumatic case where pain is found to be attacking in turn the various neural distributions arising from a common plexus, I should at once suspect the existence of an organic cause. A close search for the symptoms I have described will very often disclose the presence of an unsuspected neuritis, and I feel very sure that, far more often than is thought, some such condition lies behind very many of the cases of what we treat as sciatic neuralgia.

Sclerotic alterations of nerves may possibly arise without the aid of neuritis, but this is at least doubtful; nor do I know any signs by which old chronic neuritis can be clinically diagnosed from sclerosis.

It is surprising how great may be the apparent structural change wrought by neuritis before the power to move is remarkably interfered with. The pain on motion of course limits motility, and may thus lead to error; but, as a rule, tactile sensation is more altered than motor power, and even the former may not suffer gravely until late in the case. Nearly always I have found, somewhere in the limb, hyperæsthetic regions where a touch was more unpleasant than deep pressure. The skin over the nerve trunk is apt to be thus affected, and when leeches are used on this part, their first effect is often painful, and they sometimes occasion an unusual amount of swelling and annoyance.

Prognosis.—The future of any case of long-continued subacute neuritis is rather a dark one, and is grave in proportion to the length of nerve involved, and the extent to which it has traveled in a central direction; since if it has passed up as far as the parent plexus, so as to be beyond surgical reach, the case may usually be regarded as one to be relieved, but rarely to be cured.

Pathological results of neuritis.—The primary effect of inflammation of a nerve is to render it more vascular, to enlarge and increase its vessels, to cause an enormous development of its connective tissue elements, and at first to render the nerve less firm, owing partly to this hyperplasia, and partly to an effusion of serum within the main sheath and between the nerve fibres. The secondary consequences which may follow acute inflammation I have not seen in man, so as to be able to relate them clinically. Rokitansky has stated them concisely. The nerve, intensely injected in lines, is dotted with minute extravasations of blood, becomes œdematous, and at last firm, from a grayish or yellowish-red gelatinous fluid, which hardens soon or late, at the same time that the surrounding tissues become involved, and present the ordinary inflammatory appearances. Should resolution occur, these products are slowly reabsorbed, and a gradual return of function takes place. Higher grades of neuritis reduce the nerve rapidly to a gray or yellowish-red pulpy cord, for which the inflammation and the constricting sheath are together responsible. The nerve is then tender, and readily torn, and its tissue infiltrated with bloody pus, the color of the nerve becoming yellow or brownish-red or chocolate tinted, while abscesses may form around its track. Ulceration is described as the final stage of this destructive process.

When the more acute inflammations pass into those of a lower grade, or when these alone have attacked a nerve, a series of changes result with which I am personally more familiar.

The nerve trunk is then more irregularly vascular, and is enlarged in some places and smaller than it should be in others. The induration, which affects more or less the whole of the inflamed portions, varies in density, so that sometimes there is a long, firm swelling of an inch or more of nerve, or else in a part moderately hard there is a succession of firm little fibroid bodies imbedded, and around them a circle of greater vascularity than elsewhere. The color of the nerve is usually some tint of gray or pale lead color, and in all probability the tact corpuscles undergo enlargement and degeneration. The tendency of these cases is usually towards hypertrophy and hardening of the connective structure of the nerve; and also, as a rule, the morbid change tends to march from extremity to centre, rather than outward. The result of these alterations is a gradual increase of connective white fibrous tissue, a consequent thickening of the sheaths, and finally, a more or less complete atrophy of the nerve tubes, involving chiefly the white substance of Schwann, and leaving the nerve fibre a mere rod, hardly to be distinguished from the more wavy fibrous tissue about it. This destruction is rarely complete throughout the nerve, so that nearly always nerve tubes in every state of health and degeneration can be seen within the area of a single inflamed and hardened nerve. I have thus met with perfectly healthy tubes in a nerve which was as tough as a tendon. With every appearance of enlarging, such nerves are actually undergoing atrophic changes as to their proper tissues.

Increase of bulk, proliferation of connective tissue, and wasting of nerve tubes are common consequences of chronic neuritis; but sclerosis may also be brought about without the intervention of inflammatory conditions, or, at all events, the change which began in these may increase and continue long after they have faded or disappeared. Sclerosis without inflammation undoubtedly occurs in the nerve tissues of certain stumps where their nerve trunks are enlarged and hardened, but neither tender nor neuralgic. I have recently seen with Dr. Mears a patient whose hand was removed by Dr. W. L. Atlee, on account of a remarkable train of symptoms, which, beginning with local spasms in this part, resulted in typical epileptic fits. The median and ulnar nerves were three times their natural size, and as hard as tendons. Besides an immense proportion of fibrous tissue and degenerated nerve tubes, there were still many of the latter in an uninjured condition. The tenderness over the nerve trunks had been slight and remittent, nor was pain at all a marked symptom. This was probably a case of pure sclerosis without inflammation. It is of course very difficult to decide as to the absolute non-existence of the latter condition, but I have had every reason to believe that, in some nerve wounds, the resultant sclerosis had no connection with inflammatory states except at the very outset, and that the former, in many cases, made mischievous progress without the latter.

The final functional result is the same in either case. The nerve tubes in large part perish or waste, and the symptoms affect at first rather the sensory sphere than that of motility. We have pain and anæsthesia or hyperæsthesia, but not as a rule local convulsions.

These atrophic nerve changes, whether due to inflammatory or sclerotic pressure, or to actual nerve section, demand a more careful and specific study, since upon a clear conception of their nature and the time they need for repair depends our success in the prognosis and treatment of a large number of local maladies of nerves.

Treatment of congested or inflamed nerves.—I shall have frequent occasion to allude to this subject in treating of neural injuries, and to describe in detail the various means employed; but I have also thought best to give here a more methodical statement.

Whenever, after an injury, such as a blow or wound involving a nerve, the nerve track in its near neighborhood begins suddenly to be acutely tender and painful, especially if rigors be added, it is well to take for granted the outset of a neuritis, which we should hasten to prevent from becoming acute. As I have said, my experience of this malady, and, indeed, that of most physicians, is limited. In the only case of acute neuritis of which I had entire control from the start, the arm from above the

wound to the finger ends was enveloped in bladders of ice
and iced water, which certainly lessened the pain. The
limb was elevated above the body, and $\frac{1}{25}$ gr. hypodermic
doses of sulphate of atropia with $\frac{1}{2}$ gr. of sulph. of
morphia were given every four hours, or oftener, as
needed. This plan, with attention to the secretions,
seems to me sufficient. I have also used leeches very
freely and with good effect, the ice being afterwards
replaced. I should add that leeching is sometimes excessively painful, and that the leech bites are more apt to
give trouble than in other cases. Absolute rest is one of
the essential conditions of treatment, and if the limb can
be put upon a rigid splint it is wise to do so.

Chronic neuritis is generally subacute, and is one of the
most difficult of all maladies to treat with success. It
very often occurs in persons who are perfectly well able to
walk about; and as it is vain to hope for good results without entire repose, the comparatively good health of the
patient is a real obstacle, especially in the arm cases.

Constitutional treatment.—In the army it was above all
things needful to look for the existence of scurvy or malarial disease, and to treat these with appropriate means,
—dietetic and therapeutic. But under all circumstances,
it is well to remember that the presence of such torture as
accompanies this disorder of itself induces a lowered vital
tone, which requires tonics and support, and that sometimes the long use of opiates has a depressing effect, which
we shall be wise not to forget.

Rest.—When the disease is really subacute, and the
nerve tender on pressure for some considerable part of
its length, I insist upon the most absolute rest. If it be
the leg which is attacked, the patient must go to bed and
consent to wear a carved splint for several weeks. If it
be the arm, a splint answers to put it in a state of repose;
and without this it is vain to employ other means.

Cold should be used over the nerve track by means of Chapman's spine-bags, or better, by such as are now made by the Davidson Rubber Company, which are thinner than those of English make. The caoutchouc bag should be inclosed in an outer case of thin flannel, and may then be kept *in situ* by the splint and a bandage, if a splint be worn. In most instances I have used these ice-bags over nearly the whole length of the main nerve, and have usually contented myself with their employment in the day-time. In some cases, however, I have had them renewed twice in the night, and this plan I believe to be the better of the two. The only difficulty lies in the first pain from cold, and is easily overcome. The relief afforded is often remarkable, and the loss of the nerve in size, hardness, and tenderness most gratifying.

Counter-irritants.—Revellents begin to be of use when the tenderness has lessened or only exists in a slight degree. I like best the revulsion caused by faradising with the wire brush (secondary current) the dry skin, well powdered, at a little distance from the line of the nerve. Vesication may also be used in the same situation,—but never over the nerve,—while more extensive irritation by Pearson's plan I have also found useful; but as to all of these means I shall have to speak more fully when discussing the treatment of symptoms, which late in these cases sometimes assume so much importance.

Sedatives.—Of hypodermic and other uses of sedatives I shall also have occasion to speak elsewhere. Let us use them freely, but be mindful of the fact that when recklessly employed they bring about moral and physical conditions which are simply fatal to successful treatment.

For examples of the methods employed, and which I do not find insisted upon elsewhere, the reader is referred to the chapter upon the therapeutics of symptoms.

Degeneration and regeneration of nerves.—The history of

the subject of the wasting of nerves and of their repair
presented no great interest until the classical researches of
Augustus Waller, in 1862. This admirable observer has
been happy in the almost perfect accord with which his
researches have been met whenever they have been experimentally examined by competent inquirers. Since a
clear knowledge of his conclusions lies at the basis of the
subject of nerve changes after section, I shall endeavor to
give a brief and distinct account of these results.

Section of a nerve trunk, whether it be sensitive, motor,
or of double function, insures degeneration of the peripheral extremity. If, however, we divide the sensitive
filament (posterior root) of a spinal nerve between the
ganglion and the spinal cord, the central end alters and
the portion attached to the ganglion remains unchanged.
Section of the motor (anterior) root, between the spine
and its union with the posterior root, gives us degeneration of the external end and no alteration of the central
extremity. Connection with the spine or the ganglion
seems, therefore, to insure against degeneration the anterior or posterior root respectively. Waller himself believed
that the ganglion is the trophic, or nutritive, centre for
the posterior root, and that the gray spinal matter, in like
manner, holds the same office for the anterior root. Phy-
siologists have, however, hesitated to accept this theory,
while the facts themselves have remained undisputed.

Whenever section of a compound nerve has been made
exterior to the ganglion, the entire peripheral end of the
nerve alters, and the central end remains unchanged.
To this law, Laverran* has pointed out a supposed exception. In the central end of cut nerves he found a
few altered fibres, and in the peripheral end, a certain
number of sound fibres. The degenerating fibres of

---

* Laverran, Thèse de Strasbourg, 1864.

the central end represent, according to this observer, Bernard's recurrent sensitive loops, which, being divided, the returning thread is thus dissevered from its trophic centre, the ganglion, and therefore becomes altered. In like manner, Laverran explains the unchanged fibres, in the exterior nerve end, as the recurrent fibres derived from neighboring trunks, through which the fibrils in question retain their connection with the nutritive centres. I have myself observed such altered nerve tubes in the central ends of cut nerves, but they were exceptionally rare, while in the outer ends I have failed to notice any sound tubes after the lapse of a certain time.

The upper end of a cut nerve remains but little altered for a few days, after which a rapid proliferation of connective tissue occurs, and there is a visible enlargement formed, which, if no reunion occurs, finally gives rise to the well-known button-like growth, which we shall have to study in connection with the neural maladies of stumps. The enlargement which follows simple section rarely attains such dimensions as it does after amputations.

The peripheral end of a cut nerve undergoes inevitable alterations, as to the exact nature of which there has been some difference of opinion, so much so, indeed, that I have felt it necessary to study the subject experimentally before venturing to describe the changes in question. These researches were made chiefly on rabbits, young or old, and include examinations of the sympathetic, pneumogastric, and sciatic nerves.

From the fourth to the sixth day after section, we observe in the whole length of the peripheral end a slight alteration of tint, consisting in a loss of transparency. Laverran denies this, because, as he says, the removed nerve is never transparent. I am confident, however, that if a piece of healthy nerve be observed alongside of the altered nerve, a difference will be seen even as early as the sixth day. At all events, this change corresponds with the partial loss of excitability in animals. In man, the earliest total loss of power to respond to electricity which I have seen was on the seventh day. At or about this time the whole substance of Schwann begins, in birds, to undergo irregular segmentation, a process which is slower in dogs and rabbits. The double contour of the fibres becomes irregular at first, as though the myoline were indented more or less deeply. Then the segmentation grows more complete, and the outlines of the fibres more broken, so that the myoline is finally to be seen distributed along the sheath of Schwann in masses, which are round or elongated and irregular at first, but which, by the third to the sixth week, become smaller, more numerous, and rounder, so that, in most cases, at the close of three months, the nerve tube holds only the finest granular elements. More or less speedily this remnant of the white substance of Schwann disappears, and the sheath of Schwann becomes shrunken, and, as it were, wrinkled, the whole nerve being now distinctly of a dull gray tint, and looking like a firm bundle of connective tissue.

When the nerve has reached this final condition of degeneration, there are still present in the sheath here and there a few minute molecules of fatty matter, and occasionally such masses are also observed lying between the fibres. Laverran has noted at this period, within the sheath, certain minute collections of matter very slightly refractile, and which I have also noticed, though not constantly. They resemble, optically, colloid substance, or portions of escaped myoline. After this time, there does not seem to be any notable change in the residual sheath, except, perhaps, a slight shrinking, and in some cases an increase in the amount of interfibrillar fatty molecules. The alteration of the white matter of Schwann has been

described as fatty degeneration; but, as Robin has remarked, it is largely fatty in the first place, and the
alteration may consist only in its being broken up and
removed, there being no evidence that any such substi-
tution has taken place, as is found to occur in ordinary
instances of fatty degeneration.

The utmost difference of opinion exists as to the per-
sistence of the cylinder axis during these progressive
transformations of the nerve. The majority of observers
incline towards belief in its permanence, and so far as my
own researches are concerned, I am also of this opinion,
although regarding it as a point most difficult of decisive
settlement.*

The degeneration has been described as passing from
the centre to the periphery, but I am satisfied that it
affects at one and the same time the whole length of the
nerve. For although it is true that a current which, at
the sixth day after section may not cause motion, when
applied at the upper limit of the nerve, may still do so
when used nearer to the muscles, this is due to the fact
that in the former case it has to overcome the resistance
offered by a longer track of altered nerve.

If we ask ourselves why the nerve alters after division,
several answers seem possible. The nerve may change
because its function is abolished,—the central part of a
motor nerve failing to alter owing to its being traversed by

* The rate at which the nerve change occurs varies greatly in different
animals, being rapid in birds, and slower in the rodents. In the frog it
is most speedy in hot weather, and in the hibernating animals Schiff
states that it is so singularly slow, that five weeks elapsed in the marmot
with less change than five days produced in the dog. In the snapper,
Chelonura serpentina, I found it to be equally tardy during the winter.
Some years ago, in the autumn, I cut the left sciatic nerve in two box
turtles, which soon buried themselves in my garden. On their reappear-
ance in April, I found the nerves quite *unchanged*. Within the next
month the peripheral end of the nerve underwent complete alteration.

currents of central origin; but this would only hold good of the motor filaments, and as regards the outer end would scarcely apply even to the sensitive fibres, which would continue to be excited from without, yet the whole of the external end changes, and none of the central extremity.

Waller's theory, which attributes the preservation of the central end to the conservative power of the ganglion for the sensory root, and of the spinal centres for the motor root, still remains the most prominent explanation; but whether we are to hold, as he held, that these are, as regards the nerve, direct trophic centres or not, is still a matter of doubt.

A few observers have been inclined to refer the changes which follow section to paralysis of the vaso-motors of the nerve concerned, but such an agency seems hardly competent, nor could we, admitting it, explain the automatic regeneration of isolated nerve ends. Whatever be the character of the neural impression which, setting out from spine or ganglion, preserves the nutritive integrity of the nerve to the remotest filaments, it must, in the case of the sensory branches, be propagated in a direction opposed to that in which they are traversed by impressions from without. It would follow from this, either that the preservative influence exerted by the centres passes along special nerve fibres,—nervi nervorum,—or that the sensory fibres are capable of transmitting impressions both centrally and peripherally.

The difficulty of explanation is increased, however, by the autogenetic restoration of nerves separated from the centres, and which I shall presently have to describe, and also by the repair of motor nerve ends when united to sensory nerves which still remain connected with the centres. As regards these points, M. Laverran states with Schiff that there are numerous trophic centres, and that very certainly the nutritive centre of one nerve may serve a like end for another, and that perhaps by means of anastomoses, and after a certain lapse of time, the trophic centre of neighboring nerves may come to answer a similar purpose for the peripheral extremity of the divided nerve. Of this, however, we have no proof. We only know that completely isolated nerve ends may undergo repair without having, so far as we are aware, any connection with the centres. When, therefore, nerves are cut, the perineural covering, the sheath of Schwann, and probably the axis cylinder, rest unaltered, while the myoline or white substance of Schwann breaks up, becomes granular, and disappears completely.

Regeneration of nerves.—When the nerve has reached its final term of change, a new process begins, which may or may not result in its functional restoration. After a nerve has been divided, and a portion exsected, it either remains separated, or the two portions reunite with more or less completeness. In both cases the nerve fibrils of the peripheral extremity undergo a reparative change, so that we have two sets of conditions under which to study the progress of restoration.

Within two months after section, the upper end of the nerve is seen to exhibit a slight enlargement, from which projects a grayish, conical bundle of delicate fibres. Many of these are normal in appearance, others want, at first, the medullary matter. As this stem extends towards, and finally reaches, the peripheral nerve end with which it unites, the fibres increase in number and in bulk, the complete fibres becoming more numerous as the tint of the new formation changes to the healthy white color of normal nerve tissue. After some months, it may acquire, what at least in my experience has been rare, the full size of the nerve ends which it joins together.* In

---

* Vulpian, p. 256, op. cit.

small animals, as the rabbit, from two to four lines of lost nerve may thus be made up, and in man there are certainly instances of at least three inches having been restored.

While many of the peripheral fibres are still undergoing destructive changes, and before the nerve ends are reunited, the process of repair begins in the lower end of the cut nerve, so that, in young animals, degeneration and regeneration are going on in separate fibrils side by side. Among the wasted tubules appear others, in which the medullary matter is replaced, and in this manner gradually the atrophied nerve tubes undergo a process of reparation until the nerve is recomposed, the newer elements being smaller for a time than the original fibres. The change thus effected appears to go on alike at one and the same time in the whole length of altered nerve.

Waller was of the opinion that the fibres thus formed were throughout new formations, but this view has been refuted by both Schiff and Vulpian, and there is now but little doubt that they are merely restorations of the original tissue.

Until the reuniting tissue contains a considerable number of healthy filaments, and until the lower nerve end has undergone a large amount of restoration, the functions of the nerve remain in abeyance, and the question as to the time needed for repair, and of the extent of this process, are therefore of the utmost importance in connection with the prognosis and treatment of nerve injuries.

Autogenetic restoration of nerves. — Vulpian and Phillipeaux have shown that even when the divided nerve ends do not reunite, the peripheral extremity undergoes after a considerable time a more or less complete process of repair, precisely such as occurs when reunion has taken place. This reparation may occur even when a portion

of nerve has been transplanted and grafted upon foreign
tissues; but although physiologically interesting, these
observations have no practical bearing upon the subject
of nerve wounds, except to show that the severed nerve
does not so alter as to forbid in the future any operation
looking to its reconnection by suture, or otherwise, with
the parent stem.

CHAPTER V.

NERVES, like other parts of the body, are subject to a great variety of lesions from physical agencies. In some cases these act without breaking the overlying skin, while in others the cut or wound involves the integuments so as to make what may be called a compound nerve wound, a condition involving, however, none of the added danger which an open wound brings to a broken bone. In fact, a clean cut through a nerve trunk is often far less grave than a contusion sufficiently severe to cause complete loss of power, or even, I might say, to produce less severe consequences.

Direct lesion by a missile of war or by incision.—Gunshot wounds, and, more rarely, sabre cuts, are the most frequent injuries of nerves during war, and they may present every variety in degree of severity, from the slightest abrasion to absolute loss of considerable nerve substance, as was certainly the case in many instances of wounds by conical balls observed by my colleagues and myself at the U. S. A. Hospital for Nervous Diseases. With us, at least, and the same remark applies generally, sabre wounds and bayonet injuries were very rare. I have seen no nerve lesion from the latter weapon, and if we except scalp wounds involving nerves, only one from the sword.

Seat of wounds.—The large number of wounds in the upper half of the body seen by us admit of the explanation that they bore transportation better than did those of

(82)

the legs, which involved usually far longer and more serious ball tracks.   Perhaps their frequency may have been
due in part to the greater proportion of all wounds of
the upper limbs.   Lesions of the cranial nerves were
rarely seen by us, because these injuries were so often
accompanied by fatal results at an early date, owing to
grave brain or face lesions.   One wound of the sympathetic, the only one on record, and several of the seventh
nerve, with one of the fifth nerve, complete the sum of
our hospital experience in this direction.

In the table of nerve lesions reported by Londe, and
also in Hamilton's cases, the proportion of injuries of the
upper limbs is far larger than that of the legs; so that in
civil practice as well as in war the nerves of the arms
especially are most apt to suffer.

Incised wounds of nerves.—In civil life the most common
examples of nerve wound arise from thrusting a hand
through a glass window-pane, both nerve and vessel being,
generally, severed.   I have seen one case of this kind,
in which the ulnar nerve was divided without the artery
being cut.   Knife wounds and the like of course exhibit
a variety of incisions of nerves, resulting in greater or
less loss of sensation and of motor power as the division
of the nerve is more or less complete.

Amount of injury.—The extent of injury to a nerve is of
course of the utmost importance, and is learned only by
the most careful examination of the parts to which the
nerve is finally distributed, in order to ascertain what
movements are lost and what skin surfaces show defects
of sensibility.

I shall have occasion to treat more fully of this subject
in connection with gunshot wounds of nerves; but even
here, it will be well to notice certain points which, if neglected, are apt to lead us astray.   Thus in studying loss of
motion, we should remember how closely related are the

regions of the hand, for example, and that many of its
parts are stirred by more than one muscle or set of
muscles.

In examining the sensibility, too much care cannot be
observed, since there is a natural instinct which causes us
to use any power of motion we may have in order to press
upon and so examine the touching body. Care as to these
points, and minute attention to the anatomical distribution of nerves, will usually decide the extent to which a
nerve may have been divided, where the accident is a
simple incision.   Although there is a general impression that a clean cut of a nerve, partial or complete, is
likely to result in total restoration of function, I am sorry
to state, as my own experience of such cases years after
the accident, that the histories of entire restoration are
sadly rare, and that most instances of divided nerves, if
abandoned to themselves, result in deformities and functional losses such as characterize, though in far graver
degree, gunshot lesions.   I suspect that the experience
of most physicians will support me in this statement,
which is amply sustained by Mr. J. Hutchinson's* series of
histories, nearly all of which were glass wounds, resulting
in serious and lasting loss of sensation or motion, with
marked nutritive changes.

Among cases of this nature, of which I have seen
several, but always late in their history, the burning pains
are certainly more rare than in wounds by missiles, yet
they are not altogether wanting, as Mr. Paget's cases show.
The two following examples may answer as illustrations
of this class of injury and of the consequences which
are apt to follow it.   In these, as in other neural lesions,
the nerve section is certainly followed by the usual degeneration of the peripheral end, just as is seen in animals.

_____

* Clinical Lectures and Reports, London Hospital, 1866.

Whether in man autogenesis of this extremity occurs when the part remains isolated from the central stem, is as yet unknown; nor have we learned to what degree the defect of arterial circulation, which in one of the cases must have followed ligature of the ulnar and radial arteries, is capable of affecting the process of nerve repair.

Case 4.—*Section of median nerve ; abscess at the site of the wound ; loss of sensation and motion.* R. L., farmer, Delaware County, was brought to me by his brother, one of the former patients of our military hospital. Two years before he had been accidentally wounded by a reaping cradle, the point of the scythe entering the forearm and dividing the median nerve just below the elbow. Unfortunately the wound, which was closed with care, suppurated freely at the third week, and an abscess was opened alongside of the older scar. It is said that there was at this time some sensibility on the outside of the forefinger, but it disappeared soon after the abscess formed, and not the least sign of returning function was ever seen in any part supplied by the median nerve. The skin on the radial side of the palm was thick and rough, and the limits of loss of sensation absolutely distinct, while all the muscular dependencies of the cut nerve were in the last degree of atrophy and contraction.

I proposed to my patient to cut down on the nerve and to bring the two ends together, when I hoped by galvanism to complete the cure, which, without the operation, I had failed to effect by prolonged faradisations. He declined to submit to the knife, and finally abandoned all hope of relief.

I felt well assured that the suppuration in this case interfered with, and terminated, the early efforts at repair. The very slight skin changes in this history contrast remarkably with those of the following case :

Case 5.*—*Division of the ulnar nerve and vessels and of the median nerve; anæsthesia of the parts supplied; inflammation of the tips of three fingers, unattended by sensation; diminution of animal heat in all the parts paralyzed; increase of heat during inflammation, but still not up to the normal standard.*— " A healthy girl, aged twenty-two, cut the ulnar side of her right forearm very deeply on a broken window-pane. The wound was at the upper part of the lower third, and passed across the ulnar vessels and nerve deeply into the mid-structure, probably dividing the median nerve. It bled very freely indeed. She was taken to the hospital, where the hemorrhage was arrested and the wound dressed.

" She came under my notice three weeks afterwards, the wound being then just healed. The scar was puckered in. She stated, as regards pain, that she had had very little in the wound, but much aching in the palm.

" The hand of the wounded arm looked a little thinner and a little paler than the other, but there was no other difference to the eye. All the fingers were kept bent slightly in the palm, and she was unable to straighten them, owing, as she believed, to the effort to extend dragging on the scar. In the attempt to extend, the scar was moved. She was able to flex the fingers fairly, but could not contract her palm or bring the thumb into apposition with any of the fingers. The muscular mass between the thumb and forefinger was thin and flabby. The beat of the ulnar artery could be detected below the scar.

" *Sensation.*—Immediately below the scar she could feel the prick of a pin, but not acutely; an inch or two lower, she could scarcely feel it. To the radial side, and at all parts above the scar, she could feel well. At the level of the wrist, in front, all sensation was lost, excepting over

---

* Hutchinson, op. cit., p. 314.

the ball of the thumb, where it was retained in an imperfect degree. The little finger had no sensation on either side, nor had the ring, middle, or forefingers. There was no sensation at the backs of the little, ring, and middle fingers; very little at the back of the forefinger, but somewhat more behind the thumb. Over the back of the hand, sensation was imperfect, being more so as the ulnar border was approached. The extremity of her ring-finger was inflamed, and presented an open sore, on the face of which, however, the prick of a pin was not felt in the least. The ends of the middle and little fingers were also inflamed. She had had no pain during the formation of these whitlows, but a continued aching in the palm of the hand. The palm, it should be observed, was not in the least swollen, nor was it tender to pressure.

"*Nutrition.*—About ten days after the accident, the tips of the little, ring, and middle fingers inflamed. In each the exact tip was affected, and serum was effused beneath the skin over the entire extremity; the finger-ends were slightly swollen, reddened, and, in the case of the ring-finger, somewhat tense. No pain was felt. The effusion in the little finger was absorbed. The skin at the end of the ring-finger died over the space of the size of a six-pence, and there is now an open sore at that part. On the middle finger, the subcutaneous bulla still exists. The cuticle is elevated by effused serum (subcuticular whitlow), and there is an areola of reddened skin about it.

"*Temperature.*—On cursory examination, no difference from normal heat would have been observed in the affected hand (the weather being sultry). On comparison with the other hand, a difference is, however, very perceptible; the nails of the affected hand feel, indeed, slightly cold. By the thermometer, a difference of about nine degrees is shown between corresponding parts of the two hands. On the finger most inflamed, the heat is

greater than in the others, but still does not rise quite to
that of the same finger of the other hand."

Right forefinger	(paralyzed), side,	79°;	front,	78°
Left "	(sound), "	90	"	87
Right little finger	(paralyzed), labial side,	80	ulnar side,	79
Left "	(sound), "	89	"	89*
Right ring-finger	(paralyzed, but inflamed), front,	89	"	89
Left "	(sound),	89	"	91
Right middle finger	(paralyzed, but slightly inflamed),	89	"	87½
Left "	(sound),	89	"	91

Lancet wounds of superficial nerves.—In civil practice, it
was common at one time to meet with injuries of the
musculo-cutaneous or the anterior branch of the internal
cutaneous nerves, the result of lancet wounds in bleeding.

One of the earliest reports of such injuries is Ambroise
Paré's† brief account of the case of Charles IX., who
suffered from a nerve wound thus described by his
attendant:

" Or pour instruire le ieune Chirurgien, et le dresser
mieux à la pratique dessusdite, ie reciteray ceste histoire,
qui n'est hors de propos pour la curation des piqueures
des nerfs.

"Le Roy ayant la fiéure, monsieur Chapelain, son premier Medecin, et monsieur Castelan, aussi Medecin de sa
maiesté, et premier de la Royne sa mere, luy ordonnerent
la saignée: et pour la faire on appella vn qui auoit le
bruit de bien saigner, lequel cuidant faire ouuerture à la
veine, piqua le nerf; qui fit promptement escrier le Roy,
disant auoir senti vne tres grande douleur."

Contraction of the muscles followed, with continued
pain, and during three months the king could neither flex
nor extend the arm; but, nevertheless, was in the end
happily cured.

---

* The sides exactly alike.
† Œuvres complètes, éd. Malgaigne, t. ii. p, 115. Paris, 1840.

Abernethy,* Mr. Swan,† Hamilton,‡ and others relate numerous instances of such accidents with more or less disastrous consequences than chanced to Paré's royal patient. These are in many respects among the most curious histories of nerve wounds with which I am acquainted, and would lead us to suspect that more extensive reflex symptoms are likely to be aroused by wounds of small cutaneous nerves than by those of larger trunks, and perhaps also that certain central conditions are needed to determine the grave symptoms which in numerous cases of slight nerve wounds are altogether wanting.

Nowadays these injuries are so rare that in my own experience I can recall but two, both of which date back several years, so that for instances of this nature we must resort to the older treatises.

Mr. Swan has detailed a number of slight wounds involving small nerve branches. In some of them there was instantly acute pain in the track of the nerve distribution, which speedily subsided, while in others it grew more severe, until general convulsions resulted. In certain cases the pain began after some hours, and rapidly increased, with the addition of hyperæsthesia, fever, local twitchings, and general convulsive disorder, which in very rare examples assumed an epileptic type.§

It is principally notable in these histories that the gravest symptoms were due to wounds of small filaments, few instances of like severe symptoms having followed those of great trunks; a fact which accords, as I have said, with what we now know of the larger capacity of nerves for evolving reflex phenomena as they approach

---

* Surgical and Physical Observations.   London, 1793.
† Swan, op. cit., p. 110.
‡ Hamilton, Jr., Dublin Journ. Med. Sci., March, 1838.
§ Swan, case, p. 117.

sensitive surfaces. Moreover, the greater number of such cases were women, and the hysterical element comes largely into view as the disorder progresses.

The following case from Swan* may answer as an illustrative example:

Case 6.—"I was desired to visit Mr. B.'s housekeeper at ——. I found my patient in strong convulsions, and held upon the bed by several assistants; her hands were strongly clinched, and she was struggling greatly; she soon after became comatose. I was informed that she had been let blood two days before by a gardener; that she complained very much of the arm where she was bled, and of a pain shooting from thence to the shoulder.

"I examined the orifice of bleeding, which was in the median veins; it had not healed, was somewhat inflamed, and a thin liquor oozed from the lips of the wound. While I was making this examination she became again strongly convulsed, as I supposed, from the irritation I had caused. With a view to interrupt the communication from the diseased point to the sensorium, I applied a tourniquet above the part; a remission of the spasms soon followed, and I administered an anodyne; but the convulsions, after a short interval of ease, recurred as before, and the application of the tourniquet was again made without any good effect. As I had no doubt that the cause of the disorder was an injury of a cutaneous nerve in the operation of venesection, I determined to endeavor by a transverse incision to divide the nerve above the injured part, and to destroy its connection with the sensorium; I therefore made an incision while the convulsions were most violent, of about an inch in length and small depth just above the orifice: no mitigation of symptoms was perceived; but on making another incision

---

* Swan, op. cit., p. 121.

above the former one, somewhat deeper and longer, she cried out immediately, to the astonishment of the attendants, 'I am well, I am quite well; I can stir my arm;' which she began to move, and continued to do so with great delight for some time in various ways. She had no return of the spasms, and very soon got well."

Slight' injuries of the digital nerves seem especially prone to occasion distressing symptoms and to awaken widespread reflex sympathies. Mr. W. M. Banks* has recently reported several cases of this nature, for which Mr. Bickersteth removed portions of the affected nerves with excellent results. No lesion of the exsected portion could be discovered. The Paccinian corpuscles were probably increased in number and size,—an observation not elsewhere made, but deserving of remembrance in future examinations.

Punctured wounds of nerves.—If we include only those histories which strictly deserve the name, punctured wounds are excessively rare, but are apt to be followed by very serious accidents, owing to secondary changes in the nerve, and occasionally also by grave constitutional disturbances.

As I have before remarked, some additional element in the way of a tendency towards neural malady seems to be essential to these and to the cases of lancet cuts resulting in serious symptoms; because it is only in rare cases after all that we meet with the consequences in question. Thus in bleeding it was common enough to cut a small nerve and see no result save a limited numbness which gradually faded away, while in animals I have always failed to excite any of the symptoms so dreaded, by causing punctures of nerves, nor has it been found that the wounds caused by acupuncture are to be greatly feared even when purposely involving nerve trunks.

---

* Liverpool Medical and Surgical Reports, Oct. 1869, vol. iii. p. 73.

M. Bérard has described a case of true puncture of a nerve which may be taken as a typical example. For certain galvanic experiments, he passed a needle into the supraorbital nerve. The electric current was then sent through the nerve, causing great pain, which soon passed away, to return again and again, until it took on a quotidian type, which yielded for a time to quinia, but recurred at intervals with great violence.*

I saw many years ago, in Paris, a man in Prof. Roux's wards who had driven an awl through the ulnar nerve. Excruciating pain followed, with choreal twitchings of the flexors of the fingers, which in the end gave way to spasm. I believe that the case was finally relieved by applications of the actual cautery along the nerve track.

The passage of a needle into the nerve of an animal causes usually a little intrafibrillar bleeding, which passes away without grave result. Bérard describes punctures as occasioning inflammation and final thickening of nerves. He quotes Descot to like effect, but I have been unable to find that this author makes any such statement regarding simple punctures.

Contusion ; pathology.—The only pathological study, and that a brief one, of bruised nerves has been made by Tillaux, who subjected nerve trunks to slight blows from a hammer, and then examined the injured part. He found that the neurilemma remains unbroken, but that numerous hemorrhages occur within the main sheath, and that the blood gliding along between the fibres may pass to some distance beyond the part affected.

Lesser collections exist even within the perineural sheaths, and traverse, in places, the intervals between the broken nerve tubes. At the seat of injury, many of the fibres are lessened in calibre, and beyond it, on either

---

* La Nouvelle Encyclographie, 1846, p. 37.

side, nerve tubes are seen irregularly dilated, and presenting the usual alterations in calibre which are observed in
nerve bundles teased out for microscopic study.   Three
or four days later but little effort at repair is visible, and
at the point struck the nerve tubes seem to be lost
in a granular mass.   Below the contusion, they present
the appearance of granular fatty degeneration, with the
well-known coagulation of the medullary sheath.   Tillaux's account is thus far perfectly correct.   In like injuries which I have followed up in rabbits, the so-called
fatty alteration of the nerve progressed exactly as in cases
of section, save that it was more or less complete as the
original injury was more or less destructive, many fibres
in the latter case escaping change altogether.

I was impressed, however, with a fact which finds
ample clinical illustration.   In some cases where I struck
the nerve smartly with a smooth, broad whalebone slip,
allowing a thin layer of muscle to intervene, the paralysis
which ensued, although often temporary, was in degree
complete.   In these instances there was usually little
hemorrhage, but a few fibres were torn, and a large proportion suffered simply a mechanical disturbance, which
gave them for the time a baccated look and irregularities
of outline, due to displacement of their semi-fluid contents.   If a nerve, disturbed only to this degree, be examined within a few days, when the paralysis is no longer
discernible, the nerve tubes present but very slight traces
of mechanical alteration, and a still later inspection rarely
shows greater alteration of the nerve save in a very few
fibres.

It is therefore probable that the condition described is
one which is for the most part rapidly repaired, and that
the temporary symptoms which follow slight nerve contusions may be due to the definite mechanical disturbance
here spoken of.

More severe lesions break the fibres, and subject the entire tubes to the pressure of multiplied clots of blood and to the destructive effects of compression by the material poured out for purposes of repair.

In two of these cases artificially produced in the rabbit, the nerve trunk became considerably enlarged, so as in one case, at least, to be fitly described as a neuroma.

Symptoms and results of contusions.—Contusion of nerves is a common incident of civil practice. In military experience contusions are met with arising from the impact of fragments of shell or entire round shot, and are of course sufficiently grave in their results, whether the skin be broken or not. I have seen in the United States Hospital for Nervous Diseases, and elsewhere, a number of instances of contusions from blows, kicks, or falls, some of them slight in character, and others causing the most entire crushing of the nerve involved. As a rule, a blow with any blunt instrument over the length of a nerve is unlikely to be serious; but when the same injury falls upon the nerve at its exit from a bony foramen, or where it rests in a furrow of bone, or lies superficially on the prominences of a joint, the consequences may be much more severe, as I have already pointed out, when speaking of certain wounds in relation to the spinal nerves at their points of exit from the intervertebral foramina.

As a rule, contusions, unless violent, do not cause immediate symptoms of loss of function. A little numbness and tingling may succeed to the first shock of pain, and only after a time be replaced by grave troubles, as changes by-and-by occur in the bruised nerve; changes only too apt to result in evils quite as permanent as those which arise from more immediate injuries. I have several times met with bad cases of atrophic alterations of muscles, the result of a contusion of a nerve, which for some time after the injury gave few signs of latent injury. Some such evidences of hidden mischief do, however, exist in nearly every case, and should be taken as indications for anticipative measures of treatment. Considering the number of nerves exposed to this form of injury, it is surprising that it is not more frequent. The nerves, however, yield somewhat to sudden pressure, and roll aside with great readiness, so that, except when they are firmly bound to a bone, it is not easy to hurt them with any weapon except one which possesses a blunt surface.

I have seen the supraorbital and infraorbital both contused by a single blow from the head of a cane. The lower nerve suffered most, and it was some months before the parts to which it runs regained sensibility.

The slighter results of blows on the ulnar nerve behind the elbow are within every one's experience, and occasionally this nerve is so injured as to involve permanent results.

I saw, some years ago, a singular instance of this, which arose during play between two lads who were striking each other with knotted ropes. One of them, in protecting himself, threw the elbow upward and outward, receiving a severe blow upon the ulnar nerve, thus stretched and held steady by the bent elbow. The tingling pain soon passed away, but in the course of the third week an attack of measles resulted in the return of pain and tingling in the ulnar distribution. These assumed a distinct intermittent type, became very violent, and were at length relieved by placing the arm at rest in half extension on a splint and by the use of morphia subcutaneously.

Causard,* Descot,† Hamilton,‡ and Duchenne all report cases of contusion of more or less interest. Examples are

---

* Essai sur la Paralysie suite de Contusion des Nerfs. Thèse de Paris, 1861.

† Affections locales des Nerfs. Paris, 1825.

‡ Arch. Gén. de Méd., 1838, t. ii.

also to be found in the work of my colleagues and myself, and two very illustrative histories, one of a blow on the neck and one of a contusion of the musculo-spiral, are related in the Sanitary Commission Reports.*

Case 7.—David Franklyn, aged twenty-two. In October, 1820, was seen by Mr. Swan. Seven years before, he was holding a restive horse by a halter wound tightly around his hand and wrist, when the animal, running back, drew the halter tight, and bent the wrist, pulling on it violently. Great pain ensued in the hand and wrist, and continued ulceration of the dorsal skin of the hand followed. The thumb and three fingers were bent back towards the wrist, and so remained, there being loss of sensation and of touch-sense. Mr. S. amputated the hand, and found hypertrophy of the median beneath the annular ligament, and several gangliform enlargements of the digital nerves.†

Case 8.— *Contusion of right brachial plexus; pain; consequent loss of motion in the deltoid muscle; wasting; cure by electricity; rheumatism a year later, with renewed neuralgia and weakness; final relief.* Mrs. K., aged fifty-two, fell and struck the right side of her neck against one of the round knobs of a brass fender. There was early swelling, and also a good deal of pain felt in the right arm for a few minutes, owing, as I supposed, to violence done to the brachial plexus. In a few weeks the blood extravasated at the spot struck was absorbed. Slight pain was, however, felt in the fore-arm and hand at intervals, until the twelfth week, when it became extreme around the shoulder-joint. Next came loss of motion, and wasting in the deltoid, with increase of tenderness at the site of the blow. Leeches were freely used every third day at this point until the soreness diminished, when I blistered the part twice. The shoulder pains were now lessening, and at the fourteenth week I began

* Medical Reports, 1867, p. 412.   † Swan, op. cit., p 60.

to use hypodermic injections of one-eighth grain of sulphate of morphia with one-fiftieth grain of sulphate of atropia. Under this treatment, employed daily, she lost all pain, except when the arm was moved. I made two efforts to faradise the deltoid, but each time caused increase of pain. At the fifth month I was able to resort to the battery, under the use of which the muscle gained bulk and power very rapidly. After twenty sittings, she could raise the arm outward to an angle of 43°.

A year afterwards Mrs. K. had an attack of inflammatory rheumatism, which left her with distressing neuralgia of the ulnar distribution chiefly, and with some weakness of the forearm.

This attack was treated by leeching, blistering tender points in the nerve, and absolute rest of the member, a measure which I have sometimes found of the utmost value. The arm finally remained feeble, and the pain is now, a year later, so rare and so slight as to give but little annoyance.

A very interesting case of contusion of the ulnar nerve will be found among the cases at the close of the chapter on Treatment.

Injuries to nerves from dislocations or their reduction.—One of the most interesting forms of contusion is that of the axillary plexus in certain dislocations of the humerus. In considering this accident, it will be convenient at the same time to treat of the less common palsy caused by the reduction of the displaced bone, and due most probably to laceration or stretching of a nerve more or less fixed or anchored by inflammatory processes in the surrounding parts.

Some slight degree of nervous disturbance is liable to show itself upon the reduction of any old dislocation of the head of the humerus into the axilla. I have seen several such patients, whose arms had been replaced by the

late Prof. Mütter after considerable lapse of time, and in
all the reduction was followed for some weeks by pain,
numbness, and muscular feebleness.　What is here exem-
plified in a mild form is more gravely illustrated in two
cases reported by Flaubert.*　In one of them a complete
palsy of the arm followed reduction, and, upon examination
post mortem, "the four lower nerves of the axillary plexus
were found to have been torn across."　In his fifth case,
the traction being more moderate, the paralysis is conceived by him to have been due to a simple elongation of
the nerves involved.

Desault† and other surgeons report histories of palsy instantly following reduction, or coming on within a few days
afterwards, but none of these equals in interest the case‡
of a soldier, whose right arm was reduced on the day
of the displacement with instant production of brachial
paralysis without pain, and yet with permanent reflected
anæsthesia and paralysis of the right neck and with ptosis
and partial loss of sight of the right eye.　The forearm
and hand were also insensible.

The risk of nerve injury apparently increases with the
previous duration of the luxation, but even an early reduction sometimes brings about paralysis.　In a case which
Duchenne§ relates, the palsy is stated to have been caused
by the reducing process; yet, on careful reading, there
seems to be no reason to suppose that it may not have
been produced by the accident, which preceded the reduction by only two days.　Where the remedial measure is
applied as soon as or earlier than this, it often happens that

---

* Rép. d'Anat. et de Phys., 1827.　I take this reference from Causard,
having been unable to get the Répertoire, and I am also largely indebted
to his Thesis for statements in regard to this subject.

† Œuvres compl., t. i. p. 355.

‡ Mém. de la Soc. de Biologie, 1854, p. 119, E. Le Bret.

§ De l'Electrisation localisée, p. 190, 2d ed.

no careful examination has been made as to the nervous condition, so that when, after reduction, the arm appears paralyzed, the surgeon is apt to refer it to the last disturbing cause, and not to the accident.

Dislocation causing nerve injury.—That dislocation of the humerus should sometimes cause paralysis is not surprising, since even a severe blow upon the shoulder is competent to this result, as every surgeon well knows. Cases of this nature are related by Causard, and I have faradised two patients for injuries thus produced.

Without following further the classical discussions upon this accident, it will be sufficient to state the opinions which I have reached after careful examination.

In the first place, falls on the shoulder or on the hand being competent to cause palsies of the arm, we may expect to meet with the latter even in such cases of dislocation as put out of the question any possible compression of nerves by the head of the humerus. In dislocation of the humerus backward, a rare accident, no nerve lesion is likely to occur. In luxation downward into the axilla, the capsule is of course torn, the muscles and tendons are bruised and elongated, and the circumflex nerve, extremely liable to injury from its close relation to the capsule, is very apt to be torn or stretched. This latter lesion, which has been actually found post mortem, is the cause of the atrophy of the deltoid which sometimes ensues. Hamilton thinks that the muscular loss is often due to the mere contusion of the deltoid; but on the whole it is more in accordance with modern views to see in the atrophy a consequence of nerve lesion, of which rheumatic or scrofulous inflammations of the joint are so apt to furnish examples.

In dislocations of the humerus under the coracoid process, or under the clavicle, the circumflex nerve and the muscles about the joint are prone to suffer severely, while the brachial nerves are liable to be carried forward with

the head of the bone, and to meet with injury, the amount
of which is determined by the force with which the head
of the bone breaks loose from the glenoid cavity.*

Mr. Hilton has described a dislocation downward
into the axilla, in which the humerus, although reduced
with ease, was retained with difficulty. At the thir-
teenth week the man died from disease of the chest, when
the circumflex was found to have been torn and displaced. I have seen a case in which, after a dislocation
easily replaced, the deltoid wasted, and then other muscles suffered, while neuralgia of severe type accompanied
the nutritive changes. Here the pathogenesis was, no
doubt, injury to the circumflex, atrophic alteration of the
deltoid, centripetal propagation of the neural changes,
secondary alteration of other branches of the brachial
plexus, and consequent neuralgia and muscular atrophies.

In grave cases of injury to the nerves during dislocation, they are compressed, as Nélaton† has pointed out,
between the clavicle, the first rib, and the head of the
dislocated bone. The degree of paralysis probably depends upon the violence employed in the displacement
being sufficient to drive the dislodged part against the
tissues which lie on its inner side. The theory of direct
contusion is now generally held to explain the observed
results, and but one author, Empis,‡ has offered any other
explanation than that which I have given. He reports a
case in which a man luxated his shoulder by a fall, and,
thirty-six hours later, before its reduction, was seized with
loss of power in the arm muscles without the least defect
of sensibility. Puzzled by this coincidence, he offers, in
explanation, the theory of the muscles having lost their

---

* Hamilton, p. 561.

† Elém. de Pathol. chir., t. v. p. 170.

‡ Empis, Thèse de Paris, 1850. M. Debout also attributes these palsies
to contusion of the muscles,—a strange conclusion.

irritability owing to some undetermined pathological cause. It is, of course, quite possible that there may have been here a co-operative spinal palsy, limited to nerves of movement; but he does not show that the muscles were at all insensible to electricity; and, as regards the mere fact of there being only motor palsy and no sensory loss, it may be added that this is a common incident of nerve wounds of all kinds, as I have elsewhere shown, and as I shall have occasion to point out more at length in future.

The essays of Malgaigne and Duchenne are so full of cases of palsy from dislocations as to make it needless to quote all the instances I have seen. The three histories which follow may suffice as illustrations.

Case 9.—Dislocation of left humerus from a fall; reduction in twenty-four hours; at the fourth week general loss of power; atrophy and contractions; rapid cure by electricity. A soldier fell from a tree, striking and dislocating the shoulder so as to displace the left humerus, in what direction is not known. It was replaced within twenty-four hours, and, the previous pain and numbness disappearing, he remained well for four weeks, when the arm began to waste, with loss of power, which became complete in a few months. Sensation was much less altered. At the close of a year, we found him with only partial ability to flex the arm, and with slight use of the flexors and extensors of the fingers. Marked atrophy also existed, with contraction of the pronators. Rapid relief and final cure were obtained by electricity. In this case there was plainly some trouble at the time of dislocation, and the resulting difficulties were due to secondary changes in the brachial plexus. As a rule, such cases are readily amenable to treatment.

The following very instructive case was sent to the Hospital for Deformities and Nervous Diseases, by Prof. D. H. Agnew:

Case 10.—*Dislocation of humerus into right axilla; no loss of sensation; instant palsy of arm and hand; gradual relief; reduction in third week; palsy of extensors of wrists and fingers; very slight sensory loss.*   C. B., German, aged fifty-one; well and vigorous; upholsterer.   Fell six weeks ago from a height of six feet, and, striking the right elbow, threw the head of the humerus into the axilla.   There was no pain except in the shoulder, neither was there, he insists, any marked loss of feeling; but the hand was paralyzed, semi-flexed, and, he says, stiff and numb.   After three weeks, Dr. Agnew reduced the dislocation and placed the limb at rest in a sling.   During the two days which followed, there was pricking in the ulnar region of the hand, which ceased upon the removal of the bandage.

Present state, June 23, 1871.—Shoulders alike; right arm somewhat wasted; greatest circumference of right forearm, nine and seven-eighths inches; of left, ten and one-fourth inches.   No tenderness above or below clavicle over nerves, except that the musculo-spiral was a little sensitive to pressure.   The hand experiences a general burning, but no darting pain; sensation is scarcely impaired; feels warmer to the patient, and sweats unusually.   The muscles above and below the elbow are flabby, and quiver even when not in action, and the arterial pulsation is remarkably violent.   The biceps acts well, as do the other arm muscles.   Pronation is good; supination is chiefly accomplished by the biceps, the supinator longus being feeble.   The fingers and thumb flex well, but their extensor power is partially lost, as well as abduction and adduction.   He has slight power to extend only the second and third phalanges of the first and second fingers, less of the third, and none of the fourth.   Extension of the wrist is entirely absent.

Temperature of right palm is . . . . . 96⅗° F.
     "   " left palm is   . . . . . 97⅘° F.

The flexors of the forearm, hand, fingers, and thumb move well when acted upon by induced currents. The common extensors and those of the hand respond feebly, as do all the interosseal muscles, save the fourth, which scarcely stirs under any current. The abductor of the little finger has no electro-muscular contractility. The electro-muscular sensibility is good everywhere except in the interossei.

Ordered faradisation thrice a week, from which resulted immediate and rapid improvement. The case is still under treatment.

The remarkable loss of motion, with the very slight affection of sensation, makes this case rather notable. When admitted, there was certainly no appreciable defect of the touch- or pain-sense, and no neuralgia or burning after the first days of his case. Neither was there the least disease of the joints. The following history of a similar accident is interesting on account of the presence of some of the symptoms which were wanting in C. B., as well as the fact that the motor losses were nearly the same in both men.

Case 11.—*Dislocation of right humerus into axilla; reduction at third day; palsy of extensor muscles of hand and fingers; nutritive changes; joint lesions.* W. C. S., aged fifty-four, porter; a thin, ill-nourished man, looking older than his admitted age. May 24, 1871, a drunken man seized his right arm and shook him so violently as to dislocate his right humerus into the axilla, causing pain in the shoulder and instant loss of feeling and motion in the hand.

At the third day, Dr. Knorr, to whose kindness I am indebted for the case, reduced the dislocation. The condition of the arm then began to improve, but at this time he first noticed that the hand was swelling.

July 7.—When examined by me, the whole hand and lower side of the forearm were œdematous, and the former also hard and brawnlike, resisting pressure. The fingers were in the same state, and the whole hand was dark and congested, but not shiny or smooth. The joints from the wrist to the finger-ends were sore, swollen, and very stiff. The whole palm was the seat of pretty severe burning, with no darting or other pain.

Sensation.—There was partial loss of touch- and pain-sense in the median and radial distribution.

The arms were of the same size. The elbow motions, pronation and supination, were perfect, but the latter was feeble. Wrist flexion was good, but limited by the joint lesion. Extension of the wrist was lost from paralysis. Power to flex the fingers was fair, but their movement was somewhat impaired, owing to the diseased joints. All extension power, and the lateral motions of the fingers, were absent, from palsy of the extensors and of the interosseal groups of muscles.

Electric condition.—The palsied muscles all responded to strong primary induced currents.

Injury of nerves from fracture of bones. — Contusion or laceration of nerves from fracture of bones is fortunately rare, and is most commonly encountered in such accidents as involve the humerus and the bony parts forming the elbow-joint. Similar accidents are met with in the forearm, and fractures about the face involve also, though rarely, the nerves which pierce its various foramina. In the legs, owing to their larger mass of cushioning muscles, direct injury from fracture is infrequent, but it is sometimes met with in pelvic fracture through the sciatic notch.

Ferréol-Reuillet,* who has written a very full essay on this subject, reports several cases of contusion or laceration owing to fracture. In the *Edinburgh Med. and Surg. Journal,*† Granger has three cases of fracture of the inner

---

* Etude sur les Paralysies du Membre supérieur liées aux Fractures de l'Humerus. Paris, 1869.

† Vol. xiv. p. 196. 1818.

condyle with paralysis of the ulnar nerve. Coulon relates an instance of intra-articular fracture of the external condyle of the humerus with anterior luxation of the elbow, and radial palsy, an accident which I once met with in the United States Army Hospital. The history was obscure, and the patient having been badly treated, the palsy proved very unmanageable under the most industrious and varied treatment. Mr. Swan also reports a number of interesting instances of these injuries, some of them very curious. One, a fracture of the glenoid cavity, resulted in violent neuralgia of long continuance, but was finally relieved.

Mr. Earle's* case of entire brachial palsy from fracture of the clavicle was also fortunate in its issue, which is not always the case where this accident has been due to direct violence. I have now under my care a gentleman from Maryland who suffered in this manner, and who has been for nearly a year the victim of neuralgia, in the radial distribution principally,—the attendant palsy, which was at first severe, being now but slight. The pain came on at the time he was hurt, and the amount of callus is unusually small.

Perhaps the nerve most frequently injured in the arm is the musculo-spiral. In some cases the main trunk is hurt, in others one of its two great divisions. I have met with one case of this nature resulting in wrist-drop; and very lately Mr. Erichsen has reported most valuable histories of like accidents with all possible care and fullness of detail.†

Injuries to the interosseous nerve in the forearm are sometimes encountered, but as a rule the nerve is more apt to suffer from secondary changes than from the first violence of the fracture.

---

* Med.-Chirurg. Trans., vol. vii. 1816.
† Lancet, July, 1871.

A number of such cases were seen in the United States Hospital for Nervous Diseases, all of them from ball wounds.

Two of these proved altogether hopeless, as must usually be the case with nerve wounds the result of bone fractures from missiles.

As regards the femur, lesions grave enough to break and displace fragments from one end of the bone so as to injure a great nerve, are rarely seen except as the result of machine or railway injuries. Mr. Swan reports a case of double fracture of the neck of the femur,—the patient surviving two months. There was intense pain, which proved to have been due to direct injury of the sciatic nerve by the broken bone.*

Smith† details a curious case of double fracture of both bones of the leg, in which the anterior tibial nerve had been torn across, occasioning intense neuralgia and subsequently demanding amputation. Alquié, quoted by Reuillet,‡ relates a somewhat similar history of injury to the same nerve, which I have once seen wounded by a ball fracture, where apparently the lesion had been due to a fragment of bone driven against the nerve. This case occurred in the Filbert Street United States Hospital, and was discharged uncured, and, indeed, unrelieved.

I have not met, either in practice or in my reading, with cases of injury to the intercostal nerves from fractured ribs. Yet it seems quite possible that where this accident has been due to direct force such a complication might well occur. The best collection of cases of fracture resulting in nerve wounds is to be met with in an excellent paper by Mr. Callender.§

The sole remaining instance of neural injury of the

---

* Swan, op. cit , p. 108.
† Dublin Journ. Med. Sci., vol. xv. p. 234. 1839.
‡ Bull. Gén. de Thérap. 1848.
§ St. Bartholomew's Hospital Reports, vol. vi., 1870, p. 33 et seq.

lower limbs in my own experience, I saw in consultation with Dr. W. W. Keen. The patient fell some forty feet, breaking the pelvis through the sciatic notch, and apparently bruising the sciatic nerve at its point of emergence from the pelvis. Intense neuralgia followed, with causalgia in the sciatic distribution, which was promptly relieved by a succession of blisters. The patient made, finally, a complete recovery.

In gunshot fractures, as I have before observed, fragments of broken bones are sometimes driven against distant nerves. Perhaps one of the most instructive of such histories is that of Seymour,* which I have elsewhere related more fully. A ball entered the left neck, below the left meatus auditorius, slightly splintered the posterior angle of the jaw, and emerged a little above the clavicle on the right; besides the left side injuries, the right inferior branch of the fifth nerve was cut off by a splinter of bone, which was torn from the jaw and driven across the neck.

Compression.—Either from external or internal causes, the nerves of the human frame are subject to a great variety of modes of pressure, yet very little attention has been given to the nature of the changes which they bring about, and still less to the difference in symptoms which arises from the varying rate with which the pressure is applied.

Augustus Waller,† in 1862, and Bastien and Vulpian,‡ in 1855, have done something to complete our knowledge of the phenomena which attend upon compression. In the experiments of these observers, the pressure which they made on their own nerves, or those of others,

---

* See Chapter VIII.
† Proc. Royal Society, 1860–62.
‡ Gaz. Médicale, 1855, p. 794.

was usually limited to half an hour or an hour. Their results, therefore, however valuable, fail to enlighten us as to the effects which weeks or months of gradually increasing compression may bring about. In fact, rapid or slow pressure upon nerves present distinctive differences of very striking character, so that while the former is apt to occasion most severe and positive suffering, the latter may sometimes cause extensive muscular wasting without sensory loss of any kind whatsoever. Nevertheless, in a vast number of cases of pressure on nerves, we have presented, with some modifications, the sequence of symptoms related by Bastien and Vulpian, while it is also true, as a clinical fact, that there are many and curious variations from this physiological programme.

These observers divide the phenomena of acute compression into two periods, the first extending from the moment of making compression up to that of ceasing it; the second, from this latter date up to the time of the return of the normal status. Each period is divisible into four stages, more or less distinct from one another.

First period: stage first is marked by delusive sensory impressions, such as formication, prickling, and a sense of warmth, which may exist throughout the whole period of pressure. There are also said to be false cramps, whatever these may be, while tactility and motility remain unaltered. This stage begins with the first moment of compression, and lasts from two to ten minutes.

Stage second is characterized as the intermediary stadium. It lasts from a few seconds to a quarter of an hour, and in it disappear all the symptoms of the former stage, to be followed by a seeming return to the normal condition and feelings.

Stage third. Hyperæsthesia is here the prevalent character, all the forms of sensation becoming exalted, but the muscular function still remaining unaltered.

Stage fourth. Hyperæsthesia passes more deeply into the tissues, and the exaggerated sensibilities become in turn perverted, and are lost. Before entering upon this anæsthetic condition, the tactile sense gives us false impressions of roughness on the skin, and the sense of pain furnishes the impression of peripheral burning. The successive, and, so to speak, isolated way in which each mode of sensation vanishes, explains how it is that, in this stage, at the moment when tactile sensibility is abolished, the sensibility to pain may remain unperverted, or exist for a time in an extremely exaggerated shape. Nevertheless, the deeper tissues continue in a condition of exalted sensibility. The muscles are now subject to a feeling of fatigue and weariness. Vague pains or cramps attack them, and the movements become less and less easy. We have, at length, muscular palsy, with general local anæsthesia.

The pressure is now taken off, and at once the period of decline begins.

This, like that of the augmenting symptoms, has four stages:

Stage first. For a brief period, not over two minutes, the muscles remain palsied and the skin insensible, while the deeper pains disappear.

Stage second. Passing backward, as it were, through the changes of the first period, there is now slight and improving muscular power. The sensibility to touch, pain, and tickling returns, and although perverted and hyperæsthetic, soon becomes nearly normal, the thermal sense alone remaining very imperfect. After a time, which varies from a few seconds to a minute, the third stage, which the authors term intermediate, begins, and is marked by normal motility and sensibility, and by continued obtuseness to changes of temperature.

Stage fourth. The patient has sudden sense of cold, which is centrifugal in its movement through the part

involved, and to this succeeds a local feeling of enormous
weight, which makes movement difficult. At the same
time there is general uneasiness, with possibly syncope,
and the feeling for which there is no scientific term, but
which is known popularly as a setting of the teeth on edge,
and which seems to pass inward towards the centres.

In the muscular sphere, contractions, and even cramps,
occur, and the voluntary motions are awkward and difficult, while the feeling of formication returns with marked
distinctness, and the whole limb feels as though it were
vibrating. Finally, motion becomes regular, the sensory
perversions cease, and last of all the thermal sense returns,
the duration of this stage being from some minutes to a
quarter of an hour.*

Augustus Waller† has left on record a careful study of
the effects of rapid compression of the ulnar, median, and
musculo-spiral nerves, with excellent observations upon
the temperature of the parts. The French experiments
are detailed with more method, but in essentials the two
sets of observations sufficiently agree. While, however,
Bastien and Vulpian describe as constant the curious return of normal feelings a little while after pressure has
begun, all sense of warmth, formication, and prickling
being lost for the time, Waller speaks of the same phenomena as occasional in the early stages of compression.
All of these observers agree that this affection of nerves
may produce vertigo and nausea, but only Waller has
pointed out that when a single nerve has been pressed
upon, the final loss of motility is not confined to its muscles alone, and this is in strict accordance with my own
clinical experience.

It appears, therefore, that when a nerve of sensation

---

* Mémoire sur les Effets de la Compression des Nerfs. J. B. Bastien et
A. Vulpian. Gaz. Méd. de Paris, 1855, p. 794.

† Proc. London Royal Society, May 15, 1862, p. 89 et seq.

and motion has been rapidly compressed, there are, at first, false sensory impressions, which come and go with normal intervals; then hyperæsthetic conditions of touch, pain, and temperature follow, to be succeeded by perversions of sense with spasmodic muscular movements. After these come total anæsthesia and absolute palsy. When the pressure has been removed, rapid recovery of sense and motion ensue, unless the pressure has been severe and long continued. In one instance, where Waller compressed his left radial nerve forty-five minutes, both sense and motion suffered for eleven days before the health of the part was re-established; and when repeating on myself his experiments, I found that many days were always needed to restore completely the normal feelings.

Experiments on the effects of pressure.—It has seemed to me that there was still some room for inquiry as to the mechanical influence of pressure. A nerve trunk is made up of a multitude of tubes, the contents of which are so nearly fluid as probably to be capable of more or less movement to and fro. When to such a bundle we apply a tight ligature, no matter how soon it be relaxed, we annihilate at once all power of the nerve to transmit impressions past the injured zone. If, however, in place of this, we make gradual and equal pressure, we may so affect the nerve as for a time to destroy its power to carry impressions. Now this is exactly what occurs in many cases of compression,—the nerve is for a time incapacitated, but soon regains its normal abilities. It seemed to me that the reason for such loss and such return must be purely mechanical, and that perhaps even the amount of pressure needed to arrest the passage of nerve force might be capable of mensuration.

The following experiments, which were made at various times with this intent, will not, I hope, be without interest:

A tube of glass, enlarged a little at the extremities, one-tenth of an inch in diameter and twenty-one inches long, was fitted at one end with a thin caoutchouc cover. Having laid bare the sciatic nerve of a rabbit, and slipped under it a thin cork, I allowed the bladder closing the tube to press lightly on the nerve trunk, the lateral expansion of the bag being limited by a ring of cork, nicked below so as to rest on the flat cork and yet to allow of the passage of the nerve. Two inches of mercury were then poured into the tube, so tilted as not to permit of the nerve being hurt by the fall of this heavy metal. The tube was next raised to the perpendicular position. The first effect was to cause slight twitching and some expression of pain. To save pain and to leave only the better test of muscular movement, I divided the nerve an inch from the tube on the central side. The quantity of quicksilver was now slowly increased. Each increment was apt to produce new twitches, as was also any sudden movement of the tube; but constant pressure, like an uninterrupted galvanic current, gave, after the first movements, no further result. As each half-inch or more of mercury was added to the column, I tested the nerve from time to time on the central side with a current from a small single Smee cell. The communication seemed to be unbroken, and muscular movements could be thus excited until I had put on the nerve a pressure of twenty inches of mercury. Ten or twelve seconds of this pressure gradually lessened, and at last abolished, the power of the nerve to carry to the muscles the impression made by the galvanism.

The tube was then lifted carefully, when to my surprise (and great interest) I found a gradual return of this power of transmission, although ten or fifteen seconds elapsed before the first visible manifestation occurred.

These experiments, made chiefly on rabbits, and varied

somewhat, so as to place the nerve between two caout-chouc bags of mercury, gave, on the whole, the same general result. For the sciatic nerve a few seconds—ten to thirty—of the pressure of a mercury column, eighteen to twenty inches high, broke the communications between two portions of a nerve. Relieved from pressure, the nerve speedily recovered.

It seems impossible to look upon this as other than a mere mechanical disturbance of the tubal contents, and a like mechanical restoration of their needed conditions for activity.

It is needless to speculate here upon the very suggestive character of these observations in a physiological point of view. Pathologically considered, they are not less interesting.

Remembering the delicate nature of the neural tissues, it seems inconceivable that twenty inches of mercury should not destroy them utterly. Moreover, what is the change which really takes place, and does it seem possible that the axis cylinders could be so broken as to refuse their office, and yet so reunite in a few seconds as to be fit again for functional duty?

From another standpoint the experiment seems to widen the breach between nerve force and electricity, there being, as regards the latter, no analogy to this observation.

I have made careful examinations of nerves which have been thus treated by compression. In all of them were noted some evidences of congestion, but the chief lesion lay in a very extensive disturbance of the contents of the nerve tubes. In some of them I could find scarcely an unaltered nerve tube, the neural tissues looking much as they do seven or eight days after section. Yet through the tubes so disturbed the nerve force still has power to travel.

These observations appear to me full of importance

when we come to apply them to explain actual injuries, and with their aid to recall the need for certain mechanical conditions in order to the integrity of neural function.

Various forms of pressure.—It may, perhaps, seem needless to enumerate at length the various means by which pressure is exercised upon nerves; but it does often happen that this cause of paralysis escapes notice, so that again and again, both in military and civil practice, I have met with cases in which physicians had failed to comprehend the true agency at work in producing the symptoms.

The causes productive of pressure upon nerves may be conveniently divided into those which act from within the body, and physical agents which affect it from the exterior. As a rule, the former act slowly, the latter more rapidly, so that the results vary somewhat, as I have had occasion to point out when discussing the physiological pathology of nerve lesions.

Inflammatory pressure.—It is extremely probable, as I have already stated, that inflammation occasions compression of nerve branches, and that the pain which accompanies this condition is largely due to this physical influence. It is also certain that the nerves of inflamed tissues are more sensitive than others to disturbing agencies, so that any artificial or other increase of the normal pressure still further disturbs them. Compression by inflammation is most troublesome at the points where nerves pass through bony foramina, and this is best illustrated where, as in the sciatic, the inflamed nerve is so placed as to be hurt whenever the motions of the limb alter its relation to the opening through which it escapes.

I am at present treating a man from Tennessee, who received in a scuffle a kick which injured the sciatic nerve at its point of emergence. The blow caused intense pain, and in a few hours local tenderness was followed by tingling and numbness in its track and ultimate distribution. These symptoms slowly increased for several weeks, despite local bleeding and blisters. Three months after the injury there was still tenderness on pressure in the path of the nerve, some loss of power, and intense pain whenever the leg was allowed to move backward beyond a certain limit, which the patient has learned to recognize accurately. Rotation of the leg inward also produced this result, which is due I suppose to the nerve being at these times in some way pressed upon at its outlet.

Pressure by cicatrices.—Cicatrix pressure from the healing of wounds must be unusual, as we saw it rarely in our hospital experience. Two cases which I recall were deep wounds of the thigh, and in both passive motion, and, finally, enforced activity, gave relief, which had been denied so long as we kept the patients at rest, a useful lesson as to the need for experimental treatment in individual cases. In the second of these men, the cicatrix lay across and very near to the sciatic nerve, so that whenever the leg was straightened, the man suddenly lost power and suffered pain.

In other instances where wounds had been allowed to heal with the limb bent, or otherwise misplaced, the resultant neuralgia seemed to be due to compression, and was relieved rapidly enough by restoring the normal movements and by the douche and frictions. Superficial shell wounds also were found in rare cases to occasion pain by cicatrix compression of sensitive cutaneous nerves, but none of these proved obstinate under proper treatment.

Considering broadly all cicatrices and the extent to which they contract, it seems singular that so few are sensitive or give evidence of compression on the part of the included nerves; so that I am led to suspect the existence, in the few painful cases, of some coefficient factor besides the physical condition to which I have been alluding. Painful scars have been again and again extirpated, but I have been unable to find any microscopic examination of the state of their contained nerve fibres.

The nearest approach to a satisfactory insight in this direction is to be had from a study of the terrible Spedalksed or Tubercular Leprosy of Norway.

Danielson and Boeck* have shown that in the anæsthetic form of this disease the nerves undergo certain changes which are finally propagated from periphery to centre. The earlier symptoms are neuralgia, with tingling, and hyperæsthesia, which become intense, and are followed by anæsthesia and loss of motion, much as happens in the gradual compression of nerves. The earlier of these symptoms seem to be related to simple congestion of the neurilemma; the succeeding and latest phenomena are due to a hyperplasia of the connective tissues within and without the nerve sheath, which occasions compression of the nerve fibres, and ultimate extinction of their functional life.

Perhaps some such alteration may occur in the nerves of certain painful scars, but it seems at all events quite certain than in others which have undergone like contraction no nerve injury exists, so that we must look further than the mere fact of cicatricial contractions, and concede the existence of other and unstudied pathological conditions.

Pressure from callus.—Pressure upon nerves by the excessive growth of callus used to be thought a common occurrence; but although nerves are sometimes imprisoned in forming callus, there does not seem to be in it any

---

* Recueil d'Observations sur les Maladies de la Peau. W. Boeck et C. Danielson. Christiania, 1860.

liability to contract like cicatrices elsewhere, and hence the nerve, however closely confined, may escape altogether undue pressure.

Among the many animals examined by Ollier after he had caused fractures of bones, in one only did he find a nerve caught in the callus, while every effort to place nerves so as to engage them in the callus failed altogether.

It seems, then, from experimental data, "that compression of healthy nerves in callus is not habitual" (Reuillet); whether it ever happens, this author considers doubtful, but he is inclined to believe that a nerve injured in any way, and slowly enlarging from neuritis while incarcerated in the hardening callus, may suffer severely.

This is a state of things not unlikely to occur; but there are no recorded cases which I have been able to find justifying so likely an hypothesis except that reported by Ollier.*

Case 12.— Aug. Lombard, aged twenty-two years, suffered a fracture of the humerus at the upper line of the lower two-fifths of the bone. The fracture was placed in a starch bandage for forty days, during the earlier of which the man had lively lancinating pains at the point of fracture.

On removal of the apparatus, the extensors were found to be paralyzed. Four months later, M. Ollier, after careful examination, concluded that the radial nerve was suffering primarily from compression by bony fragments, and secondarily by callus. All other means failing, Ollier cut down in the line of the nerve, and found it, as he says, " swollen like a ganglion, and strangled by a piece of bone obliquely placed and appearing to belong to the lower fragment. This point was, in fact, continuous at its base with the lower end of the bone, which was itself

---

Reuillet, op cit., p. 49.

confounded, so to speak, in a mass of peripheral callus."
"At this level the nerve was compressed as by a ligature,
and measured three millimetres in diameter, while above,
the swollen trunk attained one centimetre in width, and
below this point was only slightly enlarged. A little
lower it was of normal size, although still lying for
fifteen to twenty millimetres of its length in the heart of
the callus." The osseous point was removed, and the nerve
left resting in a gutter, broadly hollowed for it in the
bone, from which the periosteum was removed. Nearly
perfect recovery took place.

Besides this interesting history of bold and sagacious
surgical interference, there are but few instances of nerve
injury from the pressure of callus. An instructive case,
which occurred in the practice of Mr. Hilton, is related
by Sir James Paget,* and Swan has reported an instance
somewhat similar in character. In the former case, a
man who had a fracture of the lower end of the radius
had his median nerve compressed by a large mass of
callus. His thumb and first and second fingers ulcerated,
and the ulcers resisted all treatment until the wrist was
kept bent in such a way as to relieve the nerve from pressure. The ulcers returned whenever the hand was allowed
to assume its former position.

Gurlt has also related an undoubted instance of callus
pressure; but how rare these accidents are may be gathered from the fact that neither Hamilton nor Malgaigne
relates a single example. I have seen three cases, at least,
of extensive callus following gunshot wounds of bone, in
which there must have been imprisonment of nerve trunks.

In one only, a wound of the forearm, was there any
evidence of pressure, and in this case the symptoms were
most probably due to injury produced at the time of the
wounding.

---

* Surgical Pathology, vol. i. p. 43.

Verneuil communicated to Tillaux a case of formation of callus, which is probably unique as yet in medicine.

A gunshot wound broke the elbow, and after resection, amputation became necessary at the close of a month. On examination, the radial nerve, a little above the bend of the elbow, was found swollen and inflamed, and on one side of the enlargement, and penetrating it, was seen an irregular bony mass of the size of a bean, and plainly of recent formation, as the color, feeble consistence, and the form of its osteoplasts attested. As this was not a piece of old bone, it was probably due, as M. Verneuil believed, to a morsel of accidentally transplanted periosteum, which had given rise to a certain amount of ossification at a point quite remote from the callus.

Pressure by tumors.—The gradual growth of pathological new formations in almost any region of the body is a common cause of pressure upon nerves. Here, as in other examples of compression, it is important to consider two points,—the rate of growth in the compressing mass, and the anatomical relations of the nerves affected. In most cases of nerves of mixed function, we have the usual sequence pointed out by Bastien and Vulpian. First prickling, tingling, and sense of heat, then exaltation of sensory function and even hyperæsthesia, with finally loss of sensibility and motion. The speed with which these follow one another is governed by the rapidity of growth of the compressing mass, and the ease with which the nerves influenced are capable of suffering from the physical effect. This will depend in a great measure upon how firmly they are tied down. Tumors occurring in relation to the sciatic, for example, at the middle of the thigh, easily carry it with them unharmed for some time, and until the growth has become very large. But a tumor near to the outlet of this nerve, or a subperiosteal growth within the pelvis and beneath the points of emergence of the lumbar nerves, is early and disastrously evident in the way of pain and other disturbing phenomena.

These remarks apply generally to this subject, and to give examples throughout the body would be only to anticipate what I may have to say as to alterations of particular nerves. As a rule, fibroid and other formations of this nature, as well as aneurisms and syphilitic growths, give examples in their relations to nerves of simple pressure or elongation, but cancers may very early affect the nerve tissue, and occasion results which are due to other than merely physical causes.

I have seen instances of this in cases of carcinoma involving the lumbar plexus, in masses of a size too small to account by pressure alone for the agonizing pain in the lower limbs.

In two such cases I found the nerve trunks enlarged and reddened; so that here, as elsewhere, inflammatory conditions determine an early manifestation of pain in stretched or compressed nerves.*

The following very interesting history is a good example of the difficulties which sometimes surround the earlier stages of these cases:

Case 13.—In April, 1871, J. H., a porter, aged sixty-six years, presented himself at my clinic for nervous diseases. He was thin, sallow, and feeble. Three years before he had strained his back while carrying a trunk. The pain in the coccygeal region, with a sense of something having given away, was intense at the time, but slowly lessened, never, however, being wholly absent. Two years ago he began to have difficulty in urinating, with numbness in the left leg, and pain in the track of the sciatic nerve. At times the leg was weak; usually it was as strong as the other limb. When the pain in the leg was most severe,

---

* Romberg, vol. i. p. 10, Sydenham Society's Translation.

that in the coccyx also increased. The sense of touch was nowhere impaired, but the whole leg, and the anterior crural region, as well as the penis, always felt unnatural. The spine and coccyx exhibited no tenderness, but the sciatic nerve, at its exit and in the thigh, as well as the whole left buttock, were sensitive to pressure. Presuming that we had to do with a case of slight neuritis, and perhaps of inflammation of the lower end of the cord, I ordered ergot, tonics, and ice to the nerve track.

On his return, some weeks later, my assistant, Dr. Wharton Sinkler, noticed that the buttock was enlarged. On carefully re-examining the part, we then observed that it was also too firm, and that the surface was covered with dilated vessels, its temperature being at least a degree above that of the other side. To remove my doubts, I plunged a hollow needle into the mass, and after rotating it, so as with its sharp, penlike edges to cut loose small pieces of the tissue, I applied a syringe, and by its aid sucked up a little blood and several of the loosened fragments.* There was no pus, but the shreds, when examined, proved almost certainly to be cancerous.

As regards their early influence upon the nerves they stretch or compress, aneurismal growths probably act sooner than innocent fibro-plastic masses, because of their continual pulsating movement. In the abdomen, aortic aneurism is apt to occasion pain, which is one of the earlier signs of disease, and sometimes antedates all other forms of deeper constitutional disturbance.

In the chest or neck, the nerve affections due to thoracic aneurisms are seen in the form of hoarseness or aphonia, from injury to the vagus or recurrent laryngeal

---

* This method is far more sure to bring away the needed portions of tissue than Duchenne's trocar, which often fails, and has the disadvantage of not securing any fluid which may be present.

nerves, or in affections of the pupil from lesions of the
sympathetic nerve,—effects which may also arise from
glandular and other enlargements.

As interesting illustrations of some of the conditions
which have influence in cases of pressure on nerves by
tumors, as well as of skillful surgical interference, the two
following cases may answer.

Dr. D. Hayes Agnew* presented to the Pathological
Society of Philadelphia a bursal tumor, about an inch in
diameter. It had occupied a place at the bend of the
elbow, on the inner side of the tendon of the biceps,
causing pain and loss of motion in the flexors of the
thumb and fingers, and the extensors in general. It was
so bound down by the deep fascia as to project but slightly,
and to greatly exaggerate the pressure it was making upon
the nerves. After cutting through the bicipital aponeu-
rosis, the growth was found to be invested on the surface
by the flattened median nerve.

On dissecting this away, pushing it aside, and turning
out the mass, a like connection was discovered beneath it
with the posterior interosseous trunk. It was thus endan-
gering both nerves at once; but, notwithstanding this
curious complication, the recovery which followed its
removal was in all respects satisfactory.

On the same evening, Dr. Packard† exhibited to the
same society, a tumor as large as a lemon, which grew
just under the lower edge of the gluteus maximus. Its
position caused incessant pressure upon the sciatic nerve,
and made motion painful, and rest on the back or left side
impossible.

For eight months the patient had been unable to remain
in bed, and found only temporary ease in incessant
changes of posture. Removal of the mass was readily

accomplished, and was speedily followed by relief from the pain, numbness, and swelling.

Compression of nerves during delivery.—Cases of paralysis of one or both lower limbs are somewhat rare sequelæ of confinements. They may be traced to a variety of causes, among which are undoubtedly the pressure of the fœtal head or of the forceps.

Although frequently denied as a cause of palsy, pressure is now, and has been for a long time, admitted by all the prominent writers upon the complications and results of labor. The subject is admirably treated in all its relations by Bianchi,* to whose excellent pamphlet I am largely indebted.

This form of accident in some cases immediately succeeds the passage of the fœtal head; in others it is delayed several days. In the latter, however, at least in the instances I myself have seen, there were numbness and hyperæsthesia, which deepened by degrees, and finally ended in partial palsy, a sequence due sometimes to the pressure having occasioned a gradually-increasing neuritis, just as is seen in the contusion of nerves elsewhere.

In many labors, as every accoucheur is aware, cramp-pain from pressure is met with. The nerves which may be thus, or more gravely, affected, are the crural, obturator, and sciatic. The first named is apt to suffer during the earlier stages of labor, and, as Burns† has pointed out, to occasion pain in the front of the thigh.

Severer injury to this trunk is unlikely, owing to its protection by the psoas and iliacus muscles. The obturator nerve is also liable to pressure, and to give rise to similar but passing pains. Within the pelvic excavation

---

* Des Paralysies traumatiques des Membres Inférieurs chez des Nouvelles-Accouchées. Thèse de Paris, 1867.

† Burns's Midwifery, p. 14.

the sacral plexus and its greater sciatic branch are the nerve tissues most liable to serious injury, and it is usually to compression of this latter nerve that we must look for an explanation of such cases of infra-pelvic palsy as follow labor, and are due to this physical cause.

Bianchi asks, very shrewdly, if it be not also possible that compression of the sympathetic filaments may have some influence in predisposing the uterus to the congestions and inflammations which occasionally follow delivery. Considering the well-known effect, in this direction, of sections of vaso-motor nerves in the abdomen and thorax, I myself should be disposed to attribute far more to this possible cause of disease than has hitherto been done.

While it is clear from the cramps so common in labor that the nerves are frequently compressed, it is also plain that this compression is rarely adequate to a graver result, and the chief reason for this is to be found in the anatomical arrangements of the pelvis. The sciatic nerves, resting as it were in deep gutters, the projection of the sacro-vertebral spine* tends to ward off from them the pressure of the fœtal head, "while the sacral nerves resting against the back wall of the excavation are in some degree saved, owing to the fact that the inclination of the planes and axes of the bassin, direct against the anterior walls and symphysis pubis the principal effects of the greatest pressure of the fœtal head."†

I may add to these remarks that the pelvic nerves have remarkably thick sheaths; that, like other nerves, they endure a good deal of squeezing and pressure without lasting injury, and finally, that, as Bianchi has shown, it is usually the forceps, rather than the head alone, which is at fault. Indeed, he has been unable to discover any

---

* Bianchi, p. 40.   † Ibid

instance where palsy from pressure followed a labor ending without the forceps, and he seems therefore inclined to conclude that it is to the lateral movements of this instrument, combined with violent traction, that we must attribute the nerve lesion. In this view he seems to be supported by the five histories he reports, all of which were those of forceps cases. On the other hand, the cases seen by my friend Dr. Keating were not all forceps cases. And my own examples, two in number, were in fact merely prolonged labors, but in other respects natural, so that, as Jaccoud* believes and Burns taught, this accident may follow even a very regular and natural delivery. Nevertheless, histories of post-partum palsy from pressure are so rare that the cases I append may not lack interest.

Case 14.—C. L., a sturdy Irishwoman, confined with her second child, suffered excruciating cramp in the left leg during a labor which lasted nearly two days, but except as to its duration was normal. The pain of the cramp was so intense as twice to cause the patient to faint. The day after her delivery she complained of pain on the outside of the leg and foot, and of prickling and numbness.

When well enough to sit up, it was found that she had great weakness of the left leg, which increased, until within one month its use was nearly lost. A little later she began to amend, and under various treatment recovered entirely within a year.

Case 15.—M. B., aged twenty-six. The second example occurred lately in a young and vigorous woman, whose second labor, prolonged by the size of the fœtal head, occasioned great pain and numbness in the limbs. At the twelfth day she was still suffering from slight anæsthesia of the right leg, and from numbness and loss of power in both. Her recovery, under the use of vig-

---

* Sur les Paraplegies, p. 290.

orous shampooing and small doses of nux vomica, was very tardy; nor was she able to walk before the fifth week. There was no sciatic tenderness at any time.

I may add with Jaccoud, that this peculiar pathogenesis of palsy of the legs by pressure is not found in deliveries only, since any intra-pelvic tumor, sufficiently hard, may give occasion to it. I recall a case of enormous post-uterine hæmatocele, in which there was great pain in the track of the sciatic nerve, and Bernuilly has related to Jaccoud the interesting history of a post-uterine tumor causing paraplegia, which was relieved when the mass suppurated and broke into the rectum.

Pressure from fecal accumulations.—It is perhaps within every one's experience that the violent effort to expel a mass of hardened fæces is competent to cause pain down the back of the thigh, and serious compression of the nerves of the lumbar plexus is said to have been caused by accumulations in the bowels,—a circumstance which I have never met with even in the most extreme instances of this disorder.

Probably most of the cases of pain from inactive intestines are due rather to reflected irritations than to more direct physical causes. Portal* relates, however, the strange case of a certain Madame de Roye, who, being deformed by a spinal curvature, suffered intensely from pain in the left great-toe. Injections increased it, but a full stool gave relief. Upon her death, from malignant fever, it was found that, owing to the spinal curve, the lowest of the false ribs were so pressed in upon the sigmoid flexure of the colon as to cause an accumulation of excrement sufficient to compress the nerves of the lumbar plexus, and thus occasion an affection of the crural nerve, and, consequently, of its saphena branch.

---

* Cours d'Anatomie Médicale, t. iv. p. 276.

Muscular pressure from spasm.—Pressure by muscles in
a state of chronic spasm might be said to belong to the
same category of doubtful causes, were it not for Romberg's statement that he had occasionally seen enduring
spasm of the scaleni cause compression of the brachial
plexus, with resultant numbness, anæsthesia, and œdema
from venous constriction.

Compression of the facial (seventh) nerve by the forceps.—This
accident, although long known to accoucheurs, seems to
have received its first correct physical explanation from
Dubois,* who pointed out the mode in which the nerve
is affected, and showed that the resultant palsy cannot be
due, as was supposed, to cerebral pressure.

The thesis of M. Landouzy appears to have been the
first published collection of cases.

In certain labors, the blade of the forceps makes pressure either upon the diverging branches of the portio
dura or upon the main trunk of the seventh, just in
front of its outlet from the temporal bone,—an accident
rendered possible in the infant by the slight development
of the mastoid process and the comparative softness of
the parts connected with the auditory meatus and jaws.
When the force is exerted unequally on the dividing filaments of the nerve, the result will be seen in an incomplete palsy of some parts of the face, and a more perfect
loss of motion in others.†

The features are found drawn to the sound side, the
tongue and palate being unaffected, which has at least
been the case in Landouzy's cases and in those which I
have encountered.‡   These circumstances usually suffice

---

* Landouzy, Thèse, Essai sur l'Hemiplégie faciale chez les Enfants nou-
veau-nés.   Paris, 1839.

† Op. cit.

‡ I shall elsewhere discuss the views of Romberg, Todd, and Saunders
as to the value of palatal palsy in deciding the seat of the paralyzing

to determine that the paralyzing cause has been external to the track of the nerve in the temporal bone.

In the three cases which I have seen, the paralysis was very marked, the ala ceasing to move and the eye remaining open. In two there was difficulty of nursing, but little or none in the third, owing to the large nipples of the mother. All of them recovered readily within a month and without treatment. I have also seen a patient, sent to me from Delaware, the child of a physician, in whom there was left facial palsy following a failure to terminate a long labor by the forceps. The birth occurred naturally several hours afterwards. The palsy existed from birth, and at the sixth week, when seen by me, was complete. I decided against the instrument as a cause, since there was no mark of violence, and because there was not only a hanging down of the palate on the affected right side, but also of the posterior palatine arch, with œdema of these parts, and because of a slight dryness and loss of epithelia on the tongue limited to the diseased side.

The child died soon after of convulsions, with discharge of offensive and bloody matter from the left ear.

As regards the marks made by the forceps, in all of my cases there was some indentation, but not always over the line of the nerves. It is well to remember, as Landouzy has pointed out, that in some instances there is no external trace of violent compression by the forceps blade, so that we need not expect in every case to meet with this diagnostic aid. Fortunately we rarely need such assistance, the diagnosis being easy except in rare examples, like that of the last case cited.

Paralysis from local pressure on nerves owing to malposition during sleep.—Every one has awakened occasionally out of

---

cause ; but it seems to me quite certain that in these brief palsys by the forceps no loss of palate power is visible.

deep sleep to find that he has been lying upon his arm, or that it has been resting under his head, or in some awkward posture, owing to which the limb feels numb and dead, or may even be insensible to touch. The lapse of a few moments usually restores it to full feeling, after a short interval of unpleasant prickling and formication. There is probably here both nerve pressure and interrupted circulation. In rarer instances, permanent palsy has followed the malposition, and this is most apt to occur in the deep sleep of debauch.

Althaus* gives a case of this accident occurring to a lady during confinement, and while under the influence of chloroform. Her head rested so long on the left arm as to cause, by pressure on the brachial nerves, paralysis of certain muscles, with anæsthesia. It is interesting to note that there was also inflammation of the wrist-joint, such as often follows wounds of nerves.

Usually the arm is the limb involved, but there are said to have been examples of facial palsy caused by pressure of the hand on the face in deep sleep. I have met with no instances of this, either in the books or in practice.

Many examples of partial palsies of the upper extremities from pressure during sleep have come under my notice. At first, both sensation and motion suffer, but the motor palsy usually continues longer, and is more severe. The most troublesome cases are those which arise from a person having slept with one arm resting on the edge of a settee. Two such cases appeared at my clinic recently. In both there was hardly any sensory loss, but in both there were exactly the same muscular troubles. The flexors were perfect, but there was complete palsy of the extensors of the wrist, of the first phalanges of the fingers

---

* Med. Electr., 2d ed.   London, p. 489.

and those of the thumb, occasioned in both instances by pressure on the musculo-spiral nerve.

The most remarkable case within my knowledge was that of a laborer, who fell asleep in the street on a door-step, after drinking heavily. There were marks of bruises on the back or outside of both arms, as if he had slept with the two limbs crossed under and behind his head.

In fact, he was found by the police resting with one arm on the edge of the iron foot-scraper and the other on that of the step. He was so nearly poisoned by the alcohol taken as barely to escape death. On the second day he was found to have wrist-drop in both hands.

A few weeks after, he came under my care, having been treated meanwhile for lead palsy, of which he had, however, no evidence, save the extensor palsy. He recovered after very prolonged treatment by faradisation.

M. Bachon reports two cases of palsy of the radial caused by pressure during sleep, or in drunkenness. In both the arm rested on the back of a chair and the head on the arm. Mr. Walter G. Smith* has published a case of wrist-drop and anæsthesia from sleeping on the arm, the man being drunk at the time. In his second history a like result followed a healthy sleep, with the hand resting on the arm. His third case seems to have been due to long pressure of the elbow on the nerves of the opposite palm, and affected the median nerve chiefly.

Some persons seem to suffer more, and more readily, than others from light pressure on nerves or malposition. This is the case, I believe, with anæmic people and those in feeble health from any cause, but especially is it notably so in such as are in the first stages of spinal palsies or locomotor ataxia.

Some of the remaining external causes of paralysis of

---

* The Dublin Quarterly Journal, Aug. 1870, p. 21.

nerves by pressure are both curious and interesting, although but little has been said of them by medical writers.

In most of the severe cases the pressure has been long continued, but sometimes we are struck by the shortness of the time required to produce prolonged loss of power under certain forms of compression, and with the suddenness of the resultant palsy. Thus, it is not very rare to meet with such results from a child's carrying a package by means of a string looped over a finger, or from the pressure of a heavy basket on the arm. I have to thank my friend Dr. John H. Brinton, late surgeon U. S. Volunteers, for calling to my notice two causes of pressure which are very curious, but the latter, at least, I trust very rare.

During prolonged cavalry marches, the pressure of the snaffle-rein upon the radial side of the third finger causes in some men weakness of this member, distinct enough in rare cases to constitute a palsy, which is apt to invade, after a time, terminal branches of the ulnar nerve.

Dr. Brinton* has also met with two instances of local palsy which proved very tedious, and were brought about by the use of a form of restraint used by the police of Philadelphia, and perhaps elsewhere. It consists of a cord tied at the ends to two small handles. This cord is passed around the arm of a prisoner, and is sometimes twisted. The two handles are held in the grasp of the officer, who may make the pressure as light or as severe as may suit his own views. It is easy to understand how mischief may result from the cruel use of this formidable means of restraint.

Still more curious is the pressure-palsy to which the

---

* U. S. San. Com Med. Reports. Diseases of Nerves resulting from Injury. S. Weir Mitchell, M.D., p. 419.

water-carriers of the town of Rennes are liable. An account of this singular malady is given by M. Bachon.*

The water-carriers use a huge iron vessel, holding about eighteen quarts of water, and furnished with a single handle on the side. The belly of this great vase rests on the antero-lateral part of the thorax. The arm thrust through the handle, which is turned outward, embraces the circumference of the jar, which it presses against the side. At the same time the humerus is thrown outward and upward, so as to give the handle a solid support. This enormous load, which is at least seventy-six pounds, exerts by the agency of the handle a strong pressure on the external and posterior region of the arm, crossing obliquely the direction of the radial nerve. Paralysis of the extensors of the wrist and hand is a common consequence, and in some instances this is complicated by neuritis, of which the reporter gives a clear and interesting account.

Crutch palsy.—A common cause of paralysis from pressure in army practice, but one very rare in civil life, was known to our hospital staff as " crutch palsy." Early in the war a great number of instances of this malady were sent to our wards, and some occurred while patients were under our own care. Such were usually emaciated men, who, being of large stature, and therefore of great weight, bore heavily upon the cross-piece of the crutch, which was commonly of wood, and not cushioned. I do not recollect seeing this malady in any person whose axilla was well defended by adipose tissue, and by the firmness and tone of the muscular folds which bound it before and behind. Neither was it frequent after the wounded began to be supplied with a proper form of crutch. The trouble

---

* Rec. de Mém. de Méd., de Chir. et de Pharm. militaires, t. ii. (3 série) quatrième Fascicule, No. 52, Avril, 1864.

was met with, of course, in men who had to bear hard on the crutch because of a wounded or lost leg. The paralysis begins with a tingling and numbness in the little finger of one hand, ordinarily the right, with sometimes a loss of feeling in the ulnar distribution. Then the hand grows feeble, or this symptom comes on, though rarely, without previous or accompanying sensory phenomena; but at last the patient can no longer grasp his crutch, so that inevitably the disease brings its own remedy of entire rest, although it does sometimes continue to increase for a time after the crutch has been abandoned. I have seen no case which failed to get well, though in certain instances of pressure from other causes the palsy has been found to be permanent.

The following history sufficiently illustrates this form of pressure:

Q. C. Meanning, aged forty, Company B, 1st Mass. Cavalry. Enlisted Sept. 1861. He was previously well. In January, 1863, he fell, breaking both bones of the right leg. Union took place, with deformity and unusual difficulty in locomotion. From April 25th to June 20th he walked on two common wooden crutches, and then, until July 11th, on one, which he used on the right side, leaning heavily upon it. On the last-named day he walked a great deal more than usual, and immediately after found that the third and fourth fingers were benumbed. The following night he lost partially the use of the arm. The axilla felt sore, but there were no evidences of any central lesion, or of syphilitic or rheumatic antecedents.

Since then his biceps regained power, but no other muscle had improved up to July 21, 1863. At that time his shoulder muscles acted well, except the deltoid, which was feeble. The other muscles of the arm were healthy. The biceps was feeble; pronation and supination were good; flexion and extension of the wrist were nearly absent; the finger motions were all excessively weak. Sensation was absent in the ulnar side of the palm, wrist, and forearm, and nearly absent in the forefinger. In the forearm muscles, the electric contractility was lessened, and was barely present in the abductor min. dig. The axillary nerves were not tender on pressure.

Treatment.—The patient was directed to use a cane in the left hand, to have a starch bandage as a support for the broken leg, douche and faradisation daily to the forearm. The relief was very rapid and complete; so much so that within two months he recovered the full use of the weakened muscles. Sensation returned more slowly, but finally was aided by faradisation of the dried skin. He was put on guard duty after four months' treatment, but had then, I believe, some slight numbness in the fourth finger and ulnar palm.

CHAPTER VI.

THE character of the symptoms varies but slightly in the different forms of nerve injury. If we had presented to us a hand which was suffering from wound of the median nerve, there would be nothing in the symptoms to show how they were caused, and the hurt might have been due to gunshot wound, to incision, to a puncture, or to a simple contusion of the nerve. Moreover, the symptoms in nerve wounds rise into the highest practical importance as regards treatment, and are so much alike in all regions of the body, that it seems better to deal with them collectively than to describe, in tedious detail, the nerve wounds of each limb, and so to be forced into endless repetition of the same particulars in numerous cases.

I have chosen, therefore, to treat of the symptoms in successive chapters, and to reserve for separate study the wounds of such nerves as, by position or function, demand peculiar consideration.

Local symptoms.—The immediate symptoms of nerve injury are local and general. I have questioned hundreds of men who have been shot through nerve trunks, and have found a curious diversity as to their first sensations. Usually the man thinks he is struck with a stick or stone, and angrily accuses a comrade of the trick. Others suffer instant and intense pain, which is felt at the wound

(135)

and down the nerve tracks. A clever sergeant, a Canadian by birth, described his first pain as like that which is felt when a cricket-bat carelessly held is struck by a swift ball. This feeling of numbness, with tingling pain, is common in cases of slight nerve wounds or contusions. Even when the primary pain is severe, it is lost in a few moments. Indeed, cases of pain which arise at the moment of the hurt, and continue steadily, are very rare. I recall but one instance, that of a man who said he had burning pain in the hand from the instant he was hit.

In the book on Gunshot Wounds and Injuries of Nerves, by Drs. Morehouse, Keen, and myself, forty-three cases of nerve wounds are analyzed in regard to the immediate symptoms. To these I now add forty-eight. Of the ninety-one so brought together, rather more than one-third had no pain, and many did not know they were shot until weakness or the sight of their own blood betrayed the presence of a wound.

We may suspect that the difference as to pain in these cases depends upon the rate of motion of the ball, which, if slow, would be more likely to cause pain. Indeed, we all know from personal experience how little pain is given by a sharp cut made quickly, and it has even been proposed by Dr. Richardson to utilize this fact in order to open abscesses without pain. I presume that a man in a high state of excitement would be less apt to know of his being wounded, and this is certainly the case; but there are also men who have been shot through the brachial plexus while quiet spectators, and have first been informed of it by the flow of blood.

Other and rare cases have remote pain, and none at the point hurt. I have seen an instance where the ball, having traversed the inner and upper region of the thigh, partly divided the sciatic nerve. The pain was altogether in the testicle, which was retracted during several hours.*

For reasons not altogether clear, some neck wounds cause at the moment horrible pain at the insertion of the deltoid, which may possibly be due to a sudden spasm of this muscle. Commodore Stembel, whose case I have elsewhere related,† was shot in the right side of the neck, and had pain in both arms. Another officer, struck by a ball in the right thigh, felt pain only in the left limb, and throughout suffered most in that part.

Where a nerve of mixed function is slightly injured by contusion, the first impression is most felt by the sensory branches, and any motor loss is apt to be due to secondary changes. In graver lesions, as by bullets, sensation and motion are usually both lost at first, even if the ball merely grazes the nerve, so that at the outset of a case it cannot be known whether a ball may have divided a nerve or merely stunned it completely. At all events, it is common to see the functions return ing after what seem to be serious lesions, some parts recovering quickly and some more tardily, until at last we are able to decide as to what are to be permanently damaged, where motion is gone, and where sensation is lost.

---

* There is a region of skin on the thigh, extending from the groin nearly to the knee, and capable of accurate delineation, which has certain relations to the scrotum and testicle. Galvanic or mechanical irritation of this area usually causes retraction of the corresponding testicle. It is best seen in young people, and is of value in determining the presence or absence of reflex transmissions in the thigh. The sympathetic movement and pain in the testicle in the present case were curious illustrations of a regional relationship which has perhaps not been elsewhere pointed out, and which certainly is not well known or made use of for diagnostic purposes.

† New York Med. Jour., 1866. Paralysis from Peripheral Irritation, p. 49. S. Weir Mitchell.

The following case illustrates unusually well this very frequent occurrence :

Case 16.—A sergeant, wounded in the left side of the neck, was placed in our wards within four days from the date of his wound, which seemed to have directly implicated the brachial plexus. His arm was totally palsied as to motion and sensation from the moment he was hit; sensation returned within five days. Motor power was restored in all the flexor muscles of the hand within ten days; and, under three applications of electricity, it reappeared in all the other muscles except the deltoid and triceps extensor, which never perfectly regained their functions during very prolonged treatment.

This temporary though entire loss of motion and sensation in nerves not absolutely cut across, and, even in such as have been untouched by the missile which has passed near them, may find, perhaps, some explanation in the experiments upon the effects of pressure already related.

In certain cases, the nerve wound, in place of causing primary loss of mobility, occasions either sudden muscular contraction, followed by instant loss of power, or, in very rare instances, long-continued spasm. A soldier, wounded in the brachial plexus at Antietam, was obliged to ask a comrade to unclasp his rigid fingers from their hold upon the musket. A still more singular example is that of C., who was shot through the arm at Shiloh, and whom I have recently examined. When he was shot, the thumb turned inward so violently as to cut the skin of the palm with the nail. It remained in this position six hours, when the arm was amputated. I recall other cases of like nature; but lasting spasm after nerve injury is a rare occurrence.

Early constitutional symptoms ; shock.—One of the gravest of the instant consequences of nerve injuries is that which is known as "shock." This is commonly described as a condition in which the patient "becomes cold, faint, and trembling; the pulse is small and fluttering; there is a great mental depression and disquietude, incoherence of speech and thought; the surface becomes covered by a cold sweat; there are nausea, perhaps vomiting, and relaxation of the sphincters."*

Exactly such as are here described were the symptoms of shock which followed nerve wounds. In nearly every case there was more or less sudden feebleness, and in some there was the most absolute and general loss of power, accompanied in a certain number by insensibility, probably due to syncope. We have nothing in this direction to separate wounds of great nerves from those involving only muscular and bony parts, and therefore minute nerve fibres alone. Gunshot wounds, however, present us with certain possibilities which are interesting tests of the amount of shock, and which are not available in such cases as railway injuries or in any which throw a man down.

As to what percentage of men wounded through muscle, or bone and muscle chiefly, suffer from shock, and to what degree, I find no mention in surgical works, so that I cannot compare my own statistics as to the immediate shock from nerve injury with that arising from other causes.

This state of shock, so well known to the surgeon, is simply a reflex effect of the injury of nerves, large or small. In general, it affects in varying proportion all the great nerve centres which preside over circulation, respiration, and voluntary movement, and instantly brings about such a condition as follows an overdose of tartar emetic. Its symptoms and treatment are alike familiar,

---

* Erichsen's Surgery. Ed. by Dr. John Ashhurst, 1869, p. 121.

but there still are certain questions in regard to it which are answered more or less well by my own cases, all of which, it should be borne in mind, involved lesions of great nerve trunks or plexuses. To obtain a reply to these questions, I have taken only the cases of wounds of large nerve trunks, and only those of the upper half of the body, because the test of sudden fall would be valueless as regards wounds in the legs. I have also excluded every instance of early and severe hemorrhage, so that finally we have left for analysis fifty-six cases.

If we examine these with reference to the site of wound, the amount of shock, as indicated by the number who fell at once, and of those who fell insensible, and the presence of pain in such as were able to feel, we reach the following conclusions:

Those struck were nearly all of them ($\frac{9}{10}$ths) actively engaged in loading, or were charging or retreating. From the effects felt by these men as compared with what was felt by the remainder who were not in close action when hit, and also not in movement, it would appear that pain is more commonly an instant symptom of nerve wound when the man is inactive, since nearly all of these had pain when wounded, while of the remainder about one-half had no pain. Yet although such was the case, a third of the latter felt some intimation of their being hurt, in the form of a sudden numbness or other sensation, which they persisted in describing as not painful. These statements are therefore contradictory of the usual surgical opinion in regard to the instant pain arising from nerve wounds. Indeed, only two of the fifty-six cases had pain which could be called acute.

Taking all of the fifty-six cases, and studying them as regards shock and seat of wound, we get these curious replies. There were twelve wounds of the brachial plexus in the neck.

Of these, two fell senseless; seven fell with more or less confusion of mind; and three walked away.

The same nerves were wounded in the axilla ten times.

Of these, again, two fell insensible; four fell without loss of sense; and four were able to walk away.

There remain thirty-four cases of wounds of the brachial nerves, including the ulnar, radial, musculo-spiral, and median. Of these, six fell senseless; six fell, having their senses; and twenty-two were able to walk away.

The neck wounds, owing to which nine out of twelve fell, would seem to cause greater shock than arm wounds, from which only twelve out of thirty-four fell.

Taking the whole number, regardless of analysis by regions, for which, indeed, they seem scarcely numerous enough, we have of nerve lesions confined to the brachial plexus and its ultimate nerve trunks, fifty-six histories. Of these, at the instant of the wound, ten fell insensible, and seventeen dropped without loss of consciousness. Twenty-nine were able to walk away, either at once or after a few minutes, but nearly all of these (twenty-two) felt a certain loss of power at once or very soon. It is difficult, however, to carry the analysis further, because in a minute or two the flow of blood and the emotion, owing to knowledge of the loss of ability to move, come into the case, and are hard to eliminate as causes of secondary influences affecting the general result. So far as I have carried the conclusions, I believe them to be worthy of trust. While most cases of nerve wounds exhibit more or less shock in the form of cardiac feebleness and general arterial spasm, in a smaller number we meet with what might be called a localized expression of the influence of the neural lesion. Thus, in place of a general impression upon vaso-motor and cardio-motor centres, we sometimes see the shock limited to a disturbance of ideational or emotional centres, or to a single sensory ganglion, or to a group of spinal-motor cells. In certain instances, these results are temporary, in others they are lasting, and then constitute what is usually called reflex paralysis, but which I should prefer to term, where it affects muscular motion, paralysis from peripheral irritation.

Shock, then, is reflex disturbance, or, in some cases, paralysis of centres. Why in one case the cerebrum should suffer, in another the heart, and in a third the motor centres of the leg or arm, is as yet inscrutable. A ball crushes a nerve, and the tremendous shock instantly propagated to the spine falls ruinously upon some one of the numerous ganglia through which it travels. Is this because it finds a weak point, or is it that conduction checked somewhere causes at that spot destruction from dangerous accumulations of nerve force? Tempting analogies here open to certain electrical phenomena, but as yet we lack such exact knowledge as would justify further inferences.

Theories of shock.—At the present time vaso-motor agencies are called upon to explain every phenomenon in disease, and for most pathologists to-day all reflex injuries seem to be due to vasal spasm or vasal palsy in the centres affected. Elsewhere,* together with Drs. Morehouse and Keen, and since then in a longer essay,† I have stated the objections to Brown-Séquard's famous theory, which explained reflex paralysis by vascular spasm and consequent insufficiency of nutritive supplies. Gull,‡ Jaccoud,§ and the author, have all alike insisted that permanent spasm was scarcely conceivable, or, at all events, that we had no distinct evidence of its possible

* U. S. A. Circular No. 6. Reflex Paralysis. 1864.
† Paralysis from Peripheral Irritation. New York Med. Jour., 1866.
‡ Med.-Chir. Trans., vol. xvii. Dr. Gull.
§ Les Paraplégies. Jaccoud.

existence in the centres; while we have also pointed out that the reception of Brown-Séquard's theory would necessitate belief in subsequent palsy of vessels and vasal nerves as a far better explanation of the central results of reflex irritations. "Thus the stern physiological law of rest after labor, of relaxation after contraction, stands in the way of any idea which presupposes long-continued vasal spasm;"* and against it also are a number of satisfactory objections to the experiments upon which its author relied for its support. Moreover, it has been loaded with needless conditions, which make its acceptance still more difficult, since he has insisted that in reflex palsies the centres affected exhibit no lesion, which seems inconceivable in the presence of either vascular spasm or palsy, if these be long continued. Perhaps if this justly distinguished observer had more freely explained himself, some of these objections might have less weight, since he has been kind enough to assure me, after careful reading of my criticisms, that our ideas differ in reality less than I had conceived them to do.

Another theory supposes that in the ordinary instances of long-continued irritation of a part, the reflected impressions falling—why we know not—on some particular centre, either keep it in a state of excitement, resulting in pain or muscular spasm, or else wear out or suddenly extinguish its excitability so as to paralyze its dependent muscles. It becomes us, however, to be cautious as to the cases we include in this category, since science is daily opening new and different ways of accounting for many phenomena which have hitherto been confidently termed reflex. It is common, for example, so to explain cases of palsy of a leg remotely following a cut, a hurt nerve, or a wounded or crushed toe-nail. Yet, as we shall

---

* Paral. from Periph. Irrit., p. 33.

see, many of these are simply examples of disease propagated along the nerve first involved to the main trunk, and thus involving other branches.

No such objections apply to the histories of palsy reported by my colleagues and myself, since in them the wound of one part was instantly followed by loss of power in a remote region.

These, also, I prefer to explain by presuming that the shock had suddenly exhausted some ganglionic centre, and thus palsied its related muscles. This view was set forth by us in March, 1864, and more elaborately, though not more distinctly, by Jaccoud, in December of the same year. We then remarked that "either the shock of a wound causes paralysis of vaso-motor nerves and sequent congestion, with secondary alterations, or that it destroys directly the vital power of a centre. Now, there is no reason why, if shock be competent to destroy vitality in vaso-motor centres or nerves, it should be incompetent so to affect the centres of motion or sensation." Indeed, it appears incomprehensible that any vasal spasm and consequent relaxation could be competent to instantly and permanently paralyze a whole limb, while sudden deaths from shock seem also explicable in no other way than by absolute exhaustion of nerve force in some vital centre.

Explain them as we may, however, there exists a set of rare cases, for the full records of which I must refer to the essays already quoted. I give here a very brief abstract of each case, with some important additions:

Case 17.—Gunshot wound of right wrist-joint, injuring the ulnar and median nerves, and causing cerebral excitement. The patient, a colonel, ran along the line of his regiment, "half-crazed," in a state of wild excitement, and presently fell insensible,—not from loss of blood.

Case 18.—An officer, wounded in the heel, was thrown instantly into a condition of the utmost trepidation, and behaved like an insane person. His character for courage was undoubted, and a court of inquiry, for which he asked, cleared him on the surgical evidence.

Case 19.—A private, shot through the brachial plexus, became wildly excited, crying murder repeatedly, and accusing those near him in the ranks of having shot him. He did not fall.

Case 20.—An officer, shot through the right median nerve, was helped away to the rear, talking somewhat incoherently about matters foreign to the time and scene. He was very feeble, but lost little blood, and had not the least remembrance of having been shot, or of any event which followed within an hour afterwards.

Such cases as these are examples of shock affecting variously the emotional or intellectual organs. Legouest, in his "Surgery of the Crimean War," p. 219, describes them as not uncommon.

As I have had occasion to repeat, the shock of nerve wounds commonly weakens the heart; but in one case it merely interfered with its rhythm.

Case 21.—G. A., a wagonmaster, was shot through the left ulnar nerve. This trunk was totally destroyed, as well as the ulnar artery, and years afterwards he consulted me to learn whether the resultant loss of sense and motion could be again restored. When struck, he felt a sharp pang in the hand, and had at once great agitation of the heart; at all events, this was so annoying as to be for some days the dominant symptom. With occasional returns it grew gradually better, and when seen by me he had long ceased to feel it.

In the following cases a ball wound caused paralysis elsewhere :

Case 22.—R. S. Ball wound of right neck, probably involving no important nerve directly; fracture of hyoid bone; reflex paralysis of left arm; probable reflex paralysis of right arm ; early recovery of left arm ; more remote and nearly complete recovery of right arm.

Case 23.—J. D. Flesh wound of right thigh, without injury of large nerves; complete paralysis of all four limbs; left arm recovered quickly ; the other limbs slowly; final development of myelitis.

Case 24.—W. W. Wound of right thigh, with probable injury to sciatic nerve ; partial palsy of right leg ; reflex paralysis of right arm, which recovered rapidly.

Case 25.—A sergeant, shot through the right testicle. He fell, without pain, except in the back, and soon became senseless. Partial loss of power in right foot ; no loss of sensibility.

Case 26.—D. K. Gunshot wound of right thigh ; direct lesions of crural nerves ; loss of motion and sensation ; reflex paralysis of right arm as to motion.

In two remaining cases, wounds of one leg seemed to the patient to be truly in the other; and in one there was a space of anæsthetic skin on the uninjured side, symmetrically related to the site of the wound.*

Other but more doubtful cases of reflex paralysis have been seen by me, but these I have hesitated to put on record. It will be observed, also, that of the twelve cases here given in abstract, only six involved injury to large nerve trunks; and in a seventh, all the nerves of an important organ, the testicle, must have been instantly destroyed.

---

* In Case IV., Hutchinson's Series, p. 313, the median and ulnar nerves being injured, there was pain in the unhurt hand. Pirogoff, p. 384, has a similar instance from injury to the right brachial plexus.

CHAPTER VII.

Tetanus—chorea.—We have thus disposed of the early symptoms, local and general, which occur when a nerve trunk is wounded. The reunion and regeneration of the nerves have been already described; and for the rest, wounds involving large nerves heal as do others, and involve no greater constitutional dangers. The local changes in motion, feeling, and nutrition are what most interest us in these wounds, and which, indeed, continue to do so long after the wound has been healed.

The only constitutional conditions to which they may give rise during this process, or soon afterwards, are tetanus and chorea. There is a prevalent belief that tetanus is more apt to arise when large nerves are slightly hurt than on other occasions; but although there are on record many cases where this terrible malady has followed the inclusion of nerves in ligatures, in the mass of tetanic histories the causal irritation has arisen in the extreme distribution of nerves, and where there has been no proof of precedent injury to large trunks. Were it otherwise, I must more often have seen tetanus, whereas in two hundred recorded instances of wounds of great nerves which passed under my eye during the war, not a single case of lock-jaw was seen, although in perhaps one-half the injuries were recent, and we actually witnessed a part of the process of healing. In fact, the tendency towards irritation, resulting in spasm, seems to increase as the

nerves divide and approach the skin. Brown-Séquard
succeeded once in causing tetanus, by leaving a rusty
tack in the foot of an animal. I have never been able to
get this result by any method, nor in some seventy
sections of wounds of nerves in animals have I ever
encountered it.

Chorea, a still rarer consequence of nerve wounds, is
a very uncommon result of any wound, although I have
met with such cases, especially one in an adult, where
the ankle was slightly injured by a ball. Dr. Packard*
reports a case of chorea from injury to the terminal
filaments of the median nerve in the thumb. Exsection
of a sensitive point brought about relief and cure, which
all previous means had failed to effect.

I have seen no example of chorea from wounds of
large nerve trunks, but I have several times been called
upon to treat this malady in the stumps left by amputations of the arm. Here, however, it is one of the more
remote consequences of changes in the divided nerves,
and is excessively rebellious to treatment. Beginning in
the stump, it is apt to be propagated to more distant parts,
so as finally to assume, in certain cases, a unilateral character. I shall elsewhere have occasion to speak of the
tendency of muscles in stumps to twitch from excitement
or changes of weather, and to obey irregularly orders
directed by volition to parts in the lost limb.

Later local symptoms.—Long after a nerve has been
bruised or wounded, there is apt to occur in the skin or
muscles to which it is related a double series of most unmanageable symptoms—the one due to division of nerve
fibres and absence of nerve force, the other to irritations
of nerve fibres which are still more or less entire, and to
consequent disturbances of the nutrition and functions of

---

* Am. Jour. Med. Sci., April, 1870, p. 347.

the connected tissues. These irritations are in some cases of inflammatory birth, and in others purely mechanical, but in all probability they result in the propagation to the connected parts of a succession of interrupted waves of force, which give rise to many of the phenomena and appearances with which these cases present us. A part of the symptoms is due to loss of nerve force, a part to irregular nerve force; and I use this term because we are not clear as to the nature of the abnormal influences thus exerted. The separation of these two causes of evil in nerve wounds is not always easy, so that any one who sees many nerve injuries will constantly be called upon to admit that in numerous instances we cannot tell whether a given result be due to one cause or the other, since, as regards the influence of the hypothetical nutritive nerves, vaso-motor and all other, upon tissues, we know so little as to be unable to decide whether this or that condition of tissues may be caused by a non-supply of their normal nerve impulses, or by some irregularity in these. We have, indeed, as yet, no good test which shall serve us to make this distinction as clear as it is in wounds of musculo-motor nerves, in which nerve section causes palsy, and nerve irritation some form of spasm. Yet interesting as these questions may be, their settlement does not affect either our clinical prognosis or our therapeutic methods.

In considering the local symptoms which follow nerve wounds and endow them with an interest belonging to no other lesions, I shall treat, first, of the nutritive changes; second, of altered states of sensibility; and lastly, of the various causes which affect motility and mobility.

Trophic changes.—When, as rarely happens, an injury has totally destroyed a portion of all of the great nerves of a limb, and there has been no subsequent reunion, the related tissues undergo atrophic changes which are very remarkable. The muscles waste away, the areolar tissue disappears, the skin becomes dry, ragged, yellowish or brown, and rough; the nails and hair degenerate, while the veins shrink and the arterial pulse grows feeble.

Lesser nerve injuries produce, of course, muscular atrophies bearing a proportion to the fibres wounded or cut. Where a missile has divided a nerve, wholly or in part, these changes begin in the connected muscles with a slight but almost immediate loss of tension, so that the muscle feels flabby and relaxed.

This is certainly the first notable alteration in a muscle the nerves of which have been severed. It is so perceptible, within a day or two of the injury, that in some cases it is possible to tell, by handling the part, what muscles are thus isolated and what are not. Within a few hours there is, in the disordered muscle, some loss of power to move when faradised, and the difficulty increases day by day, until finally it ceases altogether to respond to this form of stimulation. For a much longer time, perhaps even for weeks or months, the same muscle may move more or less readily when traversed by a current of twenty to forty galvanic cells, while it is also noticeable that mechanical irritation may produce contractions long after induced currents have ceased to possess any such power.

The pathological changes which accompany this functional deficiency have been frequently described as fatty degeneration; but they scarcely deserve this description. The following extract from Vulpian so precisely corresponds to the alterations which I have myself seen and studied, as to require no additions:

" Muscular atrophy from nerve section is characterized by a considerable reduction in the diameter of the primitive muscular bundles, accompanied in a few localities by granular fatty changes, with total disappearance of certain fibres. In the early stages of alteration, the primitive fibres appear to be segmented, the muscular substance persisting in some places and being absent in others. At the same time, we observe the formation of a more or less considerable quantity of fat vesicles in the connective tissue which separates the secondary bundles of fibres, and much more rarely between the primitive fibres. Multiplication of the nuclei and hyperplasia of the general connective tissue of the muscle are also observed, while the vessels suffer only a loss of calibre, without other changes."

Atrophy from complete nerve division is pretty surely followed by contraction of muscles, but I have been unable to determine the time at which this begins, and the stage of atrophic change to which it is related. It is usually a remote consequence of complete division of a nerve, and is, perhaps, the worst of all the signs which foretell a hopeless loss of function. It sometimes happens that extreme atrophy takes place without consequent contraction; but we may then suspect, enough of time having elapsed to admit of the change, that the nerve communications have been in part restored, so as, in such a case, to allow of successful treatment. I have said that usually the shortening bore a strict proportion to the amount of wasting; but to this there is another exception besides the one above mentioned. In a few rare cases, the atrophy being but slight, the contraction has seemed to be excessive. I am unable to explain this to my satisfaction. The force with which the failing muscle contracts reminds me of the power with which certain scars shorten, and results, as I shall elsewhere point out, in ruin to the usefulness of the uninjured muscles, and in subluxation of the joints concerned.

Influence of nerve injuries upon the nutrition of the skin and its appendages.—As in the muscle so in the skin, the nervous lesions may fall only on the functional innervation, or

may alight upon this and on the nutrient system of the
skin at one and the same time. I have yet to see a distinct case of nerve wound affecting the latter singly, without sensory or motor disturbance.

The mode in which nerve wounds attack the cutaneous
nutrition, whether directly, by irritations of fibres leading
to the part, or reflectively, through the centres, and by
uninjured filaments upon the skin, is often, nay, generally, difficult to determine; but since in total nerve section we more rarely observe such grave disasters to skin
nutrition as follow partial lesions, it is likely that reflected irritations have their share in the mischief; yet
there is reason to believe that in one large class of skin
disease arising out of nerve wounds, the irritation is direct
rather than of reflex parentage.

The nature of the irritation which arises in nerve wounds
is somewhat doubtful. It is very rare that any of the
peculiar nutritive changes occur early. They are more
liable to arise with the inflammatory state into which most
wounds are apt to fall, or they follow the injury even
more remotely, as in contusions. We may, therefore,
suspect neuritis or sclerosis as frequent causes of mischief.
In one case I saw a sudden access of inflammation in a
healing wound over the injured median nerve determine
an immediate outbreak of neuralgia, ulcerated matrices
of nails, and vesicular eruption; while in another, a
wound of the radial, an attack of erysipelas brought about
causalgia (burning pain) and glossy skin, with eruptions,
the patient having previously only some loss of motion
and sensation. I have already stated that complete section of the nerve of a limb caused general atrophy, with
œdema, and finally discoloration of the dry and thickened
skin, the ragged epithelia hanging in patches. Some of
these conditions are, no doubt, due to want of use.

Cases of this kind are, however, very rare, and do not

exhibit the horrible lesions which in animals are apt to follow complete nerve sections. Certain instances of local ulceration, consequent upon entire nerve sections, have been recorded; but, on the other hand, Hutchinson and Paget both describe the ready healing of wounds in parts so situated, of which I have seen many examples. The former author speaks, also, of the reproduction of nails in a finger having no central nervous connections. There is, therefore, nothing in the loss of innervation to restrain cicatrization. A remarkable case in point is the ease and speed with which we can often heal the ulcers caused by pressure in paralyzed persons, when the parts have been put into conditions favorable to healing.

Slight nerve injuries from pressure, contusion, and partial division by ball or blade, occasion a variety of singular symptoms, which had been little studied before my colleagues and myself saw at Turner's Lane Hospital an unequaled collection.

Cutaneous eruptions.—At some time in the history of a nerve injury it is common to see certain forms of eruption, which are herpetic, vesicular, or in the shape of bullæ. In our own experience we saw numbers of eruptions which, as a rule, were most sure to be met with in the cases of greatest irritation, and which usually assumed the appearance of small vesicles.

Charcot* has described a case of Rayer's, of gunshot wound of the thigh, which resulted in neuralgia, and in the production at the painful spots of repeated crops of herpes. In a note to Charcot's cases, Brown-Séquard mentions a contusion of the internal cutaneous nerve of the arm, also followed by herpes; and there exist numerous histories of like eruptions consequent upon blows affect-

---

* Journal de Phys., 1859, p. 108.

ing certain regions of skin. Bullæ resembling those of
pemphigus occur in other instances. In one of Charcot's*
cases, abscesses, or the incisions needed to open them,
injured the nerves of the arm, and resulted in loss of sensation, partial paralysis, atrophy, neuralgia, and finally,
late in the case, in a peculiar eruption, chiefly about the
joints of the index, medius, and ring fingers. Bullæ
formed in a few hours, "grew as large as a nut," and,
breaking, disclosed a quickly-healing ulcer.

A case is also given by Raynaud,† in which the ulnar
nerve was compressed at the elbow, with the result of
successive groups of phlyctænula seated exactly on the
nerve track. They were full of bloody serum, and left
no ulcers when they broke. In these cases there was no
inflammation, but in those related by Earl, Romberg, and
Kuhl‡ there was inflammation about the bullæ. In a case
of nerve injury by pressure at the wrist, I saw the thumb
rapidly covered on the fourth day by a large bulla, and
looking as if blistered. Mr. Hutchinson§ reports a similar
instance where there were marked inflammation, bullæ,
and ulceration; and it would be easy to extend the list if
this were desirable.

I have already remarked that in total division of nerves,
the injuries from blows or pressure to which the part may
be afterwards exposed are apt to result in ulcers, which
require only careful and judicious treatment to enable
them to heal. But in partial nerve sections superficial
ulcers sometimes form without obvious mechanical causes,
and, according to my own experience, such ulcers usually
result from previous bullæ, or, as I have seen repeatedly,

* Mougeot, Rech. sur quelques Troubles de Nutrition consécutifs aux
Affections des Nerfs. Paris, 1867, p. 36 et seq. Also Samuel, op. cit.
† Thèse de Paris, 1862, p. 156.
‡ Samuel, Die trophischen Nerven, p. 189.
§ Clin. Lects. and Reports London Hospital, p. 314.

and as Hutchinson relates, they assume the form of whitlows, which are painful or not, as they chance to be in
anæsthetic or hyperæsthetic regions. The vesicular diseases of the skin which, in our experience, followed nerve
wounds by missiles, we described as eczematous, a term
which has been criticised by Hanfield Jones and Charcot.
In reality, these eruptions were somewhat peculiar, and
more like eczema than herpes. In a few cases they appeared upon healthy skin, but usually made one of the
features of that singular condition of atrophied skin with
burning pain which followed a remarkably large proportion of gunshot wounds of nerves. The eruption consisted of small, scattered, acutely-pointed vesicles, full of
a thin, serous fluid. On the healthy skin they were larger,
and dried up without sequelæ; but when situated on the
thin and altered teguments, they left behind them minute
ulcers, which horribly increased the itching or the burning
so constantly present.

It was somewhat rare to see any case of glossy skin,
especially with causalgia, unattended by vesicles; but
these were apt to come and go in successive crops, and
we soon observed that when present the burning pain
was lessened,—a fact which our patients also recognized.
As a rule, the eruption was widely spread over the affected
skin, and was not gathered into groups.

Atrophic conditions of the skin.—Previously to the Report
from the United States Army Hospital for Nervous Diseases, Mr. Paget had described briefly, but forcibly, a
peculiar shining, glossy state of skin, the accompaniment
of certain intractable neuralgias.* The earliest mention
of this form of pain from nerve wound is, however, to be
met with in the classical case of a portion of ball imbedded in the radial nerve which Mr. Alex. Denmark

---

* Paget's Cases, Med. Times and Gazette, March 26, 1864.

reported in 1813.*   The patient described the sensation
of pain "as beginning at the extremities of the thumb
and all the fingers, except the little one, and extending
up the arm, to the part wounded.   It was of a burning
nature," he said, " and so violent as to cause a continual
perspiration from his face.   He had an excoriation on the
palm of the hand, from which exuded an ichorous discharge.   He could not bear to be touched without evincing
additional torture."   In our wards, we found this remarkable form of skin disease associated, as a rule, with a very
characteristic burning pain, which in most of the cases
became at length the dominant symptom.†   Mougeot, in
quoting our description, labels the condition as erythema;
but no conception of erythema as known to me would at
all fill up the picture of this extraordinry malady.   Since
we published our history of numerous cases thus affected,
Hutchinson, Annandale, and others have encountered
similar instances, but as yet none have appeared which approach in severity certain of the examples furnished by us.

I shall therefore content myself with a somewhat altered
statement taken from our book, and shall refer the reader
to the annexed cases and to the chapter on sensation for
fuller details.

The state of skin to which I refer is never present
without burning pain, and commonly the earlier presence
of this form of neuralgia enabled us to predict the coming of the skin disease.   In no case did it become visible
short of two weeks, but usually it preceded the healing
of the wound, and not rarely was to be traced to an outbreak of inflammation involving the wound.

The duration of the malady varied from a few weeks
to years, but in all of the cases I have been able to follow
it has either been cured or gradually disappeared.

---

* Med.-Chir. Trans., London, vol. iv. p. 48.

† It was singularly rare in cases of ordinary shooting neuralgic pain.

Mr. Paget describes this state of skin in the following language: " Glossy fingers appear to be a sign of peculiarly impaired nutrition and circulation due to injury of the nerves. They are not observed in all cases of injured nerves, and I cannot tell what are the peculiar conditions of the cases in which they are found, but they are a very notable sign, and are always associated, I think, with distressing and hardly manageable pain and disability. In well-marked cases, the fingers which are affected (for this appearance may be confined to one or two of them) are usually tapering, smooth, hairless, almost void of wrinkles, glossy, pink, or ruddy, or blotched as if with permanent chilblains. They are commonly also very painful, especially on motion, and pain often extends from them up the arm. In most of the cases, this condition of the fingers is attended with very distinct neuralgia, both in them and in the whole arm, and its relation to disturbance of the nervous condition of the part is, moreover, indicated by its occasional occurrence in cases where neuralgia continues after an attack of shingles affecting the arm. In two such cases I have seen this same condition of the fingers well marked, and only very slowly subsiding, and seeming unaffected by the ordinary treatment of neuralgia." The following quotation from the work of Drs. Morehouse, Keen, and myself, describes the malady as it appeared in numerous cases in our own wards:

" *Glossy skin.*—The skin affected in these cases was deep-red or mottled, or red and pale in patches. The epithelium appeared to have been partially lost, so that the cutis was exposed in places. The subcuticular tissues were nearly all shrunken, and where the palm alone was attacked, the part so diseased seemed to be a little depressed and firmer and less elastic than common. In the fingers there were often cracks in the altered skin, and the integuments presented the appearance of being tightly drawn over the subjacent tissues. The surface of all the affected part was glossy, and shining as though it had been skillfully varnished. Nothing more curious than these red and shining tissues can be conceived of. In most of them, the part was devoid of wrinkles and perfectly free from hair. Mr. Paget's comparison of chilblains is one which we often used to describe these appearances; but in some instances we have been more strikingly reminded of the characters of certain large, thin, and highly-polished scars.

"Where a single nerve, as the ulnar, had been attacked, the described state of skin was seen only in its ultimate distribution; but in other instances of more extensive nerve injury, the central palm suffered, or a single finger, or the pulps of all of them. In others, the palm or fingers were dotted with islets of thin and red and glossy skin. The dorsum of the hand, as a rule, was in that member the part least subject to the alteration, while the dorsum of the foot was in that region the part most liable to suffer. Do the greater functional endowments of the palm of the hand, as compared to the sole of the foot, account for this preference?

"*Eczema.*—A very constant feature of this state of skin was the occurrence of eczematous eruptions, which appeared as minute vesicles thickly scattered over the thin and tender cutis, or else showed themselves in successive crops of larger vesicles on the skin about the altered parts, with usually a preference for the portions which lay nearer the trunk.

"In some patients this symptom was absent; in others, it was never wholly lost, but varied in amount; while in a small number it came and went, being absent for weeks at a time, and then returning. It was also remarkable in these latter, that recurrence of the eruption gave ease to certain painful symptoms to be presently described, or, to speak more cautiously, when the eczema came back the pain declined."

Since our report, Mr. Annandale* has published a very interesting history of wound of a finger with tender cicatrix, followed by glossy redness of the skin of the same hand, and finally of the opposite hand. Mr. Syme removed the finger, which soon relieved the hand first involved, but was succeeded by swelling and increase of pain in the other hand. The history, unfortunately, ends here, and there was no microscopic examination of the portion of nerves removed. This is especially to be regretted, because of the mystery which hangs over the production of this form of mal-nutrition of skin and its accompaniment of burning pain. I have never seen in these cases any distinct redness or swelling upon the opposite side, although in severe examples the sense of burning and the hyperæsthetic state of the skin was apt to affect first the symmetrically related member, and then other regions or the whole surface. In a single instance, the unwounded limb was attacked by a vesicular eruption like that which existed on the other palm. Before leaving this subject, it were well to notice the fact to which I have already called attention,† that glossy skin, with causalgia, may follow central disease, as in the following very interesting case, which was probably an example of what it is now the fashion to call "sclerosis" of the antero-lateral column of the spine. That there may also have been alterations of nerve trunks, I cannot, of course, deny. Charcot has shown that, both in old spinal sclerosis and in cerebral palsies, affections of extra central neural fibres are not uncommon, so that the present case was probably an extreme example of similar disease.

---

* Malformations of the Fingers and Toes. London, 1866, Case 35.
† San. Com. Rept., p. 429.

Case 27.—*Intense neuralgia and motor palsy of legs, with contracted toes and ankles; no loss of sensation; neuralgia of arms and hands; contraction of fingers; no palsy of upper limbs; hyperæsthesia of palms; causalgia, and glazed redness of ulnar side of palms.* October 19, 1865. Mrs. S., aged fifty-two, twice married, has had no children, and never was pregnant. During the latter years of her last marriage, and after her husband's death, she had a good deal of distress and annoyances of various kinds. In 1859, Mrs. S. had a fall, in which she struck the back of her neck. Two weeks later she felt suddenly a dull but severe pain between her shoulders. Within a few days this extended into the arms, with dragging and tearing pains down to the wrists. A few months later the pains attacked the legs, and were accompanied by violent cramps. About this time she had distinct articulation; but this did not endure. The intellect was clear throughout the case. The next symptom was feebleness in the legs, which increased until she ceased to walk. She has since remained on a couch or in bed. After a year, as well as can be recalled, her feet and hands became contracted. The toes were flexed, the feet extended. The fingers became slowly flexed to a right angle with the palm, the index-finger remaining extended. The thumb was drawn tightly into the palm, and the fingers were extended tightly on themselves. Sensation was said to have been normal at all times. It is now entire everywhere. On the ulnar half of the palm, in both hands, the skin is dark-red, shining, and glazed. It is in these parts exquisitely tender to the touch, and is the seat of a constant causalgia or burning pain. The soles also burn, but are not red nor shining. All the motions are limited by the contractions, but there does not seem to be any distinct paralysis. The flexors of the toes are somewhat atrophied, but still have voluntary motion. Her bowels are always costive, never being moved without enemata. Urine is passed with difficulty, and for some years has occasionally required the use of a catheter; it is cloudy, from deposits of urates, and very rarely uric acid sediment; it is always acid; the average specific gravity of four specimens of mixed urine of the whole day was 1025; no albumen or sugar was present. Tubercle in left lung, cough, and hectic. These are symptoms only of the last five months. *Nutrition*—general wasting. The great-toes were subject to occasional ulcers at their angles during the first two years of her malady. The index, medius, and ring fingers on each hand have a disease of the matrix of the nails, resulting in a thinning and irregular growth of the nails without incurvation.

The affection of the teeth is very curious. They were formerly regular, white, of even length, and touching one another. They are now very unequal in length, and diverge from one another, so that the space of four lines exists between the two anterior upper incisors. They all seem to be turned more or less on their long axes, and all are of a deep yellow, despite the most assiduous care. I should add that none are loose. I do not know that I can fully describe the curious appearance presented by this patient's mouth. It strongly impressed me with the idea that there had been disease of the alveolar sockets, something akin to that which is met with in the matrices of certain diseased nails.

My patient died in November, 1865. To my regret no post-mortem examination could be had.

Alterations of the cutaneous appendages.—The nails and hair undergo very curious changes consequent upon nerve wounds. After total section the nails are apt to become clubbed, and, in rare cases, to suffer from painless whitlow. I am unable to say whether or not nail growth is for a time arrested immediately after the section of the nerve; but in most of these cases it is found at a later stage to be slower than that of the corresponding healthy parts, although in no instance have I met with a total cessation of growth. In lesser nerve wounds, ulceration around the nails is common, and often very painful; but in connection with the glossy skin of certain neural lesions, we observed peculiarities of nails and hair which we described as follows:

" When the depraved nutritive state has lasted for some months, the hair commonly disappears from the fingers affected, and the nails undergo remarkable alterations. They suffer only in the fingers the neural supply of which has been interfered with, so that the nails in the median distribution may be contorted and those in the little finger be unaffected. The alteration in the nail consists of a curve in its long axis, an extreme lateral arching, and sometimes a thickening of the cutis beneath its extremity. In other cases a change takes place which is quite pecu liar, and which to us, at least, was new. The skin at that end of the nail next to the third finger-joint becomes retracted, leaving the sensitive matrix partly exposed. At the same time, the upper line of union of skin and nail retreats into or under the latter part, and in place of a smooth edge, is seen through the nail as a ragged and notched border. The patient who presented these changes in the most striking form had also lateral arching of the nail, but no longitudinal curving. It was a case of the most terrible suffering, from a combination of burning pain in the hand and neuralgic pain in the forearm.

" No deformity of the nails in tubercle at all approaches that which nerve wounds occasion. Indeed, we think it would be possible for one familiar with these cases to diagnose the existence of a nerve lesion from the form of these protuberant and oddly-curved nails.

" When the nails of the toes have been attacked, and they are very rarely so, the curving is less marked, but a distressing ulceration is apt to occur at their angles, and to break out again and again, despite of every care and attention."

Besides the curious changes here described, the nails suffer in nerve wounds other nutritive alterations which have been nowhere well delineated. In many nerve wounds, where there is only ordinary neuralgia, and not glossy skin and causalgia, I have seen the nails clubbed in some cases, and in others dry, scaly, cracked, and fragile. Occasionally they are very thin, so as to be tender,—atrophied in fact. I have not seen their growth suspended by any nerve lesion, as occurs in some fevers, or rarely in constitutional syphilis, and even complete nerve section does not prevent lost nails from being reformed. In a recent case of wound of the ulnar nerve, the nail of the little finger was marked transversely by a series of closely-set, indented furrows, such as I have since seen but once, and that in a case of hemiplegia, now under my care.

The hair is very apt to desert the red and glossy skin surfaces which accompany causalgia. In the case of Mrs. S., quoted above, the hairs on the legs were sparse, and, under the microscope, the part of the hair nearest the skin was ragged, the external cells of the hair being ruffled up in a remarkable manner.

In neuralgia or injury of the fifth pair, alterations of the hair are common, such as its becoming partially gray after an attack, or falling out for a time.

Mougeot quotes Pouteau* as having seen in traumatic neuralgia the hair growing large and hard, with an inconvenient tendency to stand erect. Larrey,† whose relations of his campaigns are rich in interesting cases, describes a like change in hairs springing from hyperæsthetic skin,

---

* Œuvres posthumes, p. 92. 1783.

† Larrey, clinique Chir., v. i. p. 200. 1829.

and unable to bear the lightest touch. Bellingeri noticed
the hair as becoming thicker and harder and as growing
faster than elsewhere; while yet more singular is the history which Hamilton* relates on the authority of Cramp-
ton. A lancet wound was followed by remarkable symptoms, probably due to neuritis affecting an hysterical
temperament. Among other changes in the part, the
arm became thickly covered with hair. Section of the
nerve gave partial relief, and finally a cure was obtained
after an attack of pneumonia, in which the patient was
salivated.

Loss of hair after nerve sections is occasionally met
with in animals, especially rabbits, and it is sometimes
renewed without reunion of the nerve having taken place.

Further study is yet needed as to the state of the hair
and nails, especially the latter, as revealing neural or other
conditions of disease. Beau has paid most attention to the
subject, but not in nervous maladies. As one of its difficulties, I may mention that while after nerve sections
the nails still grow, I have lately discovered that for
some time after certain cerebral palsies they do not do
so.† This observation was made in four instances of
cerebral palsy, by staining the nails with nitric acid. The
nails began to grow anew in every case a few days before motion returned in the fingers, but the rate of
increase was for a long time slower than upon the healthy
side. I have since observed the same facts in embolus
of the left hemisphere with right hemiplegia. It may
constitute a new diagnostic difference between central
and peripheral paralysis.

The following case is a singular example of the effects
of a punctured wound of a nerve in a child of hysterical

* Dublin Jour. of Chemical and Med. Science, March, 1868.
† Repts. Phil. Coll. Phys., Am. Jour. Med. Sci., 1871.

temperament. The nail lesions, on account of which I have quoted the case here, were very unusual in character. I am indebted to Dr. J. C. Norris for notes of the earlier history of the case.

Case 28.—D. H., a girl, aged thirteen, of highly nervous constitution, applied at my clinic for nervous disease, December 5, 1871.

May 24, 1868, while she was playing in the street, a lad accidentally ran a small penknife blade into her right hand. Dr. Norris supposed that it wounded the median nerve at the point where the digital nerves are given off, because it caused at once decided tingling in the third finger. The injury seemed trifling, and gave no further trouble until thirty-six hours later, when she became sick, and began to suffer excruciating pain in the right hand, arm, sternum, and back, with fever, rigors, nausea, and slight convulsions, without loss of consciousness. The hand and arm were slightly swollen, and the head was drawn backward, while there was also tremor of the jaw and dysphagia. She could not bear to be moved, and the least jar was intolerable. The treatment consisted in the application of ice to the spine, poultices to the hand and arm, and full doses of anodynes. After four days of acute suffering she improved, and was nearly free from annoyance until the tenth day, when she began to complain of burning pain in the injured palm. Meanwhile the hand remained slightly swollen, livid, and low in temperature. At this time all the finger-nails of the hurt hand began to turn dark from blood effused under them. In a few days they became perfectly black, and their growth, although not entirely arrested, was for a time retarded. The least touch increased the pain in the palm, but a firm pressure did not so much affect it. After a good deal of ineffectual treatment, the burning pain yielded to repeated blisters made with liq. ammoniæ fort.

At the same time she took iron, quinine, belladonna, and good diet, and after a time was induced to exercise in the open air. She continued to improve during the summer, and three months after the injury was free from pain and had good use of the hand and arm. The palm, however, remained livid, and was lower in temperature than that of the other limb. The nails were normal in form and color. At this time Dr. Norris ceased to attend, and, upon the return of pain, in September, a homœopath treated the case. During the winter of 1868 and 1869, the fingers became contracted, and the hand flexed, the palm continuing to suffer with burning pain. These conditions existed in varying degrees up to March, 1869, when the pain grew more severe, and the flexions became extreme. Six weeks' treatment by induced currents entirely relieved all of these symptoms, which remained absent until October, 1871. At this date, the flexions recurred, but only when a storm impended, or when she was under the influence of strong emotions.

When the case was seen by me, December 5, 1871, I found the fingers normal as to movement. Although she complained of weakness in the right arm, the dynamometer showed its grasp to be stronger than that of the left. The median nerve track in the arm was normal, but in the forearm it was tender, and pressure on it excited pain at the seat of wound. The nails were natural.

Nutritive change in connective tissues.—Affections of the connective tissues are common after nerve wounds, and are first seen in the shape of œdema, local or general, in the limb affected. In looking over notes of one hundred and sixty cases of these wounds, I find that œdema was apt to come on suddenly and to announce, as it were, a subsequent neuralgia. Sometimes the swelling came and went without obvious cause, and sometimes it was very persistent and accompanied with congestion of the skin. In generalized atrophic conditions of a limb, the connective tissue shared the loss which fell upon the other tissues, seeming to disappear quite as rapidly as they. It is, however, indicative of the difficulties which surround these cases, that in a single instance I have seen a nerve wound give rise to an hypertrophic state of the connective tissues. The case is so unusual that I have been unable to match it either from my own material or from the records of others. Such a condition of sclerosis of the areolar tissues is, however, a rare incident of spinal myelitis.

Case 29.—John Graham, Company E, 116th New York Volunteers. A ball entered three inches below the left axilla on the posterior face, and made exit two inches below the axilla anteriorly. The arm dropped, and the man fell, faint and bleeding freely. It is not easy to fix the date of the first hyperplastic change, but quite early in the case the first and second fingers and thumb slowly enlarged without inflammatory signs, and with slight darting pains. After the wound healed, these parts increased still more and became firm to the touch and dark-purplish in tint, the lancinating pains becoming more severe. For several months there was also burning pain in the fingers and palm, and two months after the wound occurred, the skin of the affected parts was shed almost entire.

Seven months after he was shot, I saw and examined him through the kindness of my friend Dr. Morehouse, in whose service the case at that time was.

He had loss of the sense of touch and pain in the first, second, and lower half of the third finger, as well as in the palmar face of the thumb. The index and second fingers were moveless, but chiefly because of their size and stiffness. The thumb could be stirred slightly. In all of these parts there were darting pains, and the skin

was dry, scaly, and yellow. The enlargement affected
principally the thumb and first two fingers, but it also
involved the back of the hand, which was most developed
on the radial side, the thumb being more remarkably
overgrown than the other parts. The ulnar side of the
palm and the back of the hand were a little œdematous,
but in the regions above mentioned the skin seemed thickened, and the tissues were as firm as most fibrous tumors,
and did not pit upon pressure. Dr. Packard, who also
saw this patient, pointed out its extremely close likeness
to elephantiasis.

Alterations of joints.—Of all the various forms of mischief wrought by nerve wounds, the most intractable and
disabling are the curious inflammatory states of joints to
which we were the first to call attention.

The relation of rheumatic lesions of joints to neural
injuries of centres is so interesting in its connection with
our own observations that I shall be pardoned if I allude
to its history.

In 1831, my father, the late Dr. J. K. Mitchell, described* four cases of spinal injury, which were followed
by inflammations of joints below the point of spine
affected. Upon these he based a pathogenesis of rheumatism, which connected it with affections of the spinal
centres. Since then, numerous theories of the cause of
rheumatism have held sway, each in turn to fall before
more strict analyses and later facts. In 1864 our demonstration of the relationship of joint diseases to nerve wounds
again called attention to this view of the subject. It received favorable consideration at the hands of Dr. Day,† of
Stafford, England, in an able volume of clinical histories,
in 1866, and in the same year was carefully discussed by

---

* Amer. Jour. Med. Sci., vol. viii. p. 55.
† Clinical Histories, Dr. Day. London, 1866.

Ball,* who, without going so far as to consider rheumatism a neurosis, is plainly at a loss to fasten upon any clinical distinction between neuro-traumatic arthritis and that due to common rheumatism.

In 1868 Charcot† published his excellent paper upon arthropathies consequent on spinal or cerebral lesions; and other facts resembling those which he has related have since then accumulated largely.‡

In a certain number of nerve wounds, notably most often in those of the upper extremities, one or more of the joints in the wounded limb become swollen. The nature of the injury does not seem to influence the case, as I have seen it follow dislocations, ball wounds, and contusions of nerves, while in an interesting case of Dr. Packard's, it was one of the consequences of compression of the sciatic nerve by a tumor. More lately, in the service of my friend Dr. J. A. Brinton, at the Philadelphia Hospital, I saw a man who had extensive joint lesions, owing to the brachial nerves having suffered during the dislocation, or upon the subsequent reduction of the humerus, so that I suspect these troubles are more common than has been supposed.§ In one case the joints of the fingers became swollen and tender on the third day after ball wound of the brachial plexus, but usually the swelling appears much later, and, like the glossy skin, is frequently the offspring of secondary neuritis. Often masked at first by the general inflammation of the limb, or concealed by the œdema so common after nerve wounds, it is more persistent than these, and, as they fade, begins to

---

* Rheumatism Viscéral, Benj. Ball.   Paris, 1866, p. 88.

† Arch. de Physiol., 1868, p. 160.

‡ Dr. Scott Alison (Lancet, March, 1846, p. 278) was the first to describe the arthritis of hemiplegia. Although brief, his account of the malady is clear and sufficient.

§ I have since met with similar cases.

assume importance. We may then have one articulation—
and if only one, a large one—involved, or perhaps all the
joints of a finger, or every joint in the hand, or of the
entire limb may suffer. The swelling is never very great,
the redness usually slight, and the tenderness on touch
or motion exquisite. This condition of things remains
with little change during weeks or months, and then
slowly declines, leaving the joints stiff, enlarged, and
somewhat sensitive, especially as to movement. A small
proportion of such cases find ready relief, but in many
of them the resultant anchylosis proves utterly uncon-
querable, so that it is vain to break up the adhesions
under ether, or to try to restore mobility by manipulation
or splints. All alike fail, and serve only to add to the
essential tortures of the accompanying neuralgia and hyperæsthetic states of skin. Since writing my last paper,*
I have met with some of the former patients who suffered with these troubles, but in no case originally very
severe was there any great gain,—indeed in most of them
the joints had become every year more stiff and useless.

It is then quite clear that injuries of the spine, diseases
of this organ, and of the brain, and wounds, or any form
of lesions of nerves, are capable of developing in the joints
inflammatory conditions, usually subacute, and which
so precisely resemble rheumatic arthritis in their symptoms and results, that no clinical skill can discriminate
between the two. In this state it were well to leave the
subject. The chemical theories have crumbled, and, in
the growing tendency to believe that rheumatism may
have more forms than one, it may not be amiss to recall
the facts to which we have contributed, and which are
well illustrated by the following case. Other and more
severe examples will be found in the cases appended to
the later chapters of this work.

---

* Reports of the Sanitary Commission.

Case 30.— *Gunshot wound of the right brachial plexus; caus-*
algia; tremor; arthritic lesions; nail-changes; acid sweats;
hyperæsthesia; little loss of motion from paralysis; great gain
under treatment. B. D. L., aged forty-three, a farmer
from Maine. Enlisted July, 1862. He was healthy to the
date of his wound, received July 2d, 1863, at Gettysburg.
While kneeling and aiming he was shot in the right side
of the neck. He felt pain in the wound, but none down
the arm. He spun around, feeling stunned, and fell on
his back, not unconscious. In five minutes he arose and
walked to the rear, where the wound was dressed with
cold water, no splint being employed either then or later.
At first, all motion was lost. In an hour he could move
his fingers and abduct the arm, but not flex it. He thinks
sensation was perfect, except as to the ulnar distribution.
Within an hour he had severe earache, and pain in the
shoulder, arm, and forearm. During the second week he
began to have burning pain in the hand. At this time,
which probably marked the onset of neuritis, the shoulder-joint grew stiff, then the elbow, and lastly all of the
fingers. This condition was excessively painful, and remained unchanged. The tremor which is constant in the
upper arm muscles began the day of the wound, and had
not ceased on his admission to our wards.

Site of wound.—On admission, October, 1863, it was
noted that the ball had entered the right side of the neck,
in front, three inches above the clavicle, in the outer edge
of the trapezius. The missile passed downward and outward, and struck the anterior edge of the supra-spinal
fossa of the scapula, five inches external to the spine of
the first dorsal vertebra. Both wounds sloughed, leaving
scars one and a half inches in diameter. The patient is
well and florid. The shoulder is motionless from stiffness.
The lower joints are alike stiff, swollen, red, and painful;
the arm, semi-prone and flexed, is carried across the chest,

supported by the sound hand. He has slight motion throughout, but the effort causes fibrillar-tremor and exquisite pain.

Sensation.—The sense of touch is everywhere good, save that there is slight numbness of the back of the hand and forearm. Some causalgia is felt in the palm, but no other pain, except on movement.

Nutrition.—The palm is thin and red or purplish, and on it the patient uses water, now and then, as a dressing; there is no atrophy; the wound is healed, but tender, as are also the upper nerve tracks. Muscular hyperæsthesia of the deltoid and triceps is present. The nails are remarkably curved; the hair is scanty; the sweat ill smelling and acid. The shoulder muscles alone have lost electro-muscular contractility (induction current). Under ether, the joints when moved are found to be free from well-marked organic adhesions.

Passive motion and electricity caused speedy gain in movement, and in February, 1864, he was able to move all the joints with diminished pain. The muscles were, at this time, sensitive to induced currents, and the numbness and causalgia had nearly disappeared. He was allowed a furlough, at the expiration of which he deserted.

This case is valuable as an example of arthritic changes, extreme in character, with very little sensory or motor paralysis, and seemingly aided by treatment.

Influence of nerve wounds on secretion.—It has occasionally been observed that after nerve injuries productive of neuritis, and especially in the neuralgic paroxysm, the affected parts sweat excessively; but we still need full details as to the comparative results in cases of partial and those of complete division of a large nerve trunk. As a rule, in the few cases of extensive nerve injury which we saw at Turner's Lane Hospital, and where there was evidence

of total loss of function, the skin remained dry, even in
hot weather; both the oleaginous and sudoriparous glands
having ceased to act, probably because of atrophic changes.
In certain instances this was so marked that the region
involved could be known by the want of moisture. This
was well seen in wounds of the median nerve. In the
case of Captain (now Commodore) Stembel, who had
reflex paralysis of the left arm, with a like but more permanent condition of the right arm and shoulder, there
was defective sweating of the right limb, with excessive
secretion in the left; and although some years have
elapsed, and the right arm has become nearly, and the left
entirely, well, these symptoms remain unaltered. I saw,
two years ago, an officer who had no secretion and no
odor in the left axilla, which was insensible, owing to a
ball wound of the shoulder. In many of the histories of
our cases of partial nerve wounds, I find the sweating
stated to be excessive; but in a number of instances of
glossy skin, with causalgia, the sweat was not only abun-
dant, but intensely acid, so that when some of these patients passed me in the wards I was aware of their presence because of the disagreeable odor, like vinegar, which
their hands exhaled, despite the constant use of water, to
which they resorted for relief. In one man the smell was
disgustingly heavy, and resembled that which comes from
a bad drain.

Effect of nerve injuries on calorification.—The examinations
of temperature made at the Hospital for Nervous Diseases
were more incomplete than I could have desired, but they
brought out distinctly one very important difference between cases of total section of nerves and those irritative
lesions which result in causalgia with glossy skin. Since
then I have studied my cases with great care as to this
point, and have found that my later conclusions sustain
those which we then reached. Perhaps a word as to the

method of such examinations may not be out of place. At our hospital we used the thermometer, held in succession on the skin of two parts anatomically symmetrical, and which had been subjected for half an hour to the same external conditions. More satisfactory results were obtained by the use of the thermo-electric disks of Becquerel and the galvanometer; but of late I have employed a small thermometer, the bulb of which is covered on one-half of its circumference by a piece of cork, which extends a half-inch on either side beyond and also below the bulb. By this arrangement the heat is confined, and the time needed for the observation is shortened. Some weeks or months after complete division of a large nerve, it will be found that the affected parts are colder than those which are not influenced by the injury. The range in my cases was from two to fifteen degrees Fahrenheit lower than that of the sound tissues. Mr. Hutchinson's cases were six to ten degrees colder in the parts palsied, and Mr. Erichsen had a like result.*

Where a nerve trunk had been merely injured and not thoroughly divided, we commonly found that the temperature of the affected tissues was lowered in most cases from half a degree to two or three degrees; but when there was some irritative lesion, with consequent causalgia and glossy skin, the temperature was either normal, or, as happened in the majority of such cases, slightly above that of the neighboring tissues.

At the U. S. A. Hospital for Diseases and Injuries of Nerves the records were unfortunately only comparative, owing to the galvanometer being the instrument used,

---

* See, also, Earle, Med.-Chir. Trans., vol. vii. 1816, p. 173, for observations on the low temperature of traumatic palsy, and on the effect of electricity in raising it Also, Yellowby, same journal, vol. iii. Also, W. B. Woodman, in Sydenham Soc. Translation of Wunderlich on Temperature in Disease, p. 152.

but they were still sufficiently distinct. I have since seen only two cases of glossy skin tissues from nerve wound, and in both the temperature of the causalgic region was one or two degrees higher than that of the opposite side, while above the burning parts the thermometer stood usually a degree below that of the healthy limb. This slight loss of temperature above the wound is not uncommon in any nerve lesion, and may be due in part to the long and constant disuse of the limb.

In 1867, Dr. W. W. Keen was kind enough to examine for me two of the worst of our former cases of causalgia. In both the injured parts were still a fraction of a degree warmer than those on the well side. Both of these men had improved considerably, and in both the pain had disappeared. I have been unable to study any case of nerve wound immediately after its reception, so that what I have here said applies only to dates remote by weeks or months from the time at which the wound was received. The records of other observers are also deficient in this respect, so that we still need a complete thermal study of the heat of limbs immediately after nerve wounds, both complete and incomplete, as well as a thorough knowledge of the influence of irritative lesions and of the remoter changes in temperature which time may bring about. We may suspect as probable, that within a short period after nerve section the temperature rises as it does after physiological nerve sections, owing to palsy of the vaso-motor nerves, and consequently of the vasal muscle fibres under their control. The later loss of temperature which has been uniformly observed in these cases is less easy of explanation. It does not appear to be directly related to the state of the sympathetic fibres, because when these alone are cut, as in the neck, although the first increase of heat is not preserved, the temperature does not fall below the normal standard as it does finally after total nerve section in the limbs. As regards these latter, it is likely that the utter absence of muscular movement may have some influence in causing lowered temperature, but a far larger share may be due to atrophic changes in vasal muscles and to their subsequent contraction. As the voluntary muscles and other parts waste away, the general calibres of the greater trunks, both arteries and veins, must be diminished, and the circulation lose all of those hastening influences which every muscular movement occasions, so that in time the general temperature comes at last to be distinctly lessened. The slight rise of the thermometer which is seen in parts of the body suffering from glossy skin and burning, is probably due to localized palsies of vessel walls, owing either to direct nutritive changes or to reflected impressions, competent to bring about such a condition.

There is a curious and interesting discrepancy between the physiological and the clinical results as to the local temperatures observed after nerve sections. Bernard has shown that section of the anterior or posterior spinal nerve roots, or, indeed, of both, does not materially alter the temperature of the related tissues, while, on the other hand, division of the main nerve of a limb, as the sciatic after it has been joined by sympathetic filaments from the pelvis, results in considerable elevation of tempera- ture in the leg. Schiff believes, however, that portions of the vaso-motor nerves pass with the spinal nerve roots, and that their division causes slight elevation of the ther- mometer, while a higher temperature is to be attained by section of the main nerve of the limb. Neither physi- ologist has considered the influence of partial section or of irritation of nerves. I am aware of no clinical obser- vation which records the early rise in temperature after total section of the main nerve of a member; but this may be due to the fact that the temperature examinations have been made at more or less remote periods, so that it is quite probable that were a case of divided nerve examined at all its stages, we should find at first a rise, and, after a time, a fall of temperature. Augustus Waller has left on record a valuable set of experiments which, to some extent, cast light on this subject. He submitted the ulnar nerve at the elbow to the influence of a freezing mixture of ice and salt, or to that of ice alone. At first the mercury fell slightly, but so soon as the nerve became more completely chilled, and before all sensation was absent, the temperature between the third and fourth fingers rose several degrees above that of the interspace between the first and second digits. When the cold was removed and the nerve thawed, the temperature fell, until, in the two parts mentioned, it became equal. The physiological interpretation of these phenomena is a simple one. The first influence of cold is to irritate the vasomotor nerve fibres, and thus to occasion a contraction of the related blood-vessels and a fall of temperature. Whether this be due to a direct influence on these nerves or to a centrally reflected impression, is not decided by Waller's observations. As the main nerve becomes frozen and ceases to convey messages, the vaso-motors being paralyzed, their connected vessels undergo dilatation, the temperature rises, and the part flushes, pulsates, and feels full. When, in one instance, the ulnar nerve was more severely frozen by the use of ice and salt, the temperature rose as described in the last experiment; but the application of the freezing mixture having been too prolonged, there was total loss of motion and sensation, which only very slowly grew better, and for some days the temperature remained below that of the portions of the hand to which are distributed the median and radial nerves. In this observation, the physiological conclusions as to the later stages of the paralysis were the same as those which obtain in clinical cases of nerve section. As if, however, still further to complicate this difficult question, I find, on studying with care the thermal results of Waller's observations on the influence of pressure upon nerves, that no matter how complete may be the palsy induced by this mechanical cause, it is followed only by a fall of temperature in the affected region, and never by a rise. This seems to be corroborated by clinical experience, since in two instances of arm palsy from sleeping on the member, both seen by me within twelve hours of the date of injury, there was in one case a fall of one degree, and in the other of $2\frac{1}{10}°$ F. There appears to be, therefore, some essential difference, as yet inexplicable, between the thermal results obtained by freezing and by pressure.

I may add, that I have recently repeated Waller's experiments upon my own person, and with results in no wise different from his.

CHAPTER VIII.

Alterations of sensation.—The sensory functions of nerves are affected by wounds in such a manner as to be lessened, exalted, or perverted, so that we have as results hyperæsthesia, anæsthesia, and all the varieties of pain, with numberless sensations, for the describing of which language fails us, so greatly do they vary with different cases of injury.

Hyperæsthesia.—Heightened sensibility, or that state in which agents usually felt, as touch only, become painful, is sufficiently common after many forms of nerve injury; but I cannot recall a case in which it was an immediate effect. In some of the older histories of lancet wounds, and in many instances of ball wounds, it came on after a few days, or later, and was one of the expressions of a nerve, the polarity of which had become intensified by inflammatory conditions. I have never been able to discover that the tactile sense had been thus over-excited, so that Weber's points could be distinguished as two, where otherwise they could have been felt but as one. When, indeed, there is hyperæsthesia for pain, we are apt to find it associated with lessened or lost power of tactile appreciation, and this rather because of the confusing influence of pain than necessarily from actual loss of tactile appreciation. All cases of glossy skin with causalgia were sure to exhibit hyperæsthesia of the affected surfaces, or of regions near them; and this condition, in a less intense degree, was likely, after a time, to

(179)

be found elsewhere on the skin, more and more distant sensation centres coming by degrees to possess an increased share of the excitability which at first was confined to limited groups of ganglia. I recall one very striking example of local hyperæsthesia, in which the ulnar nerve was wounded, so as to cause, in its region of ultimate distribution, pain and hyperæsthesia. Touch did not seem to be lost, but it was certainly enfeebled, and even the gentlest contact gave pain. The median nerve had been divided, and the contrast as to sensations between the skin surfaces to which the two nerves are distributed, was both striking and instructive.

In our book on nerve wounds, a case of hyperæsthesia of the thigh is related, in which there was no glossy skin or burning pain; and such instances of localized hyperæsthesia in regions remote from the wound may occasionally be met with.

I have long suspected that hyperæsthetic states are due to several causes.

In hysteria, the centres are affected, and in many cases of causalgia, when the constitutional disturbance is at its height, these are so excitable that a touch of the skin anywhere, the sound of a step, the rustle of paper, is felt to be unpleasant, and even at times exquisitely painful. In one case, the right hand having burning pain, the left palm became acutely sensitive. In other cases, as those due to lancet wounds, the arm and hand may become hyperæsthetic very early,—so soon, indeed, that we can scarcely escape the belief that something has so affected the nerve as to make it produce on the centres painful reaction from causes usually incompetent to occasion this result. The phenomena which attend upon freezing of nerves offer a remarkably instructive illustration of the suddenness with which a long line of nerve may be brought into such a state as that just described. At a certain stage of the chilling of the ulnar trunk at the elbow, the whole nerve below this point becomes so irritable that the least pressure upon it causes not only pain, but sudden motion of every muscle which it supplies. In cases of nerve wounds this condition is reached, owing to inflammatory states of the nerve; but whether the effect be not in every such case merely to heighten the central receptive impressibility, we can hardly say. The analogy to excited motor states is curious, and, if I may be allowed the use of such a phrase, I might describe the general hyperæsthesia which follows a nerve injury as sensory tetanus.

In cases of causalgia and glossy skin, the hyperæsthesia is due, I think, to nutritive conditions affecting the skin surfaces and the nerves beneath them, so as to make the latter over-sensitive. The tendency is towards atrophy, and the thinned and shining skin, constantly fretted with tiny ulcers, seems at last to fail to shelter sufficiently its included nerve ends. Finally, the centres become over-sensitive, and radiate their state of sensitive wakefulness far and wide, just as in tetanus the motor excitability floods, at length, the nearer and more distant ganglia.

Muscular hyperæsthesia.—This condition is common in gunshot wounds of nerves, and in blows on the back, injuring the outgoing nerves. It was often the sole symptom of spinal concussions, and was, in many of them, strictly limited to certain muscles. The muscle may be over-sensitive when the skin above it is not, and the degree to which it is alive to pain where pain should not exist, is measured by pressure only. We pinch the skin slightly, without giving annoyance, but deep pressure on the muscles causes soreness, and motion of these parts is nearly always productive of more or less pain.

Defects of sensation; anæsthesia.—Defects of feeling may exist to any degree after nerve wounds, from the slightest

loss of tactile sensibility to the most entire absence of
that sense, as well as of the feeling of pain and of temperature. Accurate knowledge as to these losses can
only be had through careful examination of the skin
with the aid of certain instruments.

When examining a patient as to loss of any of the
sensory functions of the skin, it is, of course, necessary
to cover his eyes, and, if possible, it is best not to acquaint
him with the methods about to be employed. We desire
to learn what change has taken place as to his power to
discriminate tactile impressions, those of pain, and those
of temperature.

As regards touch, we need practically in nerve wounds
only three tests. For rough examination, the touch of a
pencil-point on the surface, or, in dubious cases, the tip
of a feather, suffices to reveal whether the patient feels
the touch, as he should do; but incessant questioning
and repeated examinations are sometimes needed, when
the loss of tactile discrimination is slight. Perhaps the
most delicate test of all is to touch the tips of single hairs.
The very slight movement which this produces in the skin
about the bulb is plainly enough felt during health, but
a very small diminution in the acuteness of touch will
cause the motion to be unfelt. By these means we map
out on the skin the region of affected or lost touch, and I
have found it convenient, in the hand especially, to record
these results on previously-prepared drawings of the two
faces of this part,—a plan which, with slight memoranda
added, enables me to avoid tedious note-taking. Absolute annihilation of touch is noted on the diagram by a
zero within the affected space.

Having thus made out the region attacked, we wish to
learn accurately the amount of sensation still left. This
is far more difficult in local nerve lesions than in central
anæsthesia, because of the frequent causalgia, hyperæs-

thesias, and cramped positions of the part from muscular atrophies and joint-disease.

For numeral appreciations, we make use of the æsthesiometer, which consists of a compass the points of which are covered with little rounded balls, a scale placed above enabling us to learn how far apart are the points.* There is a more convenient form of instrument, in which the two limbs of the compass slide upon a graduated bar. With its aid we desire to learn what is the least distance at which the separated points can be distinguished as two. When nearer than this, they are felt only as one. Weber has given very full tables for all parts of the skin, stating the distances at which the two points are normally distinguished as a single point. Unfortunately, these are of limited value in diseased states, because the individual sensory capacity varies remarkably, so that it is always necessary to compare the part with a corresponding portion of healthy skin in order to get a normal standard. Even with this aid, the use of the æsthesiometer is not so easy or simple as might be supposed. The answers often vary when you repeat the observation at the same place a few minutes later, and in children or unintelligent patients the records thus obtained have but little utility. These are intrinsic difficulties which have somewhat lessened the practical value of the æsthesiometer. The precautions requisite to give to its answers all possible truthfulness are these: the patient's eyes should be covered, and the part to be examined should be at rest, and the compass-points, which ought to be rounded, should be lightly placed on the skin, taking care to let both come down with equal force and at once, since otherwise the succession of impressions informs the patient that

---

* Ordinary compasses, and a rule on which to ascertain the extent of separation of their parts, answer every purpose.

there are two points in use. It is also necessary, in comparing two portions of skin, as that of the forefingers, to see that the points lie each time in the same direction, since the normal sensibility varies as we test it in the axis of a limb, or across it. Above all, it is essential, in every examination of sensation, to see that the patient does not move the part during the time of testing it. There seems to be an almost uncontrollable prompting to do this in every instance where the sense of touch is puzzled; and if he be allowed to stir the part ever so little, the answer he makes will often prove correct, when in the absence of motion it would have been defective. The records obtained by the compass-points may also be written on the diagram which is kept for reference, with the notes of the case.

Much more curious illustrations of this tendency to aid the touch by movement will be met with when we come to examine the power to localize or place a tactile sensation.

It would seem as if, when a patient is aware of having been touched, he must be able to say where the touch has been. It has been found, however, that when the touch-sense is dulled, the person examined is often unable to place the sensation correctly. If we touch the finger-tip, on being asked regarding it, he is likely to say, You touched my knuckle; or if, after touching, he be allowed to look at the part, he will indicate the place which he supposed touched, and will usually make some gross blunder as to its whereabouts.

There is, regarding this matter, an approach to regularity. It was stated in our book* that the impression was apt to be falsely referred to, or towards some region of more distinct sensation. This I have frequently seen

---

* P. 116.

illustrated since then, and, although it sometimes happens that the impression is not so referred to any very remote point, when a mistake is made it is never towards locating the touch upon a region of more obscure sensation.

The error spoken of above as arising from an instinctive tendency to move the part examined, is strikingly seen in attempts to determine the place of a sensation, so that a patient who will mistake one finger for another, if these are at rest, will instantly report the matter correctly if allowed to move freely the finger examined. Now, where we are making continuous pressure on a spot, motion of the part may be useful by enabling the pressure to be increased or varied, so that the touch is rendered more distinct; but when, on the other hand, we tap a portion of skin lightly, and the impression so made is but momentary, no aid can be had in this direction; yet, as I have said, freedom to move the part will secure a correct reply in many instances where the sense of tact alone has become too dull for this purpose. The explanation seems to lie in the fact that the muscles and other parts engaged in motion do not suffer always from the defect of sensation which has attacked the skin. A touch is felt indistinctly upon a finger, for example; we at once move the suspected digit, and the sensations which reach the brain from its yet sensitive muscles tell us which finger has been touched.

Another fallacy which is apt in careless hands to occur when sensation is examined, arises from the lateral propagation of movement from defective to sensitive regions of skin. This can only be avoided by using very gentle contacts.

Finally, in all of these investigations as to the sense of tact, it is well to take care that the part studied has on any two occasions of examination been subjected to like thermal conditions, since a partly palsied hand will give us, when chilled, far different results from those which it gave when thoroughly warmed.

I am well satisfied that in some cases of nerve wounds causing atrophic contractions and malpositions, a part of the dullness of sensation may be due to the constrained postures in which the members have been kept. How this sense may suffer from such causes is well illustrated by the double sensation which is felt when we examine with crossed fingers any round object, as a marble. Parts unused to act together are here forced to do so, and in consequence we have the sensation of two balls instead of one; in other words, we have created what has been happily called by Prof. Alexander a tactile squint. In a note to the treatise so often referred to, this subject was further illustrated by a curious observation which I made at that time, and have since repeated. Let the observer put his hands behind him, and let them be placed back to back. Then let him interlock his fingers irregularly, making the positions unusual, and keeping up mutual pressure among the parts so treated. After a few minutes, should some one touch lightly one of the fingers, the tap will be felt, but now and then the person examined will find a difficulty in stating which finger has been touched, and he will also discover how strong is the instinctive tendency to aid his tact-sense by movement, and how readily such movement supplies the required information.

There is but one part of the skin which seems remarkably deficient in power to localize sensations. When, in examining the toes, especially in laboring people, we touch them in succession, the third toe is sometimes mistaken for the fourth, and this for the third; more rarely the fourth is mistaken for the fifth, or little toe, but this is hardly ever taken for the fourth. My friend Dr. J. H. Hutchinson informs me that he has made the same observation, and I doubt not that this curious fact must often have been noticed by others.

By these various means we learn the boundaries of anæsthetic skin spaces as well as the extent of the loss of tactile appreciation.

Pain-sense.—The sense of pain is, of course, readily examined by the needle, but where this and tact are so far lost as to escape all common tests, the electric brush* used on a dry, powdered skin, is the best agent we can employ, and if from it no sensation be felt, we may usually conclude that the loss of sense is absolute. I can recall several occasions where this means has saved me from despairing about cases which seemed otherwise totally hopeless.

It is important to bear in mind when examining recent cases that sensation may be quite lost for a time from shock, and yet return again very rapidly and entirely. For these reasons some caution is needed in prognosis.

When a nerve is wounded, as a rule, motion and sensation suffer alike; but it happens in some cases that while motion is utterly abolished, sensation is but slightly attacked, or does not suffer at all. It is often difficult to conceive that the two sets of nerve fibres have not equally felt the injury, so that we are obliged to seek for some reason why the force which only impairs the sense of touch should paralyze the muscle. Perhaps the explanation may lie in this direction. The nerve centres of sensation have an enormous range of appreciation, so that even when the transmissive power is weakened, there may be still enough to allow of the carriage of a vast range of messages to organs possessed of a wide and delicate receptivity. On the other hand, the motive impulse which proceeds from the will must probably reach

---

* See chapters on Treatment.

the muscle in a definite amount in order to evoke motion, and there is reason to think that this amount must be comparatively large to get from the muscle a useful motor response, or, indeed, any at all. We can thus understand that if the motor and sensory filaments be equally enfeebled as to transmissive capacity, the brain may continue to receive sensory messages, while the muscles still fail to get nerve force enough to call them into functional activity. Something illustrative of this exists normally in the ulnar nerve, which may be easily irritated at the elbow so as to cause sensation, but which needs much more severe stimulation in order to produce movement in the muscles which it controls.

There may be in other cases an anatomical cause for the total escape of one or other set of nerve fibres when the injury falls on a nerve trunk where its strands are beginning to separate. In some of the lower animals the separation of the various nerve filaments into groups, some merely sensori-motor, and others either motor or sensory alone, is well marked in the parent trunk far above the point at which they leave it to seek their points of distribution. Now, although the eye does not reveal in man any such distinct arrangement of this nature, the phenomena of a large number of nerve wounds seem to make it probable that very soon after leaving the spine the nerves become grouped, as it were, with intention towards their final distribution. In no other way can we explain some of the phenomena which arise out of such cases; but even this resource does not suffice to make clear such a case as the following, nor yet others which I have seen, where, without obvious cause, a compound nerve being hurt, motion was lost and sensation merely enfeebled or preserved entire.*

---

* In cases of contusion or compression of nerves, the first evidence of injury is usually some effect upon sensory filaments, and the mechanical

Case 31*.—*Shell wound affecting the musculo-spiral nerve; trivial loss of tactility; entire motor paralysis in the ultimate distribution of this nerve.* B. Graham, aged twenty-two, enlisted September, 1861, 5th Battery, Massachusetts Artillery. He was previously healthy. On May 12, 1864, he was struck on the back and outside of the right arm by a piece of shell, which denuded, but did not break the humerus. The wound lay immediately below the deltoid insertion, and was five inches wide as it stretched across the arm, and three inches in diameter from above downward. The arm dropped, and he had sharp pain in the wound, so that he cried aloud. The after-pain was trifling. As he went to the rear, he examined the limb, and found that he could move his fingers a little, but that there was no notable loss of feeling. The wound healed rapidly, and is now, June 10, 1864, level with the skin. Nutrition is unimpaired. The right forearm measures nine and three-eighths inches; the left, nine and a half inches.

Sensation.—Outside of the elbow, for a short space, tactility is enfeebled. In the radial distribution touch is slightly less perfect than usual; elsewhere there is no lesion of sensation. The supinator longus muscle, supplied by the musculo-spiral through the branch given off above the wound, acts pretty well. The extensors of the wrist and thumb and the extensor communis are completely paralyzed. The interossei act well. The triceps extensor is healthy.

Electric tests.—The muscles above named as paralyzed

influence may go very far before causing any notable motor indications, while as regards spasm, a nerve of double function may be slowly and gradually compressed to the utter loss of all function without any such muscular convulsion as may at any time originate under *sudden* variations in the amount of pressure.

* Mitchell, Morehouse, and Keen, op. cit.

have no electric contractility, the currents applied to them always causing contraction of the flexor group.

This case well enough illustrates how sensation may escape, and motion be largely destroyed. The triceps and long supinator were nearly unharmed, while the remainder of the extensor group was totally palsied.

Such was the nature of the wound that it was easy to see how the triceps and other brachial muscles escaped injury to their nerves. On the other hand, it was very difficult to perceive how the muscular branches to the forearm could be so completely palsied with such trivial injury to the cutaneous and radial branches of tactile endowments.

When sensation is injured, together with motion, the former is apt to return first. Thus, for example, a man is shot through the arm, so as to partially injure the bundle of brachial nerves. The first result is entire loss of both motion and sensation; but within a day or two the latter returns to a great extent, then by degrees certain muscles recover their power, and except for inflammatory accidents we are in a position, at the close of a week, to say how much of the original loss of function is to be permanent. Let us again examine this case at the close of a year, and we shall find that, counting from this time, the gain in sensation is out of proportion greater than that of motion.

In alluding to this fact in our little volume on nerve wounds, and while acknowledging the difficulty of fully explaining the matter, we sought to account for it in the following manner:

"When a function is partially paralyzed, its continued exercise is one of the conditions of its ultimate return to full activity so soon as the neural injury has become repaired. Now, the sense of touch is in constant automatic use, so to speak, every contact being a continuous stimulus to its activity, and the very fact of deficient feeling subjects the part to rough and unusual irritations. It does not seem impossible that this may explain, in part at least, the early disappearance of sensory paralysis in cases where the function of sensation seems to be quite as much affected at the outset as that of motility.

"In regard to voluntary movement, the case is quite different. When muscles are paralyzed partially, an effort of will, and a greater one than common, is demanded to call them into action. The early inflammatory conditions make motion painful. The effort is unusually wearisome, and there is no inevitable and constant stimulus, such as exists in regard to touch. Hence, perhaps, it is that motility is regained less easily than sensibility, although beyond all this, there are also certain mechanical obstacles in the way of a return of voluntary movement, which vary greatly, and constitute every single case a special object of study.

"We may sum up the matter in this briefer shape. The skin is all the time stimulated, whether we will or not. The muscles which volition has ceased to move with ease have no such incidental stimulus. Accident and position do for the skin what artificial agencies must do for the muscles, if we desire to sustain their nutrition and restore their power."

As the case advances there soon exists a new reason for the non-return of motor function in the atrophic changes which affect the muscles, and which, after a time, place the gravest impediments in the way of movement, even though the nerve itself should have become perfectly restored. The receptive centre for sensation remains always ready, and incessant stimuli play upon its connected sets of nerves. The muscles, on the other hand, the receivers of motor impulses, become diseased and unimpressible by volition even where at last this is enabled to reach them.

Loss of thermal sense.—The sense of temperature is lost with that of pain and touch, and usually in like degree, and the amount of its loss is, of course, readily measured. I have never seen it altered from nerve wounds without affection of the pain- and tact-sense. Neither have I met with any case of wound of a nerve which seemed to involve only loss of the muscular sense.

As concerns the separate existence of nerves of touch and pain, some light is cast by two cases—27 and 28—of the Report on Nerve Wounds.

In the first of these, owing to a wound of the arm, there was greatly lessened sense of pain, with no loss of touch. The patient discriminated the compass-points as well in the hand of the wounded side as in the other, while, when blindfolded, a large needle could be run nearly through the palm without his seeming to feel more than a slight pricking. I shall quote this case in full when discussing muscular lesions. I do not think it quite free from suspicion of central disease,—the result of the wound; but, as regards the other case, there cannot be any doubt as to the purely peripheral nature of the changes which resulted in very remarkable analgesia, with preservation of the tactile and localizing sensation and that of temperature. So complete was the loss of pain-sense that the electric wire brush was felt but slightly, while it was interesting to note that there was hyperæsthesia of the deeper tissues. There was total loss of motion below the knee.

Pain.—When we touch or otherwise disturb any part of the trunk of a nerve containing sensory filaments, we cause, if the irritation be feeble, subjective referred sensations, such as formication. Warmth or cold so applied usually occasions no sense of altered temperature in the skin, but only pain in the ultimate neural distribution. More severe mechanical disturbance, at any part of a nerve, is felt as pain, and into this sad language the nerve finally translates all save the mildest impressions made elsewhere than upon its peripheral expansions.

In many cases, the nervi nervorum enable us to localize the point at which the nerve is injured, as when a blow falls on the ulnar nerve at the elbow. We feel intensely the referred pain, but have also a clear sense of local hurt to the nerve at the point struck. This is, however, by no means usual as to causes which act slowly and steadily. So that when in disease we feel pain, it is often impossible to say at what point of the nerve track the pain-making cause is busy, nor how remote it is from the region where the pain seems to be.

Any mechanical or other irritation of a nerve of common sensation is usually referred to its region of peripheral distribution, so that the pain appears to exist in that part.

Nerve injuries may also cause pain which, owing to inexplicable reflex transfers in the centres, may be felt in remote tissues outside of the region which is tributary to the wounded nerve.

When the later pathological changes of an irritative nature which follow nerve injuries begin to occur, new causes of pain arise, the reflex references become wider, and when in certain cases the nutrition of the skin suffers, novel forms of suffering spring up, which are due to alterations of the peripheral nerve ends or their protective tissues.

Pain is, perhaps, the most constant sequence of nerve injuries, but it exhibits the utmost variety as to the time of its coming and the character of the torment. I have already discussed the question of pain as regards the first moments of nerve wounds. In cases of contusion, the first pain having passed, only tingling may remain, unless secondary changes in the nerve result in the production

of the pains of neuritis. In many punctured wounds, the
whole nerve seems to be thrown suddenly into an hyperæsthetic state, so that it continues to express irritation in
the shape of very agonizing pain. After a time, such a
nerve becomes congested or inflamed, and hyperplasia of
inter-neural connective tissue occurs, the pain still continuing or growing worse.

In cases of simple equal pressure on nerves, pain may
not be a prominent symptom, but will be most apt to be
felt severely when the pressure is varying from time to
time. Pressure, with inflammatory or cancerous alterations, is the parent of most horrible forms of anguish, such
as we see so often in cancer, affecting the pelvic and sacral
plexuses.

In gunshot injuries of nerve trunks, pain may be continuous from the outset, but more commonly the neuralgias date from the time of the traumatic fevers, or even
still later.

Early in this chapter I drew a distinction as to the
three methods in which nerve pains originate, and it is
again necessary here to return to the subject. In a
large number of cases, and in most of the pains of inflamed or scleromic nerves, the pain comes from irritation
of fibres in or near the wound, the nerve tubes or the
centres becoming hyperæsthetic and the sensation being
referred to the peripheral tissues. But in many instances
like pains arise, although the nerve be cut across, or the
member lost, as in stump neuralgias, there being still
the same reference of the pain to a supposed seat. The
important difference between these two conditions, both
fertile in torment, lies in the fact that when portions
of the fibres of a nerve are still uninjured, but irritated,
certain nutritive mischief may be made in the peripheral
parts, and we may thus have evolved a peculiar type of
anguish, the remote cause of which is in the wound, the

immediate cause in the region of ultimate nerve supply. In this manner are produced, as I believe, the horrible pains of causalgia.

The neuralgias common to all nerve injuries, and which I desire clearly to distinguish from causalgia, with which I should add they may coexist, are apt to affect a quotidian type, and to occupy, as a rule, the latter rather than the earlier hours of the day. It is curious, and as yet unnoticed, that the pain of non-malarial neuralgia and of neuritis and neural sclerosis never assumes a tertian or any other than a quotidian type. It is quite rare for a patient to arouse frem sleep with pain, and I have heard men remark that it took some time to get awake to the pain. This is familiarly illustrated where the toothache of the last night does not come on next day until exercise has stimulated the circulation. The tendency to intermit or remit in ordinary neuralgias frequently causes them to be ascribed to malaria; but the same tendency is seen in traumatic cases, or in the pains caused by pressure on nerves, as from aneurism, but is much more rare in those which I class as causalgia, and in which the pain usually appears at the time the man awakens and pursues him with increasing torture throughout the day.

Mr. Swan relates some curious instances of traumatic pain of an intermittent type. In one, an ulcer over the peroneal nerve occasioned a pain which recurred daily at the same hour, and I have myself seen numerous instances of pain from direct injury where this condition was met with. Usually the pains from nerve hurts are either aching, shooting, or burning, or perhaps all three at once Looking carefully through my notes as to this point, I find that in a considerable proportion of gunshot wounds of nerves there is principally burning pain, or at least that this is the prominent symptom, while in slight

injuries of nerves from compression or contusions, the
other forms of pain are more apt to prevail.

Perhaps few persons who are not physicians can realize
the influence which long-continued and unendurable pain
may have upon both body and mind. The older books
are full of cases in which, after lancet wounds, the most
terrible pain and local spasms resulted. When these had
lasted for days or weeks, the whole surface became
hyperæsthetic, and the senses grew to be only avenues
for fresh and increasing tortures, until every vibration,
every change of light, and even, as in Miss Willson's case,*
the effort to read brought on new agony. Under such
torments the temper changes, the most amiable grow
irritable, the soldier becomes a coward, and the strongest
man is scarcely less nervous than the most hysterical girl.
Perhaps nothing can better illustrate the extent to which
these statements may be true than the cases of burning
pain, or, as I prefer to term it, causalgia, the most terrible of all the tortures which a nerve wound may inflict.
In delineating this form of pain, perhaps I cannot do
better than transfer to these pages the account originally
written while I was seeing almost daily numbers of
persons suffering as I have described them :

"In our early experience of nerve wounds, we met with
a small number of men who were suffering from a pain
which they described as a 'burning,' or as 'mustard red-
hot,' or as a 'red-hot file rasping the skin.' In all of these
patients, and in many later cases, this pain was an associate of the glossy skin previously described. In fact,
this state of skin never existed without burning pain.
Recently we have seen numbers of men who had burning
pain without glossy skin, and in some we have seen this
latter condition commencing. The burning comes first,

---

* Swan, op. cit.

the visible skin-change afterwards; but in no case of
great depravity in the nutrient condition of the skin have
we failed to meet with it, and that in its forms of almost
unendurable anguish.

"We have some doubt as to whether this form of pain
ever originates at the moment of the wounding; but we
have been so informed as regards two or three cases.
Certain it is that, as a rule, the burning arises later, but
almost always during the healing of the wound. Of the
special cause which provokes it, we know nothing, except
that it has sometimes followed the transfer of pathological changes from a wounded nerve to unwounded nerves,
and has then been felt in their distribution, so that we do
not need a direct wound to bring it about. The seat of
burning pain is very various; but it never attacks the
trunk, rarely the arm or thigh, and not often the forearm
or leg. Its favorite site is the foot or hand. In these
parts it is to be found most often where the nutritive skin-
changes are met with; that is to say, on the palm of the
hand, or palmar face of the fingers, and on the dorsum of
the foot: scarcely ever on the sole of the foot, or the back
of the hand. When it first existed in the whole foot or
hand, it always remained last in the parts above referred
to, as its favorite seats. The great mass of sufferers described this pain as superficial, but others said it was also
in the joints, and deep in the palm. If it lasted long it
was finally referred to the skin alone.

"Its intensity varies from the most trivial burning to a
state of torture, which can hardly be credited, but which
reacts on the whole economy, until the general health is
seriously affected. The part itself is not alone subject to
an intense burning sensation, but becomes exquisitely
hyperæsthetic, so that a touch or a tap of the finger increases the pain. Exposure to the air is avoided by the
patient with a care which seems absurd, and most of the

bad cases keep the hand constantly wet, finding relief in the moisture rather than in the coolness of the application. Two of these sufferers carried a bottle of water and a sponge, and never permitted the part to become dry for a moment. As the pain increases, the general sympathy becomes more marked. The temper changes and grows irritable, the face becomes anxious, and has a look of weariness and suffering. The sleep is restless, and the constitutional condition, reacting on the wounded limb, exasperates the hyperæsthetic state, so that the rattling of a newspaper, a breath of air, the step of another across the ward, the vibrations caused by a military band, or the shock of the feet in walking, gives rise to increase of pain. At last the patient grows hysterical, if we may use the only term which describes the facts. He walks carefully, carries the limb with the sound hand, is tremulous, nervous, and has all kinds of expedients for lessening his pain. In two cases, at least, the skin of the entire body became hyperæsthetic when dry, and the men found some ease from pouring water into their boots. They said, when questioned, that it made walking hurt less; but how, or why, unless by diminishing vibration, we cannot explain. One of these men went so far as to wet the sound hand when he was obliged to touch the other, and insisted that the observer should also wet his hand before touching him, complaining that dry touch always exasperated his pain. Cold weather usually eased these pains; heat, and the hanging down of the limb, made them worse. Motion of the part was unendurable in some of the very worst cases; but, for the most part, it did no harm, unless so excessive as to flush the injured region.

" The rationale of the production of this form of pain was at first sought for among reflex phenomena. It then seemed to us probable that a traumatic irritation existing in some part of a nerve trunk was simply referred by the

mind to the extreme distribution of this nerve, agreeably
to the well-known law of the reference of sensations.

" Further study led us to suspect that the irritation of
a nerve, at the point of wound, might give rise to changes
in the circulation and nutrition of parts in its distribution,
and that these alterations might be themselves of a pain-
producing nature. The following considerations tend to
strengthen the view, that the immediate cause of burning
pain lies in the part where the burning is felt:

"If the burning were a referred sensation, it would
sometimes be met with in cases of complete division of
nerves, and, therefore, in parts devoid of tactile sensation.
But we have encountered no such cases; and, on the
other hand, the burning pain is often accompanied with
hyperæsthesia, while motion and touch may remain unaltered. Is it not probable that the depraved nutrition,
often so marked in the congested, denuded, and altered
skin, may give rise to a disease of the ultimate fibres of
the sensitive nerves? Just such a pain comes when we
attack the cutis with irritants; and let us add, that the
agents which help these cases of burning are those addressed to the spot where the pain is felt, and not to the
cicatrix."

Since this description was written, several years have
gone by, but new experience has only strengthened my
belief that the explanation just given is physiologically
correct, because in a large number of amputated cases—
many of them neuralgic—I have never yet seen a case
of subjective burning pain. I add two cases of causalgia
from my notes, whilst under the head of Illustrations of
Treatment the reader will find other and more severe
examples.

*Case 32.—Leg wound; causalgia; slight sensory and no
motor defects; crutch palsy; cure in four months.* Christo-
pher Beatty, aged twenty-four, carpenter, Pennsylvania,

sergeant 26th Pennsylvania Volunteers, was shot at Chancellorsville, through the leg, below the knee. He fell without pain; lost blood largely; and, after lying on the field twenty-six hours, had a water-dressing applied, at about which time the heel began to burn. A few days later, the limb being swollen considerably, the whole foot was burning and prickling intensely,—the sole being the worst part. After two weeks the prickling lessened, but the burning remained.

He was wounded in May, 1863, and admitted to the U. S. A. Hospital for Nervous Diseases, June 30, 1863, when he had no loss of motion, and scarcely any of sensation, only the great-toe and heel being not quite up to the normal standard of sensibility. The heel and the inner edge of the plantar arch burn intensely, and are dark-red and mottled, and swollen from congestion, which the dependent position greatly increases. Pressure upon the cicatrix appears to increase the burning. He had, soon after admission, crutch palsy, which readily yielded to treatment. The burning pain slowly lessened without any therapeutic aid, and within four months of the date of the wounding he was well, excepting some tenderness and slight œdema of the foot.

In the following case there were both burning pain and common neuralgic pain, and the mental condition produced by intense suffering was well marked:

Case 33.—*Wound of right arm; glossy skin; causalgia and neuralgia; joint disease; acid sweats; slight loss of tact; constitutional symptoms.* H., aged thirty-nine, New York, was shot July 2, 1863, through the inner edge of the right biceps, half an inch above the internal condyle of the humerus; the ball passed backward and downward. The musket fell from his left hand, and the right, grasping the rod, was twisted towards the chest and bent at the elbow. He walked to the rear. He cannot tell how much motion was lost, but he knows that he had instant pain in the median distribution, with tenderness of the palm, even on the first day, and a sense of numbness. My notes describe him on entering our wards as presenting the following symptoms: the temperature of the two palms is alike. The back of the hand looks as usual, but the skin of the palm is delicate and thin, and without any eruption. The joints of the fingers are swollen, and the hand secretes freely a sour, ill-smelling sweat. The pain is, in the first place, neuralgic, and darting down the median nerve track into the fingers; while, in the second place, there is burning in the palm and up the anterior face of the fingers.

Pressure on the cicatrix gave no pain, but the median nerve below that point was tender, and pressure upon it caused pain in the hand. There was slight want of tactile sensibility in the median distribution in the hand, but the parts receiving the ulnar nerve presented no sign of injury. The hyperæsthesia of the palm was excessive, so that even to blow on it seemed to give pain. He kept it wrapped up and wet, but could not endure to pour water on to the palm, preferring to wet the dorsum of the hand and allow the fluid to run around, so as by degrees to soak the palm. After a few weeks of this torment he became so sensitive that the rustle of a paper or of a woman's dress, the sound of feet, the noise of a band, all appeared to increase his pain. His countenance at this time was worn, pinched, and anæmic, his temper irritable, and his manner so odd that some of the attendants believed him insane. When questioned as to his condition he assured me that every strong moral emotion made him worse,—anger or disappointment expressing themselves cruelly in the aching limb. There was also the most marked hyperæsthesia of the skin throughout the body, so that a sudden touch anywhere was unpleasing, and reacted on the diseased hand.

It would be easy to add numerous instances of causalgia and neuralgia from nerve wounds, but as I shall have to relate cases, perhaps to a tedious extent, in illustrating diagnosis and treatment, I shall cite no more at this time.

Effects of nerve injuries upon the function of muscles.— Mechanical disturbances of nerves give rise to the various forms of spasm and tremor, and to paralysis of motion, and consequent atrophic changes and contractions.

Local spasm.—I have already described the sudden and violent form of spasm which is sometimes the first symptom of the wound of a nerve by a ball, and I have also called attention to the painful spasms which may result almost instantly from the wounding, and probably even from the division, of a small sensitive skin nerve in bleeding at the elbow. The latter variety of spasm may last for days, and even for weeks, until, as in one instance, the growing nails of the clinched hand may cause ulcers in the wounded palm. In these cases, as in wounds from missiles of war, the spasms are of reflex origin, and are often seen in the muscles of unwounded nerves. In the case of J. H. C.,—related in our Report on Nerve Wounds,— the bullet injured the left median and ulnar nerves, and caused instant cramp of the flexors of both arms, so that he clutched both gun and ramrod violently. He shook loose the latter with a strong effort, and then, with the right hand thus set free, he unlocked the fingers of the left from their clutch on the gun, after which they did not again close.

Tonic contractions of muscles are occasionally met with at a later stage of these injuries, but are, perhaps, among the rarest of the secondary symptoms. Such forms of spasm are readily diagnosticated from atrophic shortening, by the fact that muscles affected with the latter malady are unexcitable, as a rule, by induced electric currents, whilst muscles in a state of spasm are often abnormally irritable under this form of stimulation. The atrophied muscle is hard, shrunken, and motionless, and cannot be elongated. The muscle in spasm is firm, plump, often exhibits fibrillar movement, and can be lengthened when the patient has been made insensible by ether or chloroform. When awake, the effort to extend these muscles causes pain and increasing spasmodic contractions. We remarked in our wards* many cases of what might be called a tendency to spasm, which was shown by quivering and resistance in a muscle, which gave no proof of spasm until suddenly extended by the hand of the physician or by the action of its antagonists. In a case of injury of the shoulder, which I saw a year ago, the lower arm nerves became secondarily diseased; and, owing to this, the supinator longus and biceps passed into the condition described. The arm was carried slightly bent, but if I extended it, a spastic contraction of these muscles drew it into a state of extreme flexion, which lasted for some minutes, during which the fibres of the muscle could be felt to be firmly contracted.

I was lately consulted by Dr. Ellis, of Elkton, Maryland, in regard to a patient who presented a remarkable instance of this form of fibrillar spasm.

The lad, aged eighteen years, was run over five years previously by a cart, which passed across the back of the neck and the right shoulder. Both arms were palsied as to motion alone. The left recovered entirely, as did also the right forearm and hands; but the arm muscles, except the triceps extensor, remained motionless, and became excessively wasted. The atrophied deltoid, supra- and infra-spinatus, and biceps are now the seats of the

---

* Gunshot Injuries of Nerves, op. cit., p. 124.

most constant and curious quivering, while, strangely enough, every one of them is perfectly responsive to induced currents. The first electric application at once restored partial volitional control, and he is now rapidly improving.

The following case is a good illustration of tonic spasm:

Case 34.—Shell bruise of right brachial nerves ; slight loss of motion ; tonic spasm of the flexor carpi radialis, flexor carpi ulnaris, and palmaris longus, causing violent flexion of wrist ; analgesia well marked ; no loss of tactility ; sections of tendons ; relief. Lawrence Monaghan, aged twenty-six, machinist, Kentucky, enlisted January, 1863, and had been previously in the nine months' service. At Chancellorsville, May 3, 1863, he was struck by a fragment of shell on the outside of the right arm, seven inches above the external condyle. It merely scratched the skin, but bruised the subjacent parts severely and extensively. When hit, he was lying down, leaning on the left elbow. He felt nauseated; the arm dropped with general weakness and numbness, and with slightly impaired sensation. The wound swelled and grew black and red, being bruised from the shoulder to the middle forearm.

At first the pain limited movement, but in two months the motions of the arm were much better throughout. Sensation also improved, but was never quite perfect. About the second week, and while the arm was in a sling, on a pad, the wrist began to flex. The surgeon's attention being called to it, he put it on a splint and bandaged it down; but after four weeks this treatment was abandoned on account of the pain, and also because it proved useless. After this, liniments to the arm were used, but the flexion went on. Then, as the arm grew stronger, the contraction relaxed; and, finally, he was mustered out of service. Re-enlisted August 15th, Company A, 10th New Jersey Volunteers.

The handling of a musket brought back the pain, which was a numb aching, extending to the hand. At the same time the wrist began to flex anew, and forcibly, with pain also in the wrist and in the track of the musculo-spiral nerve; the hand being constantly cold, and kept covered with a glove.

March 9, 1864, admitted to Turner's Lane Hospital.— Nutrition good; skin natural, but soft and moist, from being covered and unused. Acid odor distinctly marked.

Examined by compass, no perceptible difference in tactile sensation from the other hand. He feels the cold in his right hand severely; it becomes cold easily. He has every movement; but the finger flexion is limited by the extreme bend of the wrist, for when in this condition, the two flexors of the fingers cannot shorten enough to flex the second and third digital joints. Of course voluntary extension of the wrist is impossible, but he has perfect extension of all the digital joints. The flexor carpi radialis, the palmaris longus, and flexor carpi ulnaris are very rigid, and when extended, contract violently.

These muscles appear to possess fully as much electric contractility as those of the other arm.

June 12.—Dr. Keen cut the tendons of the flexor carpi radialis and palmaris longus completely, and that of the flexor carpi ulnaris partially. The wrist was then brought to a right line with the forearm, and placed on a Bond's splint. Motion soon began to return to the fingers as the soreness arising from change of position subsided. The patient is now, July 1st, recovering rapidly.

Muscular paralysis and its consequences.—Loss of power is of course the most common result of nerve wounds, and may exist in every possible degree, from the slightest defect to the most absolute annihilation of the motor function of an entire limb. The consequences which follow, in the shape of atrophy and contractions, I have already described, but the practical difficulties as to treatment which they occasion we have yet to consider.

It is very fortunate that not every muscle palsied by nerve injury undergoes great atrophy, and that of those which endure this change, not all are affected by consequent shortening. The force with which organic shortening of muscles acts is most remarkable, and is sometimes so great as to cause dislocations and to produce the most horrible deformities, since the healthy opponent muscles are powerless to resist the steady contraction caused by morbid conditions. The most curious instances of this are to be found in what is known as the claw-hand, which is due to paralysis of the interossei of the hand, and organic shortening of the flexors of the fingers, the extensor communis remaining intact. (For examples of this condition, see cases at the close of this chapter.) The same evils result more frequently, but in less mischievous forms, from complete palsy of muscles, which undergo no further changes, but the complete relaxation of which enables their opponent groups to distort the part by slow degrees. Almost every case of nerve wound offers illustrations of this, which, like every form of unopposed contraction, is fertile in lasting evil when it exists in connection with arthritic troubles; for when this is the case, the displacements made by the muscles are rendered, as it were, permanent by the adhesions which fix the joints in their abnormal positions.

When describing the practical annoyances in treatment which arose out of these conditions, we* called attention to the loss of motion which results from a part being held in an extreme of flexion, as in the case of Monaghan, page 204. Here the hand was so bent upon the wrist that the second and third phalanges could not be completely

---

* Gunshot Wounds, etc., p. 122.

flexed, partly, as I suppose, because of the excessive
shortening needed by the flexors to enable them to act
upon their relaxed tendons, and partly because of the
extreme tension which the extensor communis exerted
upon the first phalanges. I saw, a few months since, a
case in which, owing to various causes, the hand was
fixed in extreme extension. The patient was powerless
to effect full extension of the fingers. It is easy to make
this experiment upon one's self, and thus to learn the
limitation of movements brought about by placing a
part in excessive degrees of flexion or extension.

The cases which follow are selected from notes taken
by Dr. Keen and myself, because each of them con-
spicuously illustrates some one or more of the consequences of nerve wounds.

Case 35. — *Gunshot wound of left forearm; median and
ulnar nerves involved; paralysis of motion; none of sensation;
rigid fingers from joint disease; neuritis and causalgia from
tenth day; relief by blisters; eruptions above the limit of causalgia; red palm.* J. D., aged twenty-three, carter, Ireland;
enlisted August, 1861, Company F, 69th Pennsylvania
Volunteers. His health was good until he was wounded.
While firing, he was shot in the left forearm, behind the
ulna, four and a half inches below the olecranon process.
The wound of exit was three inches above the internal
condyle of the humerus, and half an inch in front of it.
Neither artery nor bone was injured. He fell unconscious, but in half an hour, reviving, arose, and, walking a
few steps, fell again. At the expiration of three hours,
a water-dressing was applied. No other dressing was at
any time employed. Motion below the elbow was totally
lost. As to sensation at this time, the evidence is uncertain.
He was removed to West Philadelphia Hospital, where
the water-dressing was continued. The arm was put on
splint, and passive motion of the fingers made daily. On

the tenth day he had fever and rigors, with darting pains
in the wound. The nerves became tender on pressure,
and intense burning pain, beginning on the front of the
wrist, extended to the palm and the face of the index-
finger alone.

Six months later, when admitted to Turner's Lane
Hospital, he is described as thin, anæmic, nervous, and
pain-worn; sleeps badly, and has ague and dyspepsia. The
arm is generally wasted; he keeps the hand wet. Eczema
of forearm above the line of pain is present. There is no
swelling; the odor of the hand is almost fetid. The left
biceps measures seven and a half inches; the right, eight
and one-eighth. The left forearm measures eight inches;
the right, nine inches. The hand is flexed on the wrist
from contraction of the flexors; the nails are much
curved. The median nerve is exquisitely sensitive to
pressure in the forearm, the ulnar only at the wrist. Motion is entire above elbow and at the elbow, save that extension is incomplete, from stiffening of the joint. Pronation and supination are almost lost from joint-troubles.
The hand flexors retain a fair amount of power. There
is no power to extend the hand above the level of the
wrist. The thumb can be passively moved, but there is
no voluntary control over the metacarpal joint movements, although the last phalanx can be extended or
flexed. The fingers are very rigid,—their joints swollen.
They can be slightly stirred by will in abduction, adduction, flexion, and extension perhaps to one-third their
usual extent. The movements were more limited by the
state of the joints than by muscular palsy, because, except
the supinator longus and the thumb muscles, the other
muscles respond readily to induction currents. Under
cod-liver oil, quinine, ale, and good diet, the patient
speedily improved, and after a month was treated for the
causalgia by blisters, made at first with liq. ammoniæ

fort., and then with cantharides. Six blisters effected a cure of the pain, and when he left us, after three months, his state was altogether satisfactory save as to the rigid joints, which, although improved by passive movement and the cold douche, were by no means well. The paralysis remained unaltered.

Case 36.—*Bruise of left ankle; loss of motion in foot; no loss of sensation; local subcutaneous effusions of blood; electrical treatment; cure.* A. J. M., aged thirty, enlisted August, 1862, Company K, 13th Pennsylvania Cavalry. Except that he was liable to muscular rheumatism, he was healthy until hurt. On February 16, 1863, his horse fell with him, and pinned his left foot between the saddle and the ground. The foot was much bruised, but could be moved with pain until the fifth week, when he lost power. At this time, also, he had slight darting pains about the knee and thigh, and the foot became cold, although to him it felt hot. April 18, 1864, when I first saw him, the sciatic nerve was tender, and its diverging branches still more so. The foot was hot and flushed, and could not be voluntarily moved, either in flexion or extension, while the calf muscles and the anterior leg groups were only slightly excitable by the most powerful induced currents. There was very little pain. The foot and ankle were generally red, with here and there spots of more marked congestion. The instep and sides of the foot and ankle were dotted with large and small spots, some like bruise-marks, and others more defined, and resembling purpura.

Under the use of induced currents the man was rapidly cured. Alternate cold and hot douches constituted the only additional treatment. At the close of six weeks he had had twenty applications of the battery, and had nearly entirely recovered all the lost movements. The foot was cooler and the eruption gone.

Case 37.— *Wound of median and ulnar nerves; atrophy and*

*contraction of flexor muscles ; atrophy of all the hand muscles ;
neuro-traumatic arthritis ; loss of sensation ; moderate improvement; discharge.* G. L., aged thirty-one, lumberman ; enlisted, May, 1861, Company C, 1st Minnesota Infantry.
He was healthy to the date of the wound, which was
received July 3, 1863. While advancing at a walk and
capping his gun, a ball entered the right biceps three and
a quarter inches above the level of the internal condyle,
and made its exit three and a quarter inches directly below
the same condyle, wounding the main artery and the ulnar
and median nerves. The hand and forearm flexed spasmodically, and the man, tying a handkerchief around the
arm to check the flow of blood, walked to the rear, suffering with some pain down the front of the arm, but not
in the hand. Motion and feeling were both absent. Three
hours later the artery was tied. A cerate dressing was
applied, and no splint was at any time used. The wound
healed in two months, and at this time sensation and motion began to improve. He was admitted to Turner's
Lane Hospital, December 24, 1863, when his case was
thus described: the right hand is congested and a little
swollen. In the flexor carpi radialis the loss from atrophy
is one-half. In the other flexors, supinators, and pronators
the loss is one-third. In the thumb muscles proper and
abductor minimi digiti it is one-fourth.

The deep and superficial flexors and the thumb muscles
are slightly contracted. Up to the third month the fingers
were straight, but about that time they began to bend, and
on admission were semi-flexed.

The biceps acts very little; the supinator longus, although enfeebled, being competent to flex the forearm.
Extension is incomplete from partial contraction of the
biceps, owing to the prolonged flexion of the arm ; pronation is incomplete, but the supinating power is entire.
The hand can be raised only to the arm-level, when the

contractions of muscles and the state of the wrist-joint check it. The thumb has one-third flexion and extension, owing to want of power.

The first joints of the fingers are in good order; the second a little swollen and stiff; the third joints are rigid, enlarged, and painful, especially in the index-finger. The first joints have pretty fair mobility; the second but little; the third none at all. As the fingers are semi-flexed, the will can still act on the first phalanges, and slightly on the second, but the third rest bent and motionless. The same statement may be made as to the power to voluntarily extend them. The contracted state of the common flexors has now lessened, but the joint inflammations, which arose early in the case, have fixed the fingers in the vicious positions into which they were drawn by the muscular shortening.

Touch is good in the arm; absent in the palm and palmar face of the fingers, except as to the thenar eminence. It is good on the dorsum of the hand, but defective on the back of the last phalanx of the first finger, the second and third phalanges of the second and third fingers, and on the metacarpal bone of the fourth finger.

Electro-muscular contractility is lessened in the supinator longus; absent in the common flexors, although these have some voluntary power; nearly absent in the thumb muscles, the muscles of the fourth finger, and interosseal groups.

The marked feature of this case was the obstinate and painful inflammation, and stiffness of the third joints of the fingers and of the articulation of the wrist; yet these conditions were nearly entirely relieved by three months of passive motion, electrization by induced currents, and the dry wire brush, douches, and attention to the general health.

Case 38.— *Wound of left chest, causing paralysis of the*

great pectoral muscle, probably by injury to the external anterior thoracic nerve; extension of disease from the wounded nerve to the brachial plexus, with consequent loss of sensation and motion; lesions of nutrition; intense burning pains; musculo-spiral and median principally affected. Stephen Warner, aged thirty-three, farmer, New York, enlisted August, 1862, Company B, 18th Pennsylvania Volunteers. He was healthy to date of receipt of wound. At Locust Grove, November 27, 1863, a ball entered the left chest, under the first rib, half an inch below the clavicle and two and a half inches from its sternal end. Passing probably under the arch of the subclavian artery, it went backward and downward, and made its escape two inches below the inferior angle of the left scapula, three and a quarter inches from the spine. The ball was fired by a skirmisher not twenty yards distant, and was received while the patient was in the act of bending forward to aim. He fell, giddy, but conscious; tried to move, but failed, and fainted from loss of blood. After several hours he revived, and discovered that the left arm and hand were sensitive throughout. On the radial side of the forearm there was slight numbness,—a condition compatible with perfect tactile sensibility. Motion appears to have been lost, or greatly lessened during some hours, and within a day to have become restored entirely. No doubt exists as to this point.

No dressing was used until the third day, when water was applied. At this date the arm motions were complete below the shoulder, and there had been no pain. Soon after the cold dressing, to which he attributed the sequent symptoms, he was seized with neuralgic pain, which was principally in the median nerve distribution, but also on the outside of the arm and shoulder, with a spot of intense pain at the deltoid insertion. The pain was darting and pricking in its nature. Coincidently with the pain, the joints of the fingers swelled and became sore, and this was especially the case with the thumb and the first and second fingers. At the same time the shoulder muscles became weak, flexion of the fingers grew feeble, and the flexion of the forearm was affected. All of these defects increased for several months, and the flexor group in the forearm wasted so much as to attract attention. The biceps, brachialis anticus, and coraco-brachialis were in like manner atrophied. The pectoralis major was also thus altered at a still earlier period. Up to the eighth day the patient spat blood freely. Then it ceased, and he has had no pulmonary difficulties of any kind since.

February 19, 1864.—Admitted.

Atrophy of pectoralis major is great, of the shoulder muscles slight; wasting of biceps and other anterior and internal arm muscles is considerable. The left arm at the biceps measures ten inches; the right, eleven and three-fourth inches; the left forearm, ten inches; the right, eleven inches. The left hand congested, dark, and cold; is easily chilled.

Sensation is perfect. The neuralgia has nearly disappeared, except in bad weather, and about the insertion of the deltoid, where there is great tenderness, and a good deal of hardening and deposit in the subcuticular tissues and over the bone. The only muscle which is hyperæsthetic to any marked degree is the biceps. The course of the musculo-cutaneous and the median nerves is acutely tender upon pressure.

There is no motion in the pectoralis major, and it is scarcely perceptible in the biceps,—the supinator longus alone flexing the forearm. Extension of forearm is perfect. The fingers act in flexion feebly, but are improving. The thumb motions are also weak, but not lost. Motion is now most limited by the state of the finger-joints, which, although no longer tender, are stiff and enlarged. So much improvement has taken place very recently that we

cannot be sure as to what motions were lost. Probably
the principal nerves of the external cord of the plexus—
namely, the musculo-cutaneous and the median—were
those chiefly affected ; certain filaments of the posterior
strand, as the circumflex, also sharing in the diseased conditions. The remainder of the case would be irrelevant
here. It was improving when admitted, and it gained
ground with increased speed under a course of baths,
gymnastics, and faradisation.

CHAPTER IX.

Diagnosis.—In general, it is of course easy to say whether a nerve trunk has been directly injured or not. The well-known symptoms, together with an obvious lesion having a certain place or direction, usually tell us with sufficient distinctness the nature of the hurt whenever the accident has been seen in its earlier stages. Somewhat later, and in rare cases, the diagnosis of the initial injury may be difficult, owing to the reflex disturbance of remote nerves, and the fact already dwelt upon, that a subacute inflammation or a sclerotic state of nerve may pass centrally from the nerve first in fault, and thus come to affect one or more cords of the parent plexus. Whatever doubt I may once have had as to this tendency of inflammatory changes to travel inward, has been set at rest by the repeated instances which I have recently encountered. At the Hospital for Deformities and Nervous Diseases, I have lately seen a girl who met with an injury which affected an elbow already anchylosed, in consequence of which the nerves, especially the musculo-spiral, becoming sore, the arm grew hyperæsthetic, and severe aching neuralgia set in from the middle arm region to the finger-ends. This was entirely relieved by extensive counter-irritation with strong liniments. Very soon afterwards the circumflex nerve became involved, and the deltoid rapidly wasted. In this case, the local injury at the

(215)

elbow must have traveled up to the plexus and thus involved the shoulder branches.

Far more uncommon are the cases in which a bullet has split, and one fragment or a piece of splintered bone has implicated some distant nerve. Perhaps there exists no more interesting instance of this than the case of Seymour, which I transfer from my Report to the Sanitary Commission as a rare illustration of the difficulties which this singular accident may introduce into the diagnosis of a case.

Case 39.— Wound of left neck and jaw; loss of speech and deglutition; secondary hemorrhage; attempted ligature of right primitive carotid followed by palsy of right arm; anæsthesia of right side of jaw and face; loss of gustation in right side of tongue, also of touch, pain, and thermal sense; no loss of motion in right side of tongue; left side of tongue paralyzed as to motion only and atrophied; section of left lingual nerve, of hypoglossal, and of right lingual branch of glosso-pharyngeal nerve; injury by splinter of bone to inferior branch of fifth nerve; recovery. Wm. Seymour, aged twenty, sailor. On May 5, 1865, in the Wilderness, while ramming a load, he was shot from the branches of a tree on his left. The ball entered one and a half inches immediately below the left auditory meatus, touching the lower lobe of the ear; it slightly splintered the posterior angle of the lower jaw-bone, and passed across the throat much below the level of the tongue, though as to its exact path little is known. It made exit in the right side of the neck at a level with the lower edge of the thyroid cartilage, through the sterno-cleido-mastoid muscle, about one and a half inches above the clavicle, and two and a quarter inches from the middle line. He fell senseless, lay thus about an hour, and then awakening, crept half a mile, as he thinks, both wounds bleeding in jets. He now filled the wounds with dust, and so checked the bleeding. He thinks both arms were at this time equally strong. The third night his wounds were dressed. Up to this time he had taken no food, and most of the water which he drank ran out of the right wound in the neck. He was taken to the Douglas Hospital on the 10th of May.

At this point I insert the letter which Seymour brought with him from the accomplished surgeon in charge of the Douglas Hospital, Dr. Wm. Thomson, U. S. A., at whose request the patient was transferred to the United States Army Hospital for Diseases and Injuries of the Nervous System.

After describing the wound, Dr. Thomson adds:

"For a number of days he was nourished by injections of beef-tea, and by small quantities of milk introduced into the stomach through a catheter. He had had a severe hemorrhage on his way to the hospital. His wounds were dressed with cold water.

"May 19th.—He had a secondary hemorrhage, and lost eight ounces of blood. This was checked by compression.

"May 26th.—Lost four ounces of arterial blood from the wound of exit and from the mouth. The wound of entry was closed. Small bleedings occurred each day upon the least exertion, until May 30th, when it became evident that some operation would be needed to save his life. The external compression had caused an accumulation of blood about the trachea and neck generally, which, with other causes connected with the wound, made suffocation appear imminent. He was anæsthetized, and an incision made for ligature of the right primitive carotid. I should add that at this time there was good pulsation in the right temporal artery. After patient and thorough search, no trace of the right carotid, the internal jugular vein, or the pneumogastric nerve could be found. The incision was extended downward, and the sternal attachment of the sterno-cleido-mastoid muscle divided. The opening in the neck was finally carried up to the parotid gland, and the region thus exposed was submitted to the closest scrutiny, but still without discovery of any large vessel. As the oozing still continued, I made fruitless search for anything large enough to tie, and at length filled the wound of exit with charpie, and left the patient to his fate. No further bleeding took place, and recovery was henceforward rapid.

"For a long time there was complete aphonia, and after the operation he lost power in the right arm."

Admitted at Turner's Lane Hospital, September 11, 1865.

The following particulars were elicited:

Wounds closed. Right arm: sensation and motion feeble throughout the limb. I believe this to have been due to changes in the brachial plexus in the neck, consequent upon the operation. The neck has, from stiffness, only one-quarter range of movement. Face: touch is lost on *right* side of face, cheek, skin of lips, from half an inch in front of ear to line of external angle of right eye. Worst on edge of chin, fair on red part of lips, limited by middle line. Touch lessened on upper neck. Analgesia, moreover, less complete in all these parts. The nose is unaffected. Tongue: on the right side there is absolute loss of gustation, touch, pain, and sense of temperature. This defect is limited by the middle line. Very far back there appears to be considerable sensation. On the right side motion seems entire; and the right side of the tongue is firm, red, and well nourished. The left side of the tongue is paralyzed as to motion almost entirely. It is soft, flabby, wrinkled, and atrophied, rolling helplessly with the movement of the right muscles. The whole tongue, when at rest, lies straight in the mouth, but it cannot now be projected. When, early in the case, this was possible, it turned distinctly to the left side. Deglutition is imperfect; he has to take moistened food only, and coughs and chokes very frequently while eating. He is liable to fits of gaping when tired or over-heated. Voice nearly perfect. The eyes are healthy. There is no pain anywhere. The heart and lungs are sound. Appetite and digestion good.

It is clear, from the facts before us, that the ball cut the left hypoglossal nerve and also the right lingual branches of the glosso-pharyngeal nerve. The former accident sufficed to palsy the left side of the tongue. The latter may be assumed to have had some share in the destruction of gustatory sensation on the right side of that organ; but these accidents account neither for the accompanying total loss of tact and pain in the right side of the tongue, nor for that of the right side of the face. To paralyze sensation in the latter regions, there must have been either a secondary affection through induced disease of the centres, or else a wound of the fifth nerve; and if the latter took place far enough back, it would involve some of the branches which go to the tongue, and some which supply the face. The question is answered, I think, by the following facts:

Early in the case, Seymour felt a pricking in the right side of the throat, far back. At the fourteenth day a piece of bone, half an inch wide, and very thin, escaped into the throat from the part mentioned, and was coughed up. Unfortunately it was not preserved. I suppose this splinter was broken off the left jaw, and driven across the throat so as to wound the third branch of the fifth nerve.

Seymour's recovery was rapid, although I used no treatment at all.

October 10th. — The face has recovered sensation.

Taste was restored to the tongue, although not perfectly. Tact and pain were still absent.

October 20th.—There is some feeling in the tongue, but no motion on the left side, and no change in the nutrition.

Returned to duty, October 20, 1865.

Reflected palsy in remote regions, the result of a ball wound, though rare, is not to be lost sight of. Nor should it be forgotten that when one nerve of a limb has been subjected to prolonged pressure, as in Waller's experiments, the loss of power may not be limited to its own muscular distributions, but may also involve those which had not been primarily injured. This effect is too sudden to be ascribed to progressive neuritis. As yet I have not met with it in any clinical example of neural compression.

Loss of function in a part is usually sufficient to indicate what nerve has been injured, and to what degree; but as regards the hands, and perhaps also the feet, this would seem to be less valuable as a diagnostic means than might at first be supposed. There are, for example, rare instances in which section of the median has failed to cause loss of sensation or motion in the regions to which it is commonly distributed, while in other cases, quite as uncommon, the return of function after section has been so rapid as to have cast doubt upon the fact of total nerve division, had this been other than certain. In the vast majority of instances, however, the loss of motion in some muscles, and the defect of sense in definite skin spaces, will positively tell us what nerve has been hurt, and also the extent of the lesion.

In case of doubt as to the completeness of the nerve section, or in any of the anomalous examples of apparent division with continuance of sensation in the distal distribution of the hurt nerve, the use of faradaic currents applied to the nerve above the wound would surely settle the question as to whether or not it was really cut across; since if it were, it would be impossible, by this agent, to excite its related muscles. It were also well in cases like Nélaton's or Nott's* to try if, by electricity applied to the unharmed nerves, we could excite muscles usually controlled alone by branches belonging to the nerve injured. The results, whether negative or positive, would be full of interest.

M. Tillaux has made some effort to point out how we may distinguish the various forms of injury, as commotion, contusion, compression, and partial section. Of course the history of the injury may be such as to make needless this inquiry ; but it often happens that, with evidence of functional loss or injury, there is some possibility of intra-pelvic or other interior pressure, or else we may have a history of mechanical injury with that of some other probable cause of neural lesion.

As an example of this, I saw a short time ago a fine little fellow, who had a slight dragging of the right leg, following upon a fall. On inspection, however, I noticed that the affected leg was the smaller, upon which a careful questioning disclosed the fact that the child must have halted a little for some time. Then, finally, I learned that he had had, several months before, a severe attack of typhlitis, with great swelling and hardness in the right pelvic region. The fall was too recent (forty-eight hours) to have caused atrophy, which was very distinct. I concluded, therefore, that the nerves must have suffered from the gradual pressure of the confined and engorged tissues about and below the gut. Certainly no single symptom of pain or numbness indicated the progress of the evil, so that here, as in many other cases, a very gradual pressure proved competent to occasion grave nutritive and some

---

* See chapters on Treatment.

motor loss, with no distinct warning in the way of sensory disturbances.

I have, indeed, great doubt as to our capacity to distinguish the form of injury from the resultant symptoms alone. In a recent case, where there was the probability of intra-pelvic neuritis from cancer, and the certainty of a fractured thigh, with great amount of callus, so situated as to make likely some nerve pressure, I was unable positively to ascribe the signs present to either possible cause.

There are so many ways in which slow intra-pelvic pressure on nerves may occur, that a sure test of the presence of compression has always been most desirable.

As regards the accepted signs of pressure, it is quite clear that, when clinically applied, they are not competent to guide us, because the various degrees of pressure may bring about, as we have seen, the utmost variety of symptomatic results. In proof of this I need only refer to the case of the lad lately quoted, and to the various histories of nerve pressure already related.

Still more important, practically, is the decision as to whether certain neural symptoms be due to central diseases or to peripheral causes, such as intra-pelvic or other pressure. When the question lies between nerve lesion and cerebral disease, it is, as a rule, easily settled. Cerebral palsies have a peculiar history, are sudden in their onset, and are more often destructive of motion alone than of this with sensation. They are also more peculiarly distinguished by the fact that in them the muscles remain excitable under electric currents. Indeed, in the early stages of cerebral palsies with tendency to contraction (early rigidity), they are over-excitable, while the instances in which, late in old cases, they have their electric excitability lessened are very rare, and depend, I suspect, upon some of those singular peripheral neural changes which have been lately shown to attack in such cases the peripheral nerve trunks.   Perhaps the facts, as to non-growth or lessened growth of the nails in cerebral palsies which I have recently pointed out, may aid in doubtful diagnosis.   On the other hand, very soon after any grave peripheral nerve lesion, there is sure to be great loss of power in the muscles to respond by movement to faradaic currents, and, a little later, to the galvanic currents.   These facts will usually enable us to separate cases of cerebral palsy from those the origin of which lies below the brain.

I was consulted lately in regard to a lady, aged forty-three, who, four years before, had a slight left hemiplegia, the recovery from which was unusually complete.   A few weeks since she began to suffer from numbness of the left foot and leg, followed by increasing and rapid loss of power to flex the foot.   Her attendant suspected a return of the cerebral disorder, but on electrically examining the peroneal muscles they were found to have lost power to respond to the battery.   We then insisted upon a vaginal examination, when she was discovered to have a large growth behind and to the left of the womb, and of a somewhat suspicious nature.   The local palsy was probably due to this mass.

The differential diagnosis of spinal disease from peripheral lesions presents greater difficulties, and is more apt to give trouble than any of the other questions I have mentioned.   Given a case of numbness and partial paralysis, is it due to nerve disease or to some spinal alteration ?   If the former, it will probably, but not surely, be unilateral; and if the latter, it will be likely to be bilateral, and to affect both feet.   For example : if the cause should be one affecting only a limited region of the spine, the lower ganglia being left unaltered, the muscles will retain their electric irritability, which is not the case when these lower portions of the spine become themselves largely diseased,—a fact which must be settled by other symptoms connected with the existence of analgesia and the absence of reflex motions. In certain cases, then, of spinal disease, the muscles continue to respond to some form of current, and do not waste; while in others the reverse occurs, just as in injuries of extra-central nerve trunks.

When cutaneous anæsthesia exists, it is often easy to learn whether its cause lies in the nerves or the central organs by following the plan proposed by Stich.* If the insensible region can be made the point of departure of reflex movements, the anæsthesia is of central birth, because to have reflex motion an excitation must have reached the spine, by which we infer healthy nerves, while the mere presence of the anæsthesia will, in this case, indicate the existence of disease in the spine above the point which is the seat of the reflex power exhibited. If the proof be negative, and if the excitation cause no movement, we can arrive at no definite conclusion, until, following the same sensitive nerve up the limb, and by seeking to excite through it reflex acts, by touching the skin with a hot sponge or ice at successive points, we learn if at any upper portion of tegument we can produce this result. Should we get an affirmative reply, we may presume that the anæsthesia is of peripheral origin. When, finally, the answer is negative up to the spine itself, we learn nothing by this method, the total absence of all reflex movement being equally compatible with either loss of conducting power in the peripheral trunks and branches and with extensive alteration of spinal centres. The value of this means must be necessarily limited by the difficulty of exciting reflex acts from all regions of skin.

---

* Empfehlung der Erregung von Reflexbewegungen als diagnostisches Hilfsmittel (Annalen des Charité Krankenhauses zu Berlin, 1856.) Also Jaccoud, Paraplégies, p. 498, whence this account is taken

There is another peculiarity which separates all extra-central nerve lesions from cerebral, and also from spinal disease; but I do not feel that as yet it is available to any large extent. I noticed some years ago that in even the gravest lesions of nerve trunks if a touch were felt at all, it was felt with no remarkable delay; while in many central palsies, if severe, and especially in such as result from extensive spinal malady, the time required for transmission to the sensorium was, as Cruveilhier pointed out, very largely increased,—so much so, indeed, as to be readily estimated in a rough way by the hand of a watch beating quarter seconds, or still better by a metronome. The cause of this difference is still obscure to me, nor is it easy to see why diffuse sclerosis, for example, should so retard a sensory impression, while injured nerve fibres have no such effect.*

Prognosis.—The form of injury to the nerve has a large influence upon the prognosis, which, however, is always grave, so far as complete functional recovery is concerned, in every instance of severe nerve lesion. In the larger number of cases of pressure by growths, such as exostoses, aneurism, or intra-pelvic tumors, the ultimate fate of the case depends, of course, on our power to remove the cause of pressure.

For reasons not as yet clear to me, a contusion is often apt to give rise to more prolonged and serious injury than other forms of mechanical disturbance apparently more capable of locally destroying the nerve. Probably a bruised nerve is more likely to pass into neuritis than even one which has been wounded.

Partial nerve wounds have been considered more serious than entire division, but to this I can scarcely give a full assent. The cases of intense neuralgia from lancet wounds

---

* See San. Com. Med. Report, p. 438.

of sensory skin filaments have been held to support the
opinion I am combating, but probably the pains are due
to reflex radiated irritations; nor is there the slightest
proof, on the one hand, that such irritations may not arise
from the ends of fully divided nerves, nor, on the other,
is there any evidence that in these cases the minute nerves
in question are merely pricked or half-way severed. It is
certain, however, that partial nerve wounds of large trunks
alone occasion many of the distressing nutritive conditions already described; but, so far as my experience goes,
notwithstanding these results, such wounds have, on the
whole, a more fortunate *remote* history than thoroughly
divided nerves, where a missile of war has been the injuring agent.

The future of cases of entire severance of nerves will
depend upon the amount of nerve cut away, the sequent
neuritis, and the fate of the surrounding tissues; but even
when the portion lost has been an inch or more, we should
not absolutely despair of a large return of function, when
we remember the extraordinary regeneration of nerves
after exsections for neuralgia.

Given a case of severe injury to a large nerve, how shall
we make up our minds as to the probable future of the
parts over which it presides?   No early opinion is of
value. All missile wounds bruise and disturb more nerve
filaments than they cut, and these will, in a few days, recover their lost powers. This is why many muscles, which
at first seem paralyzed, come again very early under
volitional control. The extent of anæsthetized skin of
most nerve wounds also lessens within a week. Gradually
with the absorption of blood, if no neuritis interposes,
these happy changes continue until, at last, in from a month
to six weeks, we begin to be in a condition to judge what
muscles are to be more permanently palsied, what skin
spaces are to remain insensible.

To determine the future fate of the limb, we resort to the induced and galvanic currents. If, according to Duchenne, a muscle moves ever so little when faradised at a period thus remote from the wound, there is a fair chance of its recovery,—a chance which lessens in proportion to the difficulty with which it contracts under this stimulus. If, however, a muscle neither moves nor feels the pain of the current, this is an indication of so complete a separation from the centres, that from three months to a year may elapse before the probability of nerve restoration becomes such as may enable us to call the part into action. This refusal to respond to the faradaic current does not imply a certain loss of ability to act under galvanism, or of such mechanical irritation as a smart tap. In grave cases, however, there comes a period when the muscle may be dead to every form of excitation, and even to the direct effects of galvano-puncture.

My colleagues and myself had many chances of testing the value of these means, and finally we learned to rely upon them with the utmost confidence.

The sensibility is to be examined with the electric brush, and if found, after two or three sittings, to be dead to this most intense irritant, we may safely conclude that the nerves of the part are absolutely cut off from their central connections, and will require long periods for their repair, should this be ever possible. Unhappily the future dangers of the case do not end here. Apart from the chance of neuritis, which is, I am sure, a more common sequence than has been supposed, there is no time for some weeks after the healing of the original wound when the part may not begin to suffer from neuralgia or causalgia of indefinite duration, and from those obstinate arthritic states which so baffle our efforts to restore movement even when the healed nerves have made this otherwise possible.

The contracted state of the atrophied muscles also comes into the case to make its future less hopeful, and the reader will see, therefore, why I think it needful in every instance to exercise an amount of caution as to prognosis which might at first sight seem scarcely warranted.

At the same time I may add, that in the interval of three or four years, the gradual change which may occur in the worst of these cases is so great and so beneficial that only a careful study of many of them, with a comparison made from my note-books, could have induced me to credit the degree of restoration which time may bring about. In proof of this statement, the reader is referred to the cases appended to the chapters upon Treatment.

CHAPTER X.

Compression.—The treatment of compression is obviously the simple one of removing the cause, which in examples of intra-pelvic pressure is often beyond our power. Cases of compression due to disturbances arising out of the altered mechanical relations of a diseased nerve during motion, are best treated by passive movements and the most gentle but thorough shampooing; while if there should seem to be, at any stage of the case, an inflammatory state of nerve, absolute rest, enforced by a splint, with the usual treatment for neuritis, are required.

Contusions.—Contusions of nerves, when severe, are apt to be followed in a few days by slight numbness and pricking, and when these are associated with growing tenderness over the nerve track, the physician should promptly interfere, since he may feel sure he has to deal either with the commencement of a neuritis, or of that sclerotic state of nerve which may or may not be of inflammatory origin. In either case, the nerve can sometimes be felt in thin persons as a firm cord, not always entirely regular in size. As I have said before, these consequences may follow contusion of nerves at dates as distant as weeks or months, and may give rise finally to the most deplorable results.

In a certain number of contusions the evil is most insidious, and, whatever be the pathological condition, it may result in large functional losses without any notable

(229)

warning in the way of pain or tenderness. One of the best illustrations I have seen of this was in the case of C. P., a man of intemperate habits, who bruised the ulnar nerve at the elbow by a fall in July, 1862. He could use the limb next day, but for some months he had slight formication along the inside of the arm. In December, 1862, the third and fourth digits became weak, and gradually the loss of power affected the entire hand and wrist. He was admitted to the hospital in June, 1863; at this time every motion below the elbow was feeble. The sensory loss was great in the ulnar track, and was increasing in the median distribution. Both the ulnar and the median nerves were exquisitely tender on pressure. The inflammatory condition awakened in the hurt nerve, some five months after the injury, passed up the arm high enough to affect secondarily the median nerve. Leeching and blisters always greatly relieved his neuralgic pain, and lessened as certainly the tenderness of the nerve trunks; but his incessant drinking at last set all means at defiance, and he was finally discharged. The proper treatment for a contused nerve is absolute rest, with the use of leeches and cold water, when symptoms of neuritis declare themselves.

The following case is a fair illustration of contusion of nerves and its treatment:

Case 40.—*Contusion of the right musculo-spiral nerve.* Early in January, 1865, C. P., clerk, aged twenty-two, while fencing, was struck by the button of his opponent's foil upon the middle and outside of the right arm. The shirt-sleeve was torn, and the flesh bruised severely. He felt a sharp pain, which subsided into a tingling in the thumb and outside of the forearm. This continued for several days, and on the tenth day became distressing. Upon examining his arm, I found that the motions of the index-finger were feeble, and that the wrist was extended with difficulty. The track of the radial nerve was sore, and the point on which the blow fell was exceedingly tender. Notwithstanding the deep situation of the musculo-spiral nerve, it was also tender upon pressure, and continued to be so for many weeks. I had the nerve tracks leeched twice a week, and used on the same days an injection of morphia and atropia over the radial nerve. These means partially relieved the hand; but the pain along the outer aspect of the arm became worse, and assumed an intermittent type, appearing every day after twelve o'clock. I used quinine, but to no purpose; and finally I placed him upon arsenic, giving six drops of Fowler's solution thrice a day. Once a week, four leeches were applied over the injured part of the musculo-spiral nerve. The injections were only used when excess of pain demanded them, but an opium plaster was placed over the outside of the arm and forearm. These means proved successful, and the pain slowly subsided, after having lasted unchanged for four months. Exactly five months after the injury, his condition was as follows:

Extensor power nearly perfect; no pain in hand; skin on outside of forearm a little sore to the touch, and subject to slight daily pain, increased by fatigue and damp weather. The nerve tracks were still sore, but not excessively so. At this time he began to have pain in the shoulder, tenderness below it, and distinct loss of power in the deltoid muscle. These new symptoms followed great exposure to bad weather, and were synchronous with a fresh attack of neuralgia. As he was now well and strong, as to general health, I put cut cups about his shoulder, and followed their use by a blister dressed with morphia. At the same time I confined him rigorously to his bed. These measures relieved the pain, but the feebleness of the deltoid increased, and the muscle lost bulk, so that, at the close of a month from this fresh attack, he could raise the arm but six inches outward from the side.

Two weeks later, these changes ceased, and he began to improve so rapidly that, except the exhibition of small doses of arsenic and local frictions, there was no occasion for more active treatment. I believe that this rapid relief was largely due to the coming on of warm spring weather. When last I saw him, early in the summer of 1865, he was suffering trifling pain in the arm at rare intervals. There was no pain in the shoulder, but the deltoid was still a little flattened, and the extended arm could be raised only to the level of the shoulder.

Looking at the anatomical relations of the musculo-spiral to the circumflex nerve, it seems fair to infer that the disease which first involved the former came finally by direct propagation to affect the latter. So far as the mere symptoms can inform us, such would seem to be, in this case at least, the true explanation of the secondary affection which fell upon the shoulder. No opportunity has been afforded me of studying the morbid anatomy of nerves supposed to be thus altered; but I think the facts in favor of directly propagated nerve change are quite sufficient to render probable the theory I have here advocated, while for the idea of its being a reflex affection, there is simply no evidence at all.

The changes which finally occur in sensation and motion from contusions or compression, differ in no important respect from those which arise out of direct injuries; so that for the treatment of these sequelæ I may refer the reader to that portion of this chapter in which I have dealt with the therapeutics of symptoms.

Punctured nerves; wounds of superficial branches.—Punctured wounds of nerves demand no especial treatment unless they occasion grave symptoms, which is by no means always the case. They are, moreover, very rare. I saw, some years ago, a woman who had transfixed the median nerve with a steel fork. The injury at once

caused darting pain in the palm with quivering of the
thumb flexors. I gave opium freely, dressed the wound
with laudanum, placed the arm at rest on a splint, and saw
the symptoms subside and disappear within two days. At
present I should keep such a case well under the influence of morphia with the aid of the hypodermic syringe,
and prescribe in addition the local dressing described.

Lancet wounds of the sensitive cutaneous nerves about
the elbow we shall probably see no more until bleeding
is partially restored to fashion, as it is sure to be. The
older surgeons were accustomed to treat them by cautery
at the point wounded: this was effected by placing a
morsel of potassa fusa in the lips of the cut; while others
made an incision above the wound or isolated it by carrying the knife around it. Both methods answered in many
cases, while in rare instances, where no such means were
used, excruciating pain and local spasms continued for
weeks or months, until, as in Paré's royal patient, the
symptoms gradually subsided, or some such operative procedure was employed, as I have just mentioned. Swan*
speaks of cases in which the relief thus obtained was
instant and complete, and thinks that where the symptoms are not immediate the trouble has arisen from too
early use of the arm. He relates many slighter cases in
which rest, warm opiate fomentations, and the local use
of belladonna gave ready relief.

Mr. Pearson† reported in 1817 cases of extreme pain
from lancet wounds, in which, after every other means
had been exhausted, the most remarkable ease was
afforded by the use of the following liniment:

℞.—Ol. Olivæ, ℨiiss;
Ol. Terebinthinæ, ℨiss;
Ac. Sulphuric. fort. ℨi. M.

* Swan on the Nerves, p. 117.
† Med.-Chir. Trans., vol. viii. p. 252.

It was employed repeatedly, and so as to cause the most intense inflammation of the skin of the whole arm. Where it failed to irritate sufficiently, he added a larger amount of the acid. Whatever value this treatment may have, and it seems scarcely possible to read Mr. Pearson's cases without according it a large share of confidence, must be due to the *extent* of surface attacked by the irritant.

Injuries by missiles of war.—The early treatment of this class of wounds does not require any special notice. The nerve lesion need in no way modify the dressings; and the amount of inflammation attendant upon ball wounds, and the subsequent destruction of tissue in the ball track, make it unnecessary to consider whether any of those immediate surgical interferences are demanded, which are at present among the doubts of surgery in regard to cases of clean incised wounds of neural trunks.

Every possible precaution should be taken to lessen the chance of deep inflammation and the secretion of pus, since conclusive evidence has been obtained from experiments on animals, that nothing is more fatal to reunion of nerves than the formation in the wound of large amounts of matter.

Incised wounds.—An incised wound partially involving a nerve, should be carefully cleansed from fragments of glass or other foreign bodies, the lips brought together as usual, and the limb set at absolute rest on a splint, with every precaution to relax the tissues, and to keep the nerve ends from being drawn apart. Thus, in a wound of the ulnar at the elbow, the arm should be kept in extension, and a wound of the anterior nerves should exact a state of repose in flexion. These measures are rendered necessary in every case by the tendency of the nerve ends to separate, for every healthy nerve is in a state of slight tension, and, on being cut, the extremities tend to draw apart.

Sutures in nerve wounds.—Where it is plain, from a careful study of the wound and the loss of function, that the nerve trunk has been altogether divided, the surgeon is called upon to decide whether he will leave repair to nature alone, or enlarge the wound and secure coaptation of the nerve ends by the use of sutures. The propriety of this step rests upon the manner in which we answer these two questions: Will any, even the most perfect, approximation of nerve ends insure immediate union? and, failing this, will it make likely a more speedy return of healthy function? To the first, we may give a certain negative; to the second, we may, with some confidence, reply in the affirmative.

As I have already pointed out, all the physiological evidence is against the possibility of immediate useful union. Within a few days the peripheral end of the nerve surely degenerates, and in adult animals many months may pass before it is restored and the two ends reunited. Even in young animals the earliest re-establishment of function, when the ends were made to touch by suture, was seven or ten days (Schiff), and nine days (Magnien). Vulpian has no case within seventeen days; and I have never met with an instance even in so short a time as this. The physiological facts are therefore opposed to the probability of immediate union; but, on the other hand, we are met by the statement that these were derived from lower animal life alone, and that in man the rule as to the time demanded for restoration may meet with exceptions, and this possibility is supported by certain clinical histories which may not be altogether set aside.

In 1863, Paget reported two cases of nerve section in children, aged respectively eleven and fourteen years. The first had the median and radial nerves divided by a clean cut from a circular saw. The wrist was placed in flexion on the forearm, and after ten or twelve days there

was slight feeling in the median distribution. At the
close of a month sensation was still very obscure in the
thumb and forefinger, and some parts of the skin were
insensible. A year having passed there was still no feeling in the last phalanx of the thumb and forefinger,
but elsewhere in the median distribution sensation was
almost perfect.

The second lad had his hand so nearly cut off at the
wrist that it remained attached to the forearm by only a
portion of skin an inch wide, connected with which were
the unhurt ulnar vessels and nerve, and the flexor carpi
ulnaris muscle. The radial artery was tied, and the parts
having been replaced, the limb was dressed with adhesive
strips and put on a splint. In a week after the injury the
hand had become warm again, and in ten or twelve days
there was slight sensation in the fingers, but in the thumb
none was discernible until more than two weeks had gone
by. Finally, the sensation of the hand and fingers, and
most of their movements, were perfectly restored.*

Tillaux† is inclined to explain these two cases as instances of really rapid repair, such as Schiff describes as
occurring in young animals, and would not regard them
as examples of immediate union, with consequent escape
from secondary degeneration. In other words, there was
time here for such rapid partial alteration and regeneration
of the distal ends of the cut nerves, as has been shown to
be possible in the young of animals, while to constitute a
truly immediate union we should have so speedy a reunion
as to save the peripheral extremities from the certainty of
Wallerian atrophy of their tubes.

Perhaps the following observation may best illustrate
how unlikely is immediate union to take place under even

* Paget, Surgical Pathology, Am. ed., p. 187. Phila., 1854.
† Op. cit., p. 89.

the most favorable circumstances, and where young ani-mals are used. I laid bare the sciatic nerve of a young rabbit, and with a cataract needle divided the middle fibres of the nerve. There was no bleeding, no retraction, and the lips of the little wound thus made lay in close apposition ; yet, on examining the distal end at the close of six days, I found a large number of fibres undergoing retrogressive changes.

In June, 1864, M. Houel reported to the Society of Surgery, at Paris, the following case of Nélaton's, which I quote, with some abridgment, from Tillaux:

"A female, aged twenty-four years, suffered from a neuroma, situated at the internal and upper part of the left arm, and involving the median nerve. After removing the tumor, M. Nélaton united the two ends of the divided nerve by two metallic loops. It was then found that she had lost the power to move the thumb and first and second fingers, the other two retaining their motility. There was no sensibility to touch in the median distribution, but the sense of pain and that of temperature do not seem to have been examined. On the third day she complained of pain in the thumb, index-finger, and medius. She could now bend slightly the first and second fingers, but could not move the thumb. Sensibility to touch was unaltered on the palmar face of these members. On their dorsal face sensibility was absent in the two last phalanges, and preserved in the first, while on the outside of the thumb it was rather more distinct. The threads were removed, and on the seventh day she could flex easily and rapidly the three fingers to which the median passes, and could bring the thumb into apposition with the first and second fingers."

We learn nothing further as to the fuller return of sensibility in the parts concerned, while the mode of examination, where noted at all, is said to have been by pass-

ing a ribbon over the surface. Nothing could have been
less satisfactory. With regard to motion, the interoseii of
these fingers are fed largely by the ulnar, and their share
in bending the first joints is well known. As to the apposition of the thumb, the inner half of the flexor brevis
pollicis and the adductor pollicis also obey this latter
nerve, and may well have been concerned in causing
these motions. Tillaux, in criticising this case, remarks
upon the supposed return of motion before that of sensation,—the reverse of the common rule in traumatic palsy.
I am unable to concede that there was here any positive
proof of return of motion in the median distribution, and
as to sensation, the examination unhappily leaves everything to be desired in the way of accuracy.

In June, 1864, Professor Laugier reunited by suture a
divided median nerve on the day following the accident
which severed it. "From the following night sensibility
reappeared in the paralyzed parts. The day after, the
thumb had recovered its power to oppose the index-finger,
and the sensibility was much more lively."

On the eighth day, movement, sensation of touch and
of temperature had returned; "*nevertheless, a pin plunged in
the palmar face of the medius caused no pain.*"*

It is much to be regretted that this, like the former
case, should have been left so incomplete. I agree with
Tillaux in his suspicion that the analgesia leads us to suspect that the observer was deceived as to touch and temperature, and that these were perceived through the
nerves which feed adjoining tracts of skin. He remarks,
also, that the section was so low as not to involve the
muscular branches, so that it is not surprising that the
flexors of the fingers should still have enjoyed motion.
In like manner, by the integrity of the median muscle

---

* Tillaux, op. cit., p. 92.

nerves, and of the ulnar, are to be explained the motions of the thumb. Let us add, that when seen by Vulpian on the fifteenth day, he could find no trace of sensation in the median tract, and that, according to Magnien, who saw it seventeen months after the operation, sensation was not even then normal. We are told by Tillaux* that since this case occurred Nélaton and Verneuil have both used the suture in divided median nerves, but without even the approach to success above recorded.

The evidence thus offered by surgeons is too open to criticism to allow of our admitting that severed nerves may unite by immediate union; but even should we accept the facts as stated, they may still be explained with the aid of the recent researches of Arloing and Léon Tripier,† which have shown that, in the dog, and some other animals, the connections in the extremities between the various sentient nerves is such that the division of one trunk by no means annihilates sensation in the parts to which it is distributed. As yet, the evidence for a like arrangement in man is incomplete; but we are not without a few cases which, together with those above quoted, seem to make it probable that in man some such exceptional distribution of nerves may occasionally be found to exist. Paulet‡ relates several instances which favor this view. M. Richel reports a case of entire division of the median, in which the sensibility of the thumb, index, median, and ring fingers was preserved entire. In the example given by Baudens, sensation continued, despite section of all the brachial nerves save the radial. MM. Leudet and Delaboit saw a man in whom, thirty-seven years after the median had been severed, a post-

---

* Op. cit., p. 95.

† Recherches sur la Sensibilité des Téguments et des Nerfs de la Main. Arch. de Physiologie, 1869, p. 32 et seq., and 308 et seq.

‡ Gaz. Hebdomadaire, No. 18, 1868.

mortem examination proved that there had been no reunion, yet during this period the sensibility in the area
supplied by this nerve remained unaltered and entire.

Pirogoff* relates a case in which he divided a softened
ulnar nerve during a resection, and found immediately
afterwards, and at a later date, perfect feeling in the third
and fourth fingers. He quotes,† also, Naudorfer and
Schuh to like effect. Dr. Nott‡ adds to our list of sections
without disturbance of function the following history:

Case 41.—M. Wysinger, aged fifty, of robust constitution, consulted Dr. N. for a tumor on the forearm, which,
although existing for fifteen years, had given no inconvenience until three months before, when it caused pain
and partial contraction of the third and fourth fingers.
The tumor was as large as a cocoanut, and extended
from an inch below the elbow to within an inch of the
wrist. This mass turned out to be a huge sac full of
grumous blood, and was traversed on its exterior by the
flattened fibres of the median nerve. The tumor was
removed, and with it *five inches* of the median nerve; but
the functions usually assigned to this trunk were not interfered with in the slightest degree,—"neither paralysis
nor loss of motion" ensuing. The neuralgia disappeared,
and at no time afterwards was there any disturbance of
function. Perhaps this is the most remarkable of all of
these singular histories, and it is much to be regretted
that its reporter should not have given more ample details
as to the precise sensory and motor conditions.

The general evidence as to the immediate and continued loss of function when nerves are cut, is so strong
that even if we admit the cases of exception as correctly

* Pirogoff, Military Surgery, p. 377.
† Ibid., p. 30.
‡ Bone and Nerve Surgery, Appendix.

reported, and bring to our aid the explanation given by Arloing and Tripier, we shall have to conclude that in man such partition of function as they describe in animals must be singularly rare. Thus, in one hundred and fourteen cases of nerve section which I have collected, there was but one instance of no loss of sensation or motion. These rare exceptions must, then, be referred to unusual nerve arrangements in or below the plexus, such as Krause has described in his monograph on Neural Anomalies.*

The histories first quoted prove the innocuous nature of the ligature when properly applied to nerves, a conclusion for which I felt well prepared, from having in two

---

* Les Anomalies dans le Parcours des Nerfs chez l'Homme, par W. Krause et J. Telgmann, traduit par S. H. De La Harpe, Paris, 1869, p. 38 et seq.

According to Robin, the filaments which enter the touch-corpuscles arise from terminal loops formed by the median and radial. Wenzel Gruber (Archiv für Anat. Phys. und Wissenschaft Med., iv. p. 501–522, 1870, in Schmidt's Jahrbücher, Bd. cl. 1871, pp. 8, 9.), to clear up the variety of statements in regard to anastomoses between the ulnar and median nerves, examined one hundred male and twenty-five female bodies. An anastomosis took place in ten on both sides; in eighteen on one side (right, 4; left, 14). It is, therefore, normal once in five-sixths extremities. In thirty-six cases there was one anastomotic branch, and in two a double branch. Generally, there is a branch from the median to the ulnar. Sometimes there is one from the ulnar to the median, which forms a loop with a downward convexity.

In certain cases the median branch divides, one returning as a loop and one joining the ulnar. This anastomosing filament supplies the flexor profundus. It runs from the median to the ulnar below the pronator teres, and between the flexor sublimus and profundus, and either crosses or accompanies the ulnar artery, joining the ulnar nerve from one and three-quarter inches below the epitrochlea to the lower third of the forearm. Its presence does not influence the arrangements of the palmar anastomoses. The author refers to Krause, op. cit., and to Roland Martin, Institutiones Neurologicæ Holmiæ, 1763.

Messrs. Pye-Smith, Howse, and Davies-Colley (Guy's Hospital Reports, 1870) describe as a variation from the normal, a branch between the ulnar nerve and the anterior interosseous of the median.

cases left in the nerves of dogs metallic sutures which were never removed, but which apparently gave not the slightest annoyance after the nerves had reunited. M. Vulpian* regards neural suture as harmless, and thinks that the opposite opinion held by Eulenberg and Londois must have been due to their use of the rabbit only, an animal which bears badly all nerve lesions.

The evidence in favor of regarding nerve suture as not injurious, is therefore ample when we unite the clinical and physiological statements, both of which seem to decide very conclusively that after its employment the time needed for healing is notably lessened. The case of Verneuil, already alluded to, is further cited by Tillaux and Paulet to support this view. Both ulnar and median had been severed, but the suture was used in the latter alone, with the result of rapid return of sensation for parts fed by the median, and very slow sensory restoration of the ulnar territories,—exactly the result which has attended the physiological use of the suture. There seems, therefore, to be justification for the employment of sutures in any nerve wound, and especially where there has been loss of substance, as after removal of a neuroma.

The mode of using the suture is important. Nélaton found it difficult in his first case to remove the threads. In his second case he passed a thin silver wire through the ends of the nerve within three millimetres of the cut surface, so that being drawn upon, the faces of the section would meet and not ride over one another, as they might have done had he followed Laugier in passing his thread remote from the cut. The ligature drawn through one end of the nerve returns through the other, and the two ends were imprisoned in a long tube of Galli, which reposed

---

* Tillaux, p. 96.

in the wound on the nerve, or very close to it, and projected from the wound so as to allow the operator to fasten
his wires by bending them hooklike over the edges of the
tube. In disengaging the loops, it was only necessary to
lift the tube from the wound, and, releasing one end of the
wire, to draw upon it gently.

Vulpian uses in animals a single linen thread, which he
carries with a fine needle from the upper side of the nerve
obliquely through it, so as to come out about the middle
of the cut surface. It is then passed through the middle
of the exposed face of the opposite section and out at its
upper side, so that when the loop is made and drawn, it
brings the ends in exact apposition if the needle has been
made to penetrate precisely corresponding points of the
two faces.*

I myself used in animals, some years ago, a different
method. In place of transfixing the nerve, I carried the
needle through the loose tissue, which is related to its
sheath, sometimes using one thread, and at other times
two, one being placed on either side. By drawing the
loops with care, it was possible to bring the nerve ends
into close relation. With rabbits it does not answer,
because of the small amount of areolar tissue about their
nerve trunks.

When, by suture and position, or other means, we have
placed a nerve wound of any kind in the most favorable
condition for healing, we shall find that no matter how
well exceptional cases may do, we shall usually have to
treat defects of motility and mobility, altered states of
sensibility, and sometimes nutritive changes.

---

* For all that refers to nerve suture I am largely indebted to Tillaux.

CHAPTER XI.

Loss of motion.—We have already seen how motion, at first altogether lost, in cases of partial lesion reappears in certain muscles, so that after a time we may know what muscles are permanently palsied. Both for purposes of diagnosis and of treatment, it is well to faradise the part at the close of a fortnight, if the wound be such as to admit of this. We shall then discover that certain of the muscles respond readily, and others not at all, while some revive after two or three sittings. These latter have probably been isolated from the centres for a time by mere mechanical disturbance in their connecting nerves. Those which refuse all answer are completely cut off from the spine by section or grave injury of their nerves. While making this statement, I do not wish to assert, with Duchenne, that the muscular irritability is lost because the muscle does not stir when faradised, for Vulpian has shown that in rabbits, where a nerve has been cut, and the isolated muscle, faradised through the clean and shaven skin, does not move, a current applied to the exposed muscle will cause it to shorten.

Even after several weeks, the muscles in man may be made to exhibit some contraction by passing electricity directly through them with the aid of needles.* Moreover, galvanism will oftentimes elicit an answer after in-

---

* Landry, Traité complet des Paralysies, t. i. p. 103. Paris, 1859.

duced currents have failed, so that Duchenne's dictum, that after ten days of separation the muscles in man no longer reply to the most intense electric current, is scarcely correct.

Where no doubt exists that the whole nerve has been severed, the case is more simple. The muscles begin to lose irritability very early,* and continue to do so until their power to move under irritants is extinct, and only to be reawakened usefully by a repair of the connected nerves.

Meanwhile the muscles, thus set at rest, undergo atrophy, and, in some cases, shorten, while their sensibility to pain is lost, and the supply of blood diminishes, as it is sure to do in tissues which are no longer in a condition of functional activity.

According to Duchenne, it is useless to faradise muscles so situated, until many months have elapsed and the nerve has had time to undergo a process of repair and reunion. At the U. S. A. Hospital for Injuries and Diseases of the Nervous System, we very early reached the conclusion that it was wiser, in all cases, to apply to the muscle the stimulus of electricity rather than to leave it to itself. M. Duchenne informed Dr. W. W. Keen, in 1865, that he had changed his former views in regard to this matter; and my own later experience has more and more convinced me that the practice here advised is correct. I now direct the use of faradaic or galvanic currents from the earliest date at which the healing of the wound allows of their use, while with them I combine daily massage or deep kneading, and alternate hot and cold douches. The mode of using these means will presently be more exactly described. The general result which I hope to attain is the nutritive activity which electricity sustains,

* Six days, Landry ; four to five days, Duchenne de Boulogne.

and the continuance of a larger supply of blood to the inert tissues than would enter them if they were not incessantly stimulated and subjected to those alterations of temperature, rest, and motion which belong to the normal state of limbs. When once the nerve is repaired, it finds the muscles in a far better condition to profit by this than could otherwise have been the case. Electricity, in some form, manipulation, and alternate hot and cold douches are, therefore, the three means which I most rely upon to relieve atrophy and muscular paralysis.

Electricity.—It would be out of place to attempt to give here full directions as to the use of electricity, but it is necessary to offer such partial hints as may suffice to guide the physician called upon to treat the consequences of traumatic nerve lesions.

The number of sittings need not exceed one every other day, and when the physician cannot himself give the time, it is quite possible to instruct an intelligent attendant, so as after awhile to confide to such hands a large share of these repeated applications, being careful to impress upon the patient the necessity of using a less powerful current as the case improves. From fifteen to thirty minutes are required on each occasion, and a certain method should be followed, no matter what form of electricity be used.

In hospital practice, or where the physician has control both of galvanic batteries and the induced current, the question as to their relative utility in traumatic palsies may present itself. As regards this, there is but one distinct practical rule. Whatever form of current will best act on the muscles is the one to be made use of.

The interrupted or rapidly reversed galvanic current, from ten to forty cells, will frequently excite the muscle when induction currents have lost their power, so that late in bad cases galvanism is usually to be preferred.

It is common to find, after a time, that the muscle thus treated becomes sensitive to a strong induced current, which, for convenience, may be resorted to in order to complete the cure. Whatever current is the readiest excitor is the one to be preferred, and galvanism in traumatic, as in infantile palsies, is active where induced currents fail us. It is, however, very largely a question of time and patience. Muscles which seem only capable of response to galvanism, will more slowly but surely amend under the use of a good primary current.

This is fortunate, because few persons at present resort to galvanism, while induction batteries are within every one's reach. In using these, I prefer the primary current as least painful and most efficient; but none of the common machines for sale in this country have a sufficiently powerful primary current.

Whatever be the form of electricity we employ, it is advisable to lessen the power as the muscles regain their excitability, and it is to be remembered that in traumatic palsy nothing is more common than to see a muscle restored to volitional control, long before it is able to contract at all under the use of faradaic currents.

With either induced currents or galvanism, metallic or carbon conductors covered with chamois-skin or Canton flannel are to be used; and it is not only desirable to keep them well soaked with warm salt-water, but also, when the integuments are dry, as in winter, to soak the part itself previously, so as to lessen the resistance of the skin.

If in the preliminary examination, the induced current be found competent to move the affected muscles, this alone may be employed, the two conductors being carried in turn over every enfeebled muscle,—one pole being left, in each case, over the point at which the muscle nerve enters it. Since even in the induced to-and-fro current, one pole is always more positive than the other, for reasons which I need not explain, it is found that rapid reversals of the poles by a current-changer greatly increase the effect.

For galvanization, I employ a battery of sixty cells,* or Stöhrer's instrument of forty cells. The two conductors are at first placed, the one on the main nerve, the other on the affected muscle. The circuit is then completed, and the current made and broken at intervals not too short, or, for more powerful influence, the pole-changer is used by an assistant, so as to reverse the direction of the current from moment to moment. After a time the skin reddens intensely, making conduction easier, and the muscle, beginning to move, responds better and better. If, after a minute or two, there is no motion, the assistant adds pair by pair additional cells, until the muscle acts or the application grows too painful. When that amount of battery power is reached which is needed to move the muscle, it is generally found that during the remainder of the sitting the muscle will respond readily to a smaller number of cells than were at first needed to awaken its motility.

If the muscle fails to reply to galvanism or the induction coil after three or four sittings, the case is surely a bad one; but even where we obtain a response to galvanism, although we may be allowed to hope for a cure, there is not always a certainty of it; and I can recall cases in which every muscle of a limb so responded, and yet in which no step was gained by toilsome months of galvanic and other treatment. Happily such instances are rare.

It also happens, however, that in certain muscles which for a long time fail to respond at all to electricity, the persistent use of this means is competent in time to re-

---

* Made by the Galvano-Faradic Company of New York.

store functional health. Before commencing the treatment of such cases, I am always careful to measure the size of the limb, since a change in its bulk and warmth often precedes the return of irritability, and may lead us to a hopeful continuance of the treatment.

It is, in many cases, advisable to interrupt the electric treatment for a month, after it has been continued for two or three months. When, during the treatment, neuralgia comes on, it is also requisite to pause for awhile, or to make the sittings less frequent, when the pain, which is far from an unfavorable sign, will disappear.

In bad cases, I have been in the habit of heating the part before the sitting, and even of keeping it in hot water during the use of the conductors, since I have frequently observed that when a palsied part is well warmed it reacts much more readily to all forms of stimulus, whether volitional or electric.

For faradising *insensible* surfaces, I use the ordinary Duchenne brush of very fine wires, carried lightly over the skin, which has been previously dried and dusted with flour,* while one wet conductor remains pressed on the surface an inch or two distant. For this purpose the secondary current is needed.†

Manipulation.—For want of a better name I have here styled manipulation what is known as shampooing, rubbing, massage, etc. Its value in the treatment of all forms of traumatic, and, indeed, of some other palsies, is very great, and the results which I have seen obtained by practiced rubbers were certainly to be gained by no other equally rapid treatment.

* Duchenne.

† Until lately, we possessed no good batteries of American make. Those manufactured by the Galvano-Faradic Company of New York have amply supplied this want, and are in all respects equal, and in some ways superior, to any of the foreign instruments.

At the United States Army Hospital, we carefully trained several clever sergeants to act as rubbers, and some of these men became extremely expert. For success, the manipulator must be not only tender and gentle, but also strong and enduring, because a treatment by massage extending over an hour, as it should do, will severely task the strength of most men.

If only the skin is to be acted on or excited, the operator should pinch lightly every part of the surface, and move it to and fro over the subjacent parts. The most intense reddening may be brought about in this manner.

When the limb is wasted, and there is general sluggishness or loss of function, the skin may first be treated by gently pinching and tapping it; then the joints are to be moved in turn, and lastly the muscles acted upon by firmly but gently kneading, rolling, and working them,—gradually increasing the power employed. I prefer also that every sitting should be preceded by a local hot bath.

At the close of the manipulation, if it has lasted a half-hour or an hour, the limb becomes warm or even hot, the temperature rising by thermometric determination one or two degrees F.* The skin under this usage seems to become thinner, more pliable, and less bound down to the parts beneath it, while the increase of tone in every muscle at all capable of response is most remarkable.

I have several times noticed that muscles which were previously sluggish, after being thoroughly kneaded would contract far more readily when faradised.

The general result seems to show that there is also a reflex influence exerted on the centres, because excessive kneading will sometimes, like induction currents, cause

---

* In infantile and traumatic palsy.

lumbar pain and cephalalgia, or nausea, and possibly great exhaustion; but when the remedy has not been overused, the patient feels refreshed, and is sure to sleep the better for the process.

For atrophy and muscular palsy, a treatment by electricity three or four times a week, by daily massage, with local hot baths to precede each sitting, seems to me to fulfill all the needed indications.

Strychnia.—In old cases, I see a good physiological reason for giving strychnia also, because it is probable that when a group of spinal ganglia has been long unused, it may need the special increase of irritability which this potent agent produces.

I have many times employed strychnia by hypodermic injections into the limb, but as yet I have had none of the brilliant results which a few observers have obtained, nor can I conceive of any physiological grounds upon which we might reasonably hope for a greater utility from injections into the palsied part than from those made elsewhere.

Deformities from changes in the muscles.—While we are thus wisely using every means of keeping up the organic life of the limb, in a large number of cases, and despite our efforts, changes affecting mobility are taking place which I have elsewhere fully described. The muscles which remain healthy being no longer compensated by their antagonists, gradually stretch these until they cause some deformity, which alters the forms of the articulations, and is productive of the most permanent mischief when the joints are at the same time suffering from the inflammations so common in neural injuries.

A still more troublesome cause of shortening in muscles is the organic shrinking which takes place, either with or after atrophy. This occasionally counterbalances the precedent shortening which has been due to the

healthy tone of uninjured muscles, but in the end the latter yield to the diseased groups, and in turn suffer elongation.   The power with which atrophic contractions act is
enormous, and reminds us of the relentless shrinking of
cicatrices.   It overcomes the healthy muscles, distorts
the members and subluxates the joints so as to place
the most serious difficulties in the way of cure.   The
following case is a good illustration of these disastrous
results, which, however, vary endlessly according to the
part involved :

   Case 42.—*Gunshot wound of left arm ; injury of the ulnar
and median nerves ; paralysis of motion, slight of sensation ;
contraction of flexors ; relaxation under treatment ; atrophy ;
claw-hand from paralysis of interossei ; stinging pain in hand ;
great gain ; interosseal paralysis alone remains ; discharge
with prothetic apparatus.*   Henry Gervaise, aged twenty,
Canadian, blacksmith, enlisted February, 1862, in Company F, 1st Vermont Cavalry.   Healthy until shot, July
7th, 1863, in the left arm.   Probably the wound of entry
was the one over the artery, at the edge of the biceps,
six inches above the internal condyle of the humerus.
Exit on postero-internal face of arm, half an inch above
and three and a quarter inches behind the other wound.
He felt pain in the arm, but dismounted, the artery
jetting blood.   After walking a little way he fainted,
and awakening after some hours, found that the bleeding
had ceased, but that he had no motion from the shoulder
to the finger-tips and that sensation was lessened below
the elbow.   The pain in the hand grew worse gradually,
and was neuralgic in character.   On the second day he
could move the elbow, and during the first week could
stir the thumb.   About December, 1863, he began to

---

* Mitchell, Morehouse, and Keen, op. cit.

move the fingers voluntarily, and this control has continued to improve.

In January, 1864, electricity was used in the hospital where he then was, but he says it was applied only on the fingers.

Condition on entering the U. S. A. Hospital for Injuries and Diseases of the Nervous System, February 18, 1864.— Hand congested; palm purplish; nails curved. Measurements: biceps, right, eleven and three-eighths inches; left, ten and one-eighth; forearm, right, eleven and one-half inches; left, ten.

Flexors in forearm wasted considerably; thumb muscles wasted, and all the interossei much atrophied. No stiffness in the joints. The short flexor of the thumb and the flexor group in the forearm are moderately contracted. The former defect has allowed the extensors of the thumb to act on it so as to bring its metacarpal bone level with those of the fingers, and to turn the nail upward.

Sensation.—Anæsthesia and analgesia in palm and palmar face of all the fingers, but only in the dorsum of the hand, and not on the dorsal aspect of the fingers.

Motion.—Good above elbow. Supination and pronation normal. The wrist flexion is incomplete, from want of power. Extension limited by flexor contraction.

Thumb.—Flexion partly lost from want of power, and extension limited by contraction of short flexor. He has no abduction or adduction of the fingers, and cannot flex the first phalanges or extend the last two.

It is not necessary to speak in detail as to the electric properties, which were wholly absent in the interosseal muscles, and defective in some others.

Treatment.—Electricity, douches; splint to correct flexions. Under this treatment, with energetic use of passive motion, the flexions were corrected, and every motion regained, except that of the interosseal muscles. To have a prothetic apparatus, and be discharged.

Re-examined April 9, 1864.—The hand is now healthy in color, the neuralgia nearly entirely well.

April 22, 1867. *Visible condition of hands.*—Nails of the left hand slightly incurvated; palm mottled, almost normal.

Measurements.—Biceps: right, ten and three-eighths inches; left, ten and one-eighth. Forearm: right, ten and five-eighths; left, ten and a quarter. The loss in the right arm is probably due to a change in his occupation, he being now a stationer. The left arm has gained relatively.

Nutrition.—Flexors of left forearm, thumb muscles, and interossei all slightly wasted. Flexors of fingers the only contracted muscles. Thumb has very nearly regained its normal position.

Sensation normal on dorsum of hand, perfectly localized, but a little blunted on palm; dull and rather imperfectly localized on palmar surface of fingers.

Motion.—Flexion and extension of wrist natural when the fingers are flexed, as they always are except when passively extended. Extension is limited by the contracted finger flexors. Pronation and supination entire. Abduction of thumb lost; flexion weak; extension good. No abduction or adduction of fingers; no extension of last two phalanges, save through violent extension of the first phalanx; but there is some flexion of the first. It is doubtful whether this flexion is not merely a secondary effect of the flexion of the last two phalanges. The claw-hand is only manifest on extension of the fingers, the first phalanges alone being extended, the last two flexed one-half.

Electrical test.—Electro-muscular sensibility in left arm and forearm the same as in the right; in the hand, diminished nearly one-half. Electro-muscular contractility is not now absent in a single muscle. In the left arm and forearm it is very slightly, if at all diminished. In the left hand all the muscles respond, the general loss being about one-half; but in the first and fourth dorsal interosseal, about three-quarters or more.*

Temperature (the thermometer being placed in the metacarpo-phalangeal fold, where both hands could close on it about equally well), after being tested for half an hour in each hand, was, right, $95\frac{1}{2}°$; left, $96°$ Fahr.

I have alluded to the fact that the temperature in parts partially paralyzed by wounds was in some cases higher than upon the healthy side. This was especially noticeable in the instances of causalgia described by my colleagues and myself. As the facts here referred to had excited some little doubt, I lately examined in the case of Schiveley† the thermal condition three years after he left the hospital. To my surprise I found that, despite the great changes made by time, the temperature of the injured hand was still slightly higher than that of the other member. Schiveley had severe burning pain. Gervaise, the patient last described, suffered only from neuralgia of the ordinary type.

In this man, the flexors of the hand were wasted as well as the muscles of the thumb and the interosseal group. The short flexor of the thumb, and the flexor mass in the forearm, were moderately contracted. The former defect allowed the thumb extensors " to act on it, so as to bring its metacarpus level with those of the palm, and to turn the nail upward so that it lay in the same plane with the fingers." There was, therefore, palsy of the interossei, and in consequence a condition which made the hand

---

* By means of the battery he can make a good fist, being able to bring the thumb into perfect apposition with the fingers.

† Gunshot Wounds and other Injuries of Nerves.—Case.

look precisely like that of a monkey, and which also resulted in the curious deformity described by Duchenne, and which came to be known in our hospital as the "claw-hand." It is due to these facts: the interossei being palsied, the extension of the second and third phalanges and the flexion of the first are lost as independent acts. But the two common flexors bend the second and third joints, and being without antagonists, roll them into the palm; while the common extensor, which only acts on the first phalanges, having also lost its opponent, permanently extends these parts, and thus produces the claw-hand I have described.

When both sets of muscles have been attacked, we have very curious results. Thus in the case of Schiveley, the flexor carpi ulnaris, palmaris longus, and flexor carpi radialis being strongly contracted, the wrist was bent at a right angle and drawn to the ulnar side. The extensor group was also contracted, and the first phalanges, from being violently extended while the wrist was flexed, underwent subluxation.

In rare instances I have seen the atrophy and shortening confined to small tracts of a muscle, as in one instance to the portion of the extensor communis digitorum which acts on the second finger. In cases of extreme general atrophy of a whole limb, it might be expected that the groups which in health preponderate would, in contracting, always overcome the rest. Yet this seems scarcely to be the case to any marked extent, except in the hand. Certainly in the examples I have seen of general atrophy of the leg, the contractions did not usually result in marked deformities. Most commonly the knee has been slightly flexed and the foot extended, but the toes did not suffer such changes as fall on the fingers.

I am now attending a case of palsy from the pressure of intra-spinal exostosis, in which the calf muscles have undergone atrophy and excessive contraction so as curiously to distort the foot. As a rule, in the arm it is palsy of the flexors which brings about these conditions. When the more feeble extensors are thus affected, the greater mass and power of the flexors seem usually able to resist better the force of contraction.

Prothetic apparatus.—We have no early means of preventing these alterations, except by the use of prothetic apparatus, the varieties of which I do not propose to describe, since they either are well known or need to be so modified for every new case as to baffle all description. Their object is solely to strengthen in the one case the palsied group, and in the other to aid the normal muscles in resisting the shortening of atrophied fibres.

Final relief is to be looked for from the use of electricity, rubbing, baths, and time; but if these fail us, as they must sometimes do, and the limb continues to alter in form, it is often possible by cutting tendons and restoring parts to their places, by the aid of apparatus, to leave to the sufferer a limb which, in the case of the leg, may be far better than an artificial member, and in the case of the arm will be more or less valuable according to the muscles which remain in service, and, above all, the amount of joint disease which limits their usefulness.

Treatment of spasm.—Persistent spasms of muscles from neural injuries are rare. In the case of Monaghan, already described, it was necessary to divide several tendons on this account, after which extension on a splint resulted in recovery.

I have several times seen this form of spasm, owing to rheumatic causes, affecting the nerves. In one of these cases the patient suffered from intense pain in the right arm, from some loss of power in the shoulder muscles, and from spasm of the short flexor of the thumb.

We used injections of atropia, *which were thrown into the mass of the muscle itself.* At first this caused increased contraction, but within a few minutes entire relaxation ensued. The muscle never again acted as powerfully, and successive injections at intervals of a day or two brought about a cure.

The same means were used with equal good fortune in a case of spasm of the abductor minimi digiti, but unfortunately the notes of this case are lost, so that I am unable to state either the cause of the spasm or the details of its recovery. In longer muscles, such as the flexor carpi ulnaris, this treatment usually failed us. In at least two cases, however, which I have seen since then, the happiest results followed its use in spasm of unknown origin in the right trapezius muscle, and also in spastic contraction of the biceps.

I have many times endeavored to relieve these contractions, and those which succeed some cases of cerebral apoplexy, by faradising their opponents. Unlike Duchenne, I have had unvarying ill success, chiefly because the currents excite reflectively the contracted muscles, and this was also the uniform report in all such efforts made at the U. S. A. Hospital for Nervous Diseases, etc.*

Treatment of joint disease.—The most mischievous of all the consequences of nerve injuries, of all of them the most fertile in direct and indirect evil, are certainly the joint inflammations. A case may be doing perfectly well, when suddenly or slowly one joint after another becomes swollen, stiff, and painful. When this happens, the members remain, as it were, set in the false positions into which contractions, palsies, or atrophic shortenings have dragged them. Exercise becomes impossible, from the

---

* Even when some relaxation has seemed to be caused by long electrization, there has been really no gain of the least practical value.

pain it causes, and passive motions and electricity must for the same reason be laid aside.

Often, indeed, the pain from these joints is exquisite, and in the first few months of treatment defies all means of relief except absolute repose; and this, unhappily, is a fatal sentence for the limb. When left to themselves, adhesions are sure to form, and partial anchyloses occur, so that it proved best on the whole to treat them for a time with small blisters, and as early as the inflammations allowed, to anæsthetize the patient and use passive motion with freedom. This, at all events, was the method found most productive of good after gunshot injuries of nerves; and in the rare cases of arthritic trouble from nerve wounds which I have since seen, I have found it the only reliable treatment.

Where the joint maladies are of long standing and neglected, the induced current, or, still better, that from a galvanic battery, should be used, and the adhesions at once broken up under ether or chloroform, the sufferer being fortunate if the state of the muscles has been such as not to alter materially the normal relations of the articular surfaces.

After a year or two has passed, leaving the smaller joints enlarged and only slightly painful, they may be slowly reduced by surrounding them with rings of caoutchouc cut from thin rubber tubes and slipped over the joint. The pressure is borne very well for the day or night, and is pretty sure, in time, to lessen the size of the part most remarkably, while at this stage the persevering use of galvanism, of passive motion, and of all the forms of rubbing, becomes available.

Notwithstanding the obstinacy of these arthritic troubles, it is sometimes possible to overcome them when the patient is sufficiently determined; or if, as in the following example, the resolute rule of a military hospital can be called upon to replace the enfeebled will of the sufferer. In other respects this case is remarkable, since it shows that a lesion probably limited to the anterior columns of the spine in the neck, may occasion atrophy and almost universal anchylosis from arthritic lesions. Its importance must excuse my quoting at length from the little volume so often mentioned.*

Case 43.—S. Johnson, aged eighteen, Pennsylvania. No previous business. Private, Company I, 8th Pennsylvania Cavalry. Enlisted for three years, August, 1861. Health good previous to enlistment, except as interrupted by an attack of typhoid fever four years before. Six months after enlisting he had a fever, probably of a malarious character. Three weeks before he was wounded he suffered with pain in the right leg, made worse by movement, but unaccompanied by any rheumatic swelling of the joints.

May 3, 1863.—He was wounded by a small ball in the left cheek while riding at a trot. It entered at the middle of the ramus of the jaw, a little below the level of the teeth. From his position, as well as the after-evidence, it seems that the ball passed backward and inward, and finally lodged in the spinal column. The edge of the jaw was somewhat injured, and probably was the source of the small fragments of bone which afterwards escaped from the neck. When shot, the man fell forward on his horse's neck; says he was confused, though conscious, and felt as if he had been struck in the ear, and then lifted up in air. He also felt instant pain in the back of his neck, and in all of his limbs. There were no spasms. He was removed from his horse and carried to a house near by. The motion increased his pain, especially any movement of the neck. He now became aware of the

---

* Op. cit. p. 22, Injuries of Nerves, etc.

total motor paralysis of the arms and legs. He is not sure whether sensibility was also extinct. Two days after being wounded, he became delirious, but gradually recovered his senses after three or four days. He was finally sent to the Douglas Hospital, Washington, then under the charge of Assistant Surgeon Thomson, U. S. A., and was transferred to our own wards July 19, 1863.

The wound healed in nine weeks after the discharge of a few small fragments of the jaw. Meanwhile his left leg improved slightly.

His case is thus described on his entrance to our wards. A more wretched spectacle than this man presents can hardly be imagined. He lies in bed, motionless, emaciated to the last degree, and with bed-sores on both elbows and both hips. His hands lie crossed on his chest, perfectly rigid; the fingers extended; the skin congested and thin; the nails curved; false anchylosis of all the joints of the upper limbs; the head and neck rigid, with acute pain in these parts on movement. The right leg has motion of a feeble nature in all of the joints; the left only very slight voluntary movement. The hands, the appearance of which has been already alluded to, present certain characteristics which belong usually to cases in which there have been wounds of the brachial nerves. In the present instance, as in many others, these peculiarities have been modified by the long-continued rest of the limbs in one posture. The results of the nerve injury and its consequent effects on the nutrition of the part may, however, be partially discriminated, so that what is due to them and what is due to mere rest may be discerned to some extent. Thus, the shining palm, the slight eczema, the burning pain, the atrophy, and the swollen joints, whose appearance simulates subacute rheumatism, with the contractions of certain muscles, are all owing to the nerve lesion; while the anchylosis

and the peculiar flattening of the hand are perhaps owing
to this and to the long rest and disuse, the arms meanwhile lying crossed on the chest, the fingers in extension.
Disuse alone might have caused some stiffness, but never
to such a degree as occurs when the joints have been sub-
acutely inflamed at the same time. The loss of the lateral palmar arch is owing to both causes, and the monkey-
like appearance of the hand, the thumb rotated outward,
and its nail looking upward and even toward the forefinger, is caused, first, by the subluxation of the metacarpo-
phalangeal articulation, and secondly, by the weakening
and atrophy of the adductor and short flexors of the
thumb. The nerve lesion, affecting the muscles and the
general nutrition of the part, has so relaxed the unused
tissues of the limb as to make the pressure of its own
weight effective in thus altering its form.

Sensation.—Tactile sense enfeebled equally in both arms,
worse in the left. Feeble in both legs, worse in the left.
Confused power of localizing sensation in the legs. Mistakes right for left, but not left for right.

There is muscular hyperæsthesia of the upper members,
shoulders and neck; none in the legs. The left brachial
plexus is sensitive to pressure, and this causes pain in the
left arm and hand. The palms tingle, and burn a little,
the feet not at all.

Every attempt at passive motion causes exquisite pain
in the arms, hands, and shoulders, but most of all in the
back of the neck, about the first and second vertebræ.
This is due, first, to the hyperæsthesia of the muscles, and
secondly, to the state of false anchylosis, owing to rest in
one fixed posture. He either is too weak to move the
body or is really paralyzed in the spinal muscles. The
biceps, flexors, and wrist muscles are very rigid, as well
as the trapezius, and the atrophy of the muscles throughout the upper limbs is singularly well marked.

His condition was too grave to allow of an electric examination.

There was no inflammatory swelling about the neck, and it was, therefore, resolved to treat him with free passive motion, breaking the adhesions and forcing him to exert himself as far as he could. Tonics, porter, and liberal diet were ordered, and the shampooing and passive movement were vigorously carried out, despite his pain and most earnest supplications to be let alone.

The bed-sores were treated with alternate applications of iced-water for ten minutes, followed by a flaxseed-meal poultice as hot as could be borne. This local means, recommended by Brown-Séquard, succeeded marvelously, as it always does, the bed-sores healing easily within ten days.

August 25th.—He is still losing flesh. There is great pain in the neck. Moves his head and legs a little better. No change in the arms. Despite his prayers and protestations, the shampooing was continued; and on October 15th, he was greatly improved. He is fatter; the legs can be voluntarily crossed; appetite voracious.

December 7th.—Great gain. Can move right arm freely. Can raise his head; bend and turn the neck. Sits up daily.

December 29th.—Motion returning in right hand. No gain in left, but in both the malpositions have been relieved, and the hyperæsthesia reduced. From this time the improvement was manifest and rapid. On January 7th, 1864, the case was carefully reviewed with the following results:

Nutrition.—Much fatter; atrophy lessened. The hands have lost their smooth, shining look, so expressive to us of a nerve lesion. The nails are less curved. The temperature is better.

Sensation.—Right arm and hand. Tactility and localizing sense good. Left arm rather less perfect. Tactility and localizing sense in legs normal, or nearly so. Sense of pain more perfect than at first, but even now a pinch causes a feeling of pricking only, rather than the usual sensation. There has been some burning of the right face, neck, and arm within the past week.

Voluntary motion.—Left leg normal in extent of action, but still feeble. Right leg healthy. The right arm has regained all the shoulder and elbow motions, except that, owing to a remnant of contraction in the biceps, extension is not quite entire. Flexion, pronation, and supination are perfect. Extension of wrist incomplete, owing to contracted state of flexors. Flexion of wrist perfect. The thumb has lost abduction, owing to contraction of the adductor. Fingers, extension normal. The joints being still stiff and swollen, the second and third joints possess but two-thirds of their healthy extent of flexion.

Left arm.—For ten days past the shoulder has begun to exhibit voluntary power. Elbow, no movement. Pronation and supination slight. Flexion and extension of wrist also slight. Fingers, feeble, tremulous movements.

For the first time we now examined the electric state of the muscles. The electro-muscular contractility was good in the right biceps, feeble in the left. Good in the right supinator longus, feeble in the left. Good in the extensors of both hands. Good in the flexors of the right hand, feeble in the left. The interossei on both sides showed great loss of this property. The abductor pollicis on the left had no electro-muscular contractility. As a rule, this property was lessened in the left arm and shoulder, while the electro-muscular sensibility was scarcely altered in the two members, except, perhaps, some diminution in the thumb muscles of the left hand, and in the flexor group of the left forearm. The whole left arm was still very stiff.

Ordered the patient to be etherized every day, and the adhesions to be forcibly broken. Passive motion to be continued, and the limbs to be faradised daily.

The future progress was inconceivably rapid.

On January 20th, he could rise to his feet, and by February 20th, could walk a few steps. March 20th, walks well without a cane or any aid; the left hand alone has not gained to any •great extent, although the malposition has been much relieved. The patient was discharged in March, slightly shuffling in his walk, but with nearly entire use of all his limbs, except the left hand and forearm.

Treatment of lesions of sensation; anæsthesia.—As with motion, so with sensation, we shall often find that tracts of skin which soon after the wounding are devoid of feeling, recover function within a few days. Where, however, time enough has elapsed for nerve repair, and sensation is still lessened or lost, we have but few means of treatment to which it is worth while to resort, beyond the general measures employed, to sustain in the limb its nutritive life. Faradisation of the dry skin is the most efficient method of relief.

The batteries generally used are of insufficient strength when we desire to awaken sensation in parts apparently devoid of all feeling. With a strong induced secondary current the electric brush is the most violent of all the excitants of the skin which do not disorganize its structures, and under its repeated use it is common to find sensation returning to regions which are deficient in every form of sensory life, so that after two or three sittings even far slighter impressions can be felt.*

---

* The finer the wires the more severe is the stimulation. I have frequently improvised an excellent brush by fraying out the threads of a conducting cord which contains a number of fine wires.

Counter-irritation.—Of the many counter-irritants which I have employed, the most useful are lotions of oil of turpentine, which may be applied cold or hot, as we need slight or severe irritation. When a rag, dipped in hot turpentine and covered with rubber or oiled silk, is laid on the skin, we get the most powerful stimulation which this agent affords. No agent affects more unequally different persons, so that some care may be needed in using it. I have known it to produce for hours the most unbearable pain, while some patients seem scarcely to feel it at all. I do not know why we gain by using an irritant over very large surfaces, extending far beyond the region involved; but advantage certainly seems to arise from it. I recall, in this connection, the case of a soldier, whose whole arm was insensible from a fall on the shoulder. He suddenly recovered full feeling after the entire limb and back had been severely blistered by exposure to the sun. In injuries of nerves we rarely see sensation fully and perfectly restored; and for a long time, even in the best cases, the power to localize touch is more or less defective.

Treatment of pain, neuralgia, causalgia.—Neuralgic pain from nerve injury may depend upon pressure or the presence of foreign bodies, and, if such causal relations can be made out, its relief, of course, becomes in some cases easy; but in general we shall have only to settle the question of whether the nerve be inflamed or in a state of sclerosis; while, if neither of these states can be shown to exist, we have to fall back upon the pathological phantom which we call irritation, and are driven then, and indeed very often, in every case, to treat the pain alone, without true knowledge of its immediate cause.

The treatment of the pain from acutely-inflamed nerves is simply that of inflammation, which has already been described in full.

With a history of wound or blow, and that of inflammation, subsiding to a subacute stage, or never rising to an acute grade, we fall within a larger class of cases. The pain which comes from such pathological states is very varied in type; but so long as the nerve was tender it was our custom, in the U. S. A. Hospital, to resort to repeated leeching, which proved the most potent remedy. Since the war, I have frequently used dry cold, in any case of violent pain with steady local tenderness of the nerve. Employed for a week or two, it is sure to be of service, and, under its use, the nerves lose their irritability and distinctly shrink in size; but, to make this method most available, it must be kept up unfailingly both day and night. The certainty with which dry cold will break up the tendency of these cases to intermit, is most remarkable. I have under my charge at present a manufacturer of plumbers' materials, who has for three years suffered intensely from neuritis of the left sciatic nerve, with constant increase of the pain at two o'clock every morning. The speed with which this habit broke up, and the neural tenderness lessened under the use of ice, was most satisfactory. When dry cold cannot be applied, I resort to moist heat, in the form of poultices, in which the whole limb should be wrapped, the heat of these applications being sustained by the aid of salt- or sand-bags, placed on their outside.

A variety of local remedies have found more or less favor in the treatment of traumatic neuralgia, whether related plainly or not to inflammatory causes. They passed successively under trial in our vast experience during the war. For the most part they may be classed with the therapeutics of despair, the use of narcotic injections having allowed us to dispense with them altogether.

Counter-irritation.—The use of irritants over the cicatrix or the nerve track we found but rarely of value, and they were sometimes most distinctly hurtful. In a few instances I have followed Pearson's counsel, in irritating the whole skin of the member, and have occasionally found the plan serviceable.* Veratria, so available in common neuralgias, I do not employ in cases arising from injuries, nor has the local use of chloroform been of more than temporary benefit. Aconite, the most powerful of all the local agents, I used with good effect in the only case of neuralgia from wound of a small sensory nerve of the skin which I have lately seen; but it is a drug the employment of which demands extreme caution, not less on account of its great power to depress the heart, than because of the mode in which it sometimes acts locally. I saw, several years ago, a gentleman who had received a blow on the supra-orbital region, which was followed by severe neuralgia, assuming a quotidian type, and for which the tr. aconit. fort. had been very freely used as a local measure. The space covered by it soon began to tingle and burn severely, and continued to do so for several weeks, although the sense of touch in the affected region was absolutely abolished. In another instance I employed it to relieve the pain which followed an injury of my own thumb. Within an hour it caused the most severe tingling, which soon attacked the skin of the whole body, and for many days I was eased only by dressing lightly and exposing myself to the cold January air. The effects lasted for a week.

Acupuncturation.—Of acupuncture in traumatic neuralgia, I have nothing good to say; it was repeatedly used by our staff, without the slightest advantage.

Hypodermic injections, narcotics.—The pains of traumatic neuralgia are so terrible that we are usually driven at once to the use of narcotic hypodermic injections, without which it would often be impossible to relieve such cases.

---

* See p. 233.

In neuralgia, from what we call, for want of a better term, irritation of nerves, there is reason to believe that some of the opiates in the form of hypodermic injection may prove more or less curative in their action; but where, as in most traumatic neuralgias, there is manifest organic alteration of the nerve, such agents are chiefly of service because they relieve pain, and thus enable us to bridge over, so to speak, the many months of torture which are needed to bring the nerve back to health again, or to afford time for electrical or other treatment. Without some such heroic means of dulling pain, few men would be contented to await in patient agony the long months which must often pass away before relief may come, if it come at all. This method therefore has, within my own knowledge, been the saving of a number of nerves and of many limbs which otherwise must have been sacrificed for the purpose of relieving unendurable pain.

At the present time this mode of using narcotics has grown into common use, but even yet it is scarcely estimated at its full value. In the wards for nerve wounds in the U. S. A. Hospital it was almost the only plan of treating severe neuralgic pain, so that twice or thrice a day the resident surgeons passed around these wards with their narcotics and hypodermic syringes, seeing, as a physician observed to me, anguish and troubled faces before them, and leaving behind them comfort, and even smiles. The picture is not overdrawn, since, perhaps, few hospitals have ever embraced at one time so many cases of horrible torture. It was usual at one period, I believe, for the assistants to give every morning and every night between sixty and eighty hypodermic injections.

During one year at least forty thousand doses of various narcotics were thus administered without an accident, and in certain single cases upwards of five hundred hypodermic injections were used, so that if there were no other evidence of the innocence of this mode of medication, our own experience would have been amply competent to settle the question.

I have had large opportunity for studying in traumatic neuralgia the comparative merits of narcotics used by the mouth or under the skin, and I have no hesitation in stating as my opinion, that the latter method is not only the more effective, but also the less harmful constitutionally.

For the easing of neuro-traumatic pain we tried,* in turn, the whole range of medicines known as narcotics, such as conia, hyoscyamus, daturia, atropia, and morphia. None of them, save the last, seemed, when singly used, to be of the slightest value, and one by one they were laid aside until, in the vast mass of cases, the salts of morphia alone were employed. A careful series of examinations showed very distinctly the trifling influence of atropia upon this form of pain. Several cases of intense neuralgia from wounds were treated with injections of sulphate of morphia under the skin in rising doses. When we learned the amount needed to give entire ease, we used in its place, next day, a full dose of atropia, our largest injection having been one-fifteenth of a grain. The most absolute failure attended these efforts, so that without denying to this latter drug the power ascribed to it of relieving certain neuralgias, I am sure that it is in the traumatic species simply useless.

The morphia salts, on the other hand, are invaluable. For hypodermic use I usually employ at first one-fourth of a grain of the sulphate, but I have given as much as a grain and a half twice a day. When continuously used, it is very curious that its hypnotic manifestations lessen, while its power to abolish pain continues, so that the

---

* Mitchell, Morehouse, and Keen, op. cit., 146.

patient who receives a half-grain or more of morphia may become presently free from pain, and yet walk about with little or no desire to sleep. The ability to lessen pain is not therefore of necessity connected with the sleep-compelling potency. Where, however, the latter is inconveniently felt, and we desire the former only, it is possible to attain the end in view by using with the morphia a certain share of atropia. Thus, if we inject half a grain of sulphate of morphia, and with it the thirtieth of a grain of sulphate of atropia, the anæsthetic force of the morphia will rest unaltered, but the tendency to sleep will be greatly diminished. The views here set forth were reached after long and careful experiments on large numbers of men,* and seem to justify the practice of using atropia and morphia together.

As regards the place of injection, I agree with most observers that it is generally of little moment, the effect being the same whether it be thrown into the affected limb or into a remote part. The single exception to this I shall presently mention.

Manipulation.—I have elsewhere spoken of the use of *massage* in restoring the nutrition and motions of a limb. It is only of late that I have sought to control pain and alter the nutritive state of a diseased nerve trunk by this means. A case of contusion of the ulnar nerve became subject to intense neuralgia, the nerve being hardened and enlarged, owing, probably, to subacute neuritis. It was very tender, and no application of electricity was borne with any patience. The pain was relieved by hypodermic injections, but after using many remedies,

---

* Antagonism of Atropia and Morphia, etc., S. Weir Mitchell, W. W. Keen, and G. R. Morehouse, Am. Journ. Med. Sci., July, 1865. These researches led us to the conclusion that the two drugs are mutually antagonistic through a part only of their range of symptoms, even agreeing as to some of their modes of activity.

and at last the actual cautery over the nerve trunk, without altering its size or tenderness. .I patiently tried whether by slow and careful manipulations I could enable it to bear pressure. After a course of gentle friction, lasting half an hour, I succeeded in my object, and three sittings enabled me to rub, and even knead quite roughly, the diseased part. I then taught the lad's sister to execute the same manœuvres, and was pleased to find that after some thirty sittings he could readily bear the use of ice, which before he could not endure, and that the nerve was plainly less in size and of diminished density.

This very instructive case has taught me in other instances to help the progress of the nerve towards health by like means whenever there are tenderness and sclerotic conditions. I need not say that some tact is needed in slowly increasing the force of the friction and the depth of the pressure employed. Moreover, to be of value each sitting should last from half an hour to an hour. Any intelligent attendant can readily be taught the art of methodical rubbing, and for a nurse there is no more useful attainment.

Causalgia or burning pain; water-dressings.—A vast number of means were tried to ease or cure causalgia, but the one essential for comfort was the use of water-dressings, which were unceasingly renewed, the sufferers carrying a bottle of water and a sponge and keeping the part covered. I have never known a man afflicted with causalgia who did not learn very soon the use of this agent, and I never knew one who could be induced to exchange it for any other permanent dressing.

Hypodermic injections.—Further relief was given by hypodermic injections of morphia, used twice a day *and injected into the tissues of the affected part.* I am aware that this is not in accordance with recent views as to the equal efficacy of injections at points remote from the seat of pain; but I am well satisfied that in causalgia something is gained by the local proximity. Numerous experiments were made to determine whether as full relief might not follow injections at distant points, but although the injecting of the burning hand produced in many cases torture, the patient was sure to insist upon it after a few trials of other localities.

Symptoms of neuritis, where this was plainly the pain-cause, were met by the means already described; but the use of ice on the burning part was commonly too painful to be long endured.

Blisters.—The curative treatment was simple. It consisted in blistering the burning part repeatedly with Granville's lotion or cantharides. Nor was it necessary to merely blister until we lessened or destroyed the burning pain, since relapses were common; and, to avoid these, the part required to be several times vesicated after an apparent cure had been effected. In light cases two or three blisters have answered; in others, ten or twelve have been needed, and, in very rare examples, this and every method failed us, although such was never the case in any instance which was treated early,—only the oldest cases being thus obstinate. The following history is a good illustration of the varieties of treatment essayed, and of the terrible nature of this most interesting symptom:

Case 44.*—*Gunshot wound of the left brachial plexus; paralysis of motion and sensation; muscular hyperæsthesia; intense burning in hand and arm; nutritive changes; atrophy; contracted extensors; relief; discharged.* A. D. Marks, sergeant Company C, 3d Maryland Volunteers, aged forty-three, enlisted August, 1861. Previously healthy.

---

* Gunshot Wounds and other Injuries of Nerves, p. 148.

May 3, 1863, at Chancellorsville, he received two
wounds, one in the neck and one in the chest. The first
ball passed in below the anterior boundary of the left arm-
pit, through the margin of the great pectoral muscle, the
arm being raised at the moment. The missile glanced on
the neck of the humerus, and made its escape anterior to
the coracoid process, apparently wounding the plexus. As
he turned to leave the field, a second ball entered the right
side of the back, to the right of the eighth dorsal vertebra,
and, crossing behind the spine, entered the left side of the
chest. The first wound caused palsy of motion and feeling
in the left arm. The second gave rise to cough, spitting
of blood, dysphagia, etc. It finally caused pleurisy, and
large escape of pus during breathing. The wound is now
closed, July 4, 1863, but the lower half of the lung is
consolidated. The second wound brought him to the
ground. He was taken prisoner, exposed a good deal to
bad weather, and finally exchanged, and sent to Satterlee
General Hospital, West Philadelphia, June 10, 1863.

During the first week, the arm, though palsied, was
painless. Then he began to feel a knifelike pain from
the wound down the inside of the limb, and also on its
front, and on the ulnar side, half-way to the wrist. With
these pains came a tingling and burning sensation, as
when the blood returns into a limb said to have been
asleep. Soon afterwards this extended to the hand also,
and he became able to feel the touch of foreign bodies.

Present state, July 5, 1863.—He lies on his back, anx-
ious-looking and pain-worn. The left arm rests on a
pillow. It is cold, mottled, and swollen. The skin of the
hand is thin, and dark-red, but presents no eruption.

Tactility, nowhere absent, is dull on the dorsum of the
hand and fingers. Except in these parts, localizing sensation is good. The whole arm and hand, except its back
part, is, as he says, alive with burning pain, which warmth

and dependence of the limb increase, and which cold and wetting ease considerably. It is subject to daily exacerbations about mid-day.

Motion.—The shoulder muscles act well. The deltoid is feeble. There is no motion below the elbow. The fingers are half flexed, and their joints swollen, sore, and congested. The deltoid is atrophied one-half. The extensors in the forearm are flabby, but the general œdema prevents us from telling whether the forearm muscles are wasted or not. Pressure on the cicatrix gives no pain.

While at Satterlee Hospital, Dr. Walter F. Atlee used ice to the arm, and on the shoulder a blister, dressed with morphia. These measures relieved the arm for the time without aiding the hand.

Ordered hypodermic injections of the fourth of a grain of sulphate of morphia, near the scar, twice a day. This relieved the arm; the hand growing daily worse, so that even ice ceased to afford ease, and he constantly prayed us to amputate the arm.

July 7th.—Erysipelas set in about the seat of the injections, and they were discontinued for a time, morphia being used internally, and lead-water locally.

On the 9th, the disease had left him, and two drops of conia were injected into the shoulder. This was thrice repeated, but gave no relief. Atropia, one-twenty-fifth of a grain, was next essayed, three times successively, at intervals of two hours. It caused dilatation of the pupils, flushed face, giddiness, and dry tongue. The only valuable result was a relaxation of the flexors of the fingers, which had become contracted, but which never afterwards became so rigid as they had been. The patient himself called attention to this singular effect. Again morphia, one-third of a grain, was injected into the arm without aiding the hand.

July 15th to July 20th.—Injections of morphia were made into the hand twice a day. They gave so much ease that the ice was temporarily abandoned.

July 21st.—For the first time we were able to examine the limb with electricity.

Tactile sensation was good in the arm, and absent in the ulnar distribution. In all other parts of the hand tactile sensation existed. In the portions insensitive to touch, deep pressure and pinching caused pain, which was very severe, but was indistinctly localized by the patient.

Electro-muscular contractility was absent in the whole hand and forearm. The currents caused everywhere great pain, so that we could not tell if it were muscular or not. Probably the muscles still had sensation, since pressure on them was agonizing. Every electric examination necessitated the immediate use of morphia injections.

August 14th.—The recent warm weather has increased the pain, so that he moans and weeps incessantly.

Up to September 9th, various means were employed. The injections have been so numerous that the part is dotted with punctures, and their irritation has aggravated his sufferings to such a degree that they have been permanently laid aside for the internal use of narcotics. As local agents, we have had recourse to laudanum, lead-water, ice, oil, poultices with and without soda, and poultices of carbonate of soda, with vinegar to release carbonic acid. Of these the soda poultice did best; but in this, as in every instance, the ease lasted but for a day or two. In despair, leeches were placed about the cicatrix, and blisters were applied over it and kept open, and also over the nerves which were tender on pressure; neither aided him.

Meanwhile the pain increased, but became limited to the palm and fingers, and lower forearm, with darting

pains up the arm. The tactility improved and the muscular tenderness lessened. The general œdema disappeared, and the atrophy was seen to be extreme, while
the finger-joints remained sore and swollen. Every motion or vibration caused pain.

October 18th.—A blister on the palm failed to draw,
but a blister on the dorsum of the hand acted well,
and gave very marked relief. It was followed by ammonia blisters on the palm and arm. These were repeated,
with, finally, cantharidal blisters. And now for the first
time the ease was complete. Incessant blisters gradually
ameliorated the pain. They were continued every few
days for two months, until every trace of burning left
him. He was so sure of the relief from this application,
that he was unwilling to allow the hand to heal before
using a new one.

December 1st.—Slight pneumonia of right lung.

December 10th.—Electricity ordered. Immediate return of pain. Ceased its use. His arm and hand were
shampooed daily, passive motion was employed, and he
began to sit up and move about.

January 6, 1864.—Careful re-examination. Arm gaining flesh. Cicatrix shrinking. Atrophy general. Worst
in the extensor group, in the forearm. Sensation good
throughout, but not quite perfect.

Voluntary movements.—Shoulder abduction, one-third;
other actions perfect. Elbow extension complete. Flexion,
by biceps alone, two-thirds. Supination affected only by
biceps. Pronation, one-third. Wrist extension and flexion
about one-sixth of usual range. Passive extension to line
of forearm, where the flexors, which are contracted, limit
the motion. Thumb everted, and flattened like that of a
monkey. Slight flexion and abduction. Muscles utterly
wasted. The finger-joints are no longer swollen, but are
excessively rigid, and have no movement.

Electric test.—Below the shoulder no muscle has any electric contractility, and the sensibility to induced currents is also diminished. Again the electricity brought on the burning, and was abandoned.

Ordered daily etherization, and the fingers to be then freely moved. Shampooing to be continued, and the douche twice a day, with occasional blisters.

January 29, 1864.—Electricity no longer renews the burning, and is to be daily employed. The gain was now rapid. Flexor power over the fingers came back, but no extension and no thumb motion.

February 23d.—Supination and pronation improving. Atrophy lessening. Ordered bandage roller to be placed in the palm, the fingers to be bound down over it, to overcome the extensors, which, within a month, have been contracting.

On April 10, 1864, he was discharged, free of pains and having only three-fourths flexion of the fingers, without power to extend them. All the other motions were improving, and the thumb muscles began to respond to the will. Sensation perfect.

The following case, which occurred recently in the practice of Dr. W. W. Keen, is a striking instance of the value of blisters in causalgia :

Case 45.— *Wound of musculo-spiral nerve.* Dr. W. W., in 1855, received a ball through the arm, which injured the triceps and biceps and the musculo-spiral nerve. The wound healed readily. The patient thus describes his condition at the present time, March, 1871: " Numbness on back of arm,—more numb on back of hand, thumb, fore and little finger. The thumb and little finger can be but slightly extended, and the latter stands off from the ring-finger and cannot be adducted. The arm motions were feeble for several years, and are not yet fully restored. Nutrition much impaired, the shoulder flattened.

Its muscles, and those of the arm, somewhat wasted, and the areolar tissue between the triceps and biceps so far lost that the finger-tips can feel the hurt nerve enlarged and tender. No other part of the nerve is sensitive. There are tremors of the anconeus and supinator longus when in action. Injuries of the arm heal slowly.

"Burning pain began soon after the wound healed, and has lasted to date. It affects the back of the arm and hand; is worse in warm weather, in daytime, and when the part hangs down. A dull ache is felt in the nerve track, on the shoulder and over the scapular spine. At times the arm and hand swell, and are then more painful. The skin of the hand is dark, glossy, and tender. Douches, shampooing, and morphia, subcutaneously, have been of the most use. The constant use of water affords some relief. Found value in tonics, but has consulted many physicians in vain."

Dr. Keen advised blisters upon the burning surfaces. Dr. W. writes, "I have tried the blisters, and desire to say that since they took effect the burning is entirely relieved. If I feel it again I shall, of course, return to them."

This interesting history of relief from causalgia after sixteen years of pain, also illustrates the tendency of neural trouble to pass towards the centres, and so to involve nerves unaffected by the primary injury.

Constitutional treatment of traumatic neuralgia. — I have found no alterative remedies which seemed to me efficient in these cases. In old neuritis or sclerosis of nerves I have followed the popular therapeutics by giving iodide of potassium, and, in rare cases, corrosive chloride of mercury; but I am not sure that they did any more effective service than by satisfying the patient to gain that time which is essential to the relief of almost all traumatic neuralgias.

Large numbers of our army cases were intensely poisoned by scurvy or malaria, or both, and in these persons the traumatic neuralgias seemed to me to be increased in severity by the general lowering of tone, and to react on the system with exaggerated power. In many cases it was only necessary to treat successfully the scurvy or ague in order to see very speedily diminish the pain which seemed to be due to the wound alone.

The malarious element, even more than the scorbutic, appeared to foster neuralgia; but the presence of any cause tending to lower the standard of health was sure to make this affection doubly unmanageable.

As regards the presence of ague in neuralgic cases of traumatic origin, it is to be remembered that the latter disease is sometimes most distinctly periodical, but is not made so by the most severe ague poisoning in a case with no original tendency to recur at a fixed hour. I saw at the Filbert Street Hospital a very instructive case of traumatic neuralgia, in which the pain returned daily between 4 and 5 P.M., the cause having been a gunshot injury of the crural nerve. After being some time in the wards, the patient was seized with a morning quotidian ague, which yielded easily to quinine, although the most liberal use of this drug and of arsenic failed to disturb the regular recurrence of the evening neuralgia.

The malarial element, when present, is only an additional cause of enfeeblement, and just to this extent serves to make more severe and lasting the recurrent neuralgia. In a word, there is apt to be, in any traumatic neural pain, a tendency to periodicity which seems to be a part of the natural history of such cases.

Quinine in the largest doses exercised, as a rule, no certain control over traumatic neuralgia; and the same may be said of arsenic, which, in functional neuralgias, has so good a reputation.

It is needless to dwell further upon the indications in ague or scorbutic cases, but it should be clearly understood that, in every case, lowered tone is to be regarded as a serious obstacle to success in the treatment of these patients. We should always bear in mind that pain itself slowly but surely assaults the nutritive functions, and that it may be necessary to aid the system by iron, cod-liver oil, extracts of malt, and change of air.

CHAPTER XII.

Neurotomy.—When every other means of relieving pain has been exhausted, the very grave question of the propriety of nerve section arises. As regards the simpler cases of lancet wounds and the like, requiring division of superficial filaments, nothing more need be added; but when the nerve to be divided is a great trunk, more serious considerations present themselves. In deciding for an operation, we are, of course, influenced by the extent and duration of the pain and by the fact that cases of common, aching, traumatic neuralgia depend very often on morbid nerve states, which, unless checked, gradually but surely extend up the nerve, and may thus get beyond the reach of the knife, and so make permanent the tortures they occasion. On the other hand, causalgia, in my experience, gets well in time; nor should we forget that in severing a great nerve we are probably condemning certain parts to perpetual functional idleness; yet the earlier the operation the lower down it may be done, and the less will be, therefore, the loss of motion and sensation.

When, after due regard to these points, an operation is decided upon, it becomes requisite to determine at what point it shall be done. To settle this, the limb concerned should be inspected with extreme accuracy, to learn what regions of skin or tissue seem to be painful, because it is essential to cut the nerve above all the pain-yielding branches.

(282)

Next the nerve should be examined with the utmost care, in order to ascertain how far up it is hardened and enlarged. The examination in these cases is far more easy than might be supposed, because in many instances, owing to muscular wasting, the nerve trunks can be readily felt. By rolling or compressing the diseased nerve under the finger-tips, an attentive observer can very often learn whether or not it has undergone inflammatory or sclerotic change.

It is, as a rule, desirable that the section should be made a short distance above the point at which the nerve ceases to feel enlarged and hard. If it be practicable to find even a little farther up the limb a spot where the nerve is neither swollen nor tender upon pressure, the operation should be done at that point. Usually, however, nerves long diseased are sensitive up to and into their parent plexus, so that in practice the surgeon must content himself with a division some distance above the point where the nerve is obviously diseased. When it lies too deep for examination, it will be safest to operate high up in the limb, and, indeed, as a rule, the older the neuralgia, if of traumatic origin, the wiser it is to divide the offending nerve as near to the body as possible.

The necessity for making section of the nerve at a point where its tissues are sound, arises out of the fact, so often insisted upon in these pages, that subacute neuritis and sclerosis inevitably travel inward along the nerve attacked, and that if above the line of division the surgeon should leave any considerable amount of diseased tissue, his operation may be useless, and the morbid change continue to ascend the nerve, inflicting new tortures, and perhaps calling for further operative interference. The popular medical view attributes the return of pain after neurotomy to a reunion of the nerve ends;

but unless there should be at the same time some return
of the normal function of the divided trunk, it is more in
accordance with the observed facts to believe that renewed
pain, after section or exsection, is most often due to the
presence or to the gradual increase in the central end of
a nerve of the same disease which necessitated an operation. In other words, the section should have been made
higher up the nerve.

Where the neuralgic cause is purely local, and the
trunk unaltered by sequent changes, the operation ought
of course to be done at the lowest point possible, and will
then offer the best chance of success.

The operative procedure must vary with the nerve,
but there are certain indications to be fulfilled in every
instance. If, when the nerve has been fully exposed, it
should prove to be hard, red, and congested, the track
should be followed upward, or a new incision made above,
until a healthy point has been found.

Simple division of the nerve is at present scarcely ever
practiced. Not less than two inches of its length ought
to be removed, our object being to make reunion impossible, or at least very remote in point of time. It has been
advised to cauterize the cut ends, but a more sensible plan
is that of Malgaigne, who counsels us to double the nerve
ends on themselves,—a measure which I should think
very unwise as regards the central end, while I see no
reason why the peripheral extremity should not be thus
reverted, and, if necessary, secured by a removable loop
of silver wire.

With this precaution, reunion would be out of the question, but assurance may be made doubly sure by further
following the French surgeon's advice, and interposing a
piece of muscle or fascia.

Such precautions are not vain, since even where two
inches of nerve have been cut out, function has returned,

and neuralgia also; and although, for reasons already stated, neither the return of sense nor of pain is in all cases conclusive as to the reunion of the nerve ends, it were wise to take every precaution against this occurrence.

It is desirable also to make, at the time of operation, a rapid microscopic examination of the portion of nerve removed, because only the microscope is fully competent to decide whether or not we have reached the region of normal nerve tissue, and until this is done we can possess no certainty that the operation will prove successful.

On pages 288–291 will be found the statistics of these operations, but a careful study of the individual case and of the state of the nerve will offer far better ground for prognosis than any table of cases can ever furnish us.

Should the pain recur, it has been advised to amputate the member, and this grave step has been frequently taken, although I do not conceive that it can ever be justified except where more than one nerve is involved, or where grave injury has rendered the limb altogether useless.

We are certainly able to make neural reunion impossible, and, if so, I cannot see what advantage amputation offers which resection higher up does not also afford. Moreover, when resection has failed, this more extreme step is not always successful, as the following curious case will show :

Case 46.—A soldier had his leg crushed in a railway accident, August 1, 1862. Amputation was done August 12th, at the junction of the lower and middle third. The stump was conical, the bone bare. In 1863, after a journey, in which he was exposed to cold, he consulted Dr. Nott for intense neuralgia of the stump, which, in September, 1863, Dr. Bayless amputated without relief. In May, 1864, Dr. Nott removed the stump again, taking off an inch of bone. Portions of two large nerves were found enlarged and engorged. The pain continued, and was intolerable.

June 1st.—Dr. Nott opened the popliteal space and took out an inch of the trunk of the sciatic, and apparently about three inches of the popliteal and peroneal nerves, all of which were enlarged. No relief followed, and in May, 1865, Dr. Nott, evidently thinking there might have been reunion, and, as he justly says, with "no very good physiological reason for so doing, dissected out the two large nerve trunks completely down to the extremity of the stump." He does not say whether or not there had been reunion. Naturally, no relief ensued, and, in despair, the thigh was removed four inches above the knee, when the sciatic nerve was seen to be engorged and double its normal size. The neuralgia continued, and in August, 1865, Dr. Nott exsected the sciatic nerve at its point of pelvic exit, removing an inch and a quarter. The upper half only of this portion seemed healthy, but whether it was studied with the microscope or not we are nowhere informed. Some relief was thus obtained, but the next day the pain returned, and then, as always, was referred to the end of the existing stump, and not to the lost limb,—a rare anomaly.

Dr. Nott believes that his patient was really much eased by this final procedure, but that his craving for opium caused him to malinger.

As an illustration of the tendency of neuritis to pass centrally, of its sclerotic results, and of the need for early resection higher up the nerve, this case is most instructive.

I have stated in the accompanying table the more important particulars of twenty-three cases of exsection of portions of nerves for traumatic neuralgia, with one of simple division.

These include a variety of nerves, in five of which the

exsected portion is described as variously altered, reddened, indurated, or thickened, no statement being made as to the pathological condition of the remainder.

In two only was there no immediate relief from the operation. In four the relief was partial, or came gradually, and in the rest it was entire and immediate.

The future of these latter cases was less happy, since in five the pain returned at remote periods. As a final result, we learn that in sixteen the excisions effected lasting ease for the patient, although in several the announcement as to the cure has been made too early to leave us sure of its permanency.

In one case six excisions were practiced before relief came, and there was a relapse in eighteen months.

Dr. Morton's case was an interesting example of causalgia. Five inches of the radial nerve were removed, without any good effect, and relief was gained by amputation. In Nausick's case, excision also failed, and amputation succeeded. In the former example it is clear that the patient's statements as to the seat of pain led to a diagnostic error with regard to the nerve involved. It is difficult to see why, in these cases, amputation should be allowed to replace neurotomy.

If the statements as to loss of function and its return are to be trusted, they show how rapid, in some cases, is the recovery of function, and how incomplete is its loss in others. The general conclusion is favorable to neural resection as a means of relief in extreme cases of traumatic neuralgia. I am quite confident that if the operation were not delayed so long the percentage of recoveries would be greater. I am equally certain, that were it always done in accordance with the very obvious rules which I have here laid down, it would be far more often successful.

OPERATIONS FOR RELIEF OF

AUTHOR.	AFFECTED NERVE.	OPERATION.	CONDITION OF NERVE.
Schuh, Op. Surg., p. 922.	Inferior dental and mental.	Excision.	Not stated.
Wardrop, Med.-Chir. Tr., vol. xii. p. 206.	Digital of thumb.	Division.	"
Davies, Dublin Medical Jour., vol. xxx. p. 331. (From fracture.)	Ant. tibial and musculo-cutaneous.	Excision of one inch of popliteal.	"
Davies, Dublin Medical Jour., vol. xxx. p. 331.	Posterior tibial.	Excision of one inch.	"
"	Ulnar.	One-half inch excised.	"
Schuh, Op. Surg., 783.	Inf. orbital and inf. maxillary.	Excision of parts of both nerves.	"
Schuh, Op. Surg., 791.	Inf. max. and inf. orbital.	Excision of part of inf. max.	Inflamed sheath and altered nerve.
Schuh, Op. Surg., 791.	Inf. max. and inf. orbital.	Excision of part of inf. orbital.	Normal.
Schuh, Op. Surg., 829.	Radial.	Excision.	Not stated.
Buzzell, J. M., Med. World, vol. i. p. 10.	Int. plantar.	Excision.	Not stated.
Teevan, Lancet, 1832-33, vol. i. p. 654.	Radial.	One-half inch excised.	Highly inflamed.
Bickersteth, Ranking's Abstract, vol. li. p. 221.	Digital.	Excision.	Not stated.
"	Digital.	One-half inch excised.	"
Wormald, Med. Times, 1863, vol. i. p. 343.	Inferior dental.	Three-quarter inch excised.	"

TRAUMATIC NEURALGIA.

IMMEDIATE RESULT.	REMOTE RESULT.	REMARKS AND RESULTS AS TO FUNCTION.
Entire relief.	Return of pain at fourth month.	Not stated.
"	Pain returned at intervals, finally disappearing after twenty months.	Numbness on end of thumb.
"	Continued relief; no pain after three months.	Paralysis of extension of foot. Partial sensory palsy, which was improving.
"	Continued relief; well after two years.	Not stated.
"	Continued relief; time not stated.	Slight loss of tactile sense.
Entire relief as to inf. orbital.	Continued relief for a time; return of pain in one year.	Not stated.
Entire relief.	Pain returned in four months.	Loss of sensation, which returned in one month.
"	Pain returned in fifteen months.	Not stated.
Partial relief.	Paralysis in radial distribution.	Six excisions of this nerve were practiced. The last caused entire relief, with return of pain in eighteen months.
Entire relief.	Continued relief.	Not stated.
Entire relief after three weeks.	Unknown.	Numbness in thumb, middle and index fingers. Sensation finally restored.
Entire relief.	Continued relief.	Loss of sensation in side of finger supplied by nerve; great gain in sensation in eight days.
"	Continued relief during three weeks.	Sensation incompletely lost.
"	Continued relief dur six weeks.	

OPERATIONS FOR RELIEF OF

AUTHOR.	AFFECTED NERVE.	OPERATION.	CONDITION OF NERVE.
Morton, T. G. Unpublished.	Radial.	Five inches excised.	Not stated.
Agnew, D. H. Unpublished.	Ulnar.	Two and a half inches.	Thickened and indurated.
J. C. Warren, Boston Med J., vol. i. p. 101.	Thumb nerves.	Division.	Not stated.
"	Peroneal.	Excision.	"
"	Inf. plantar.	Excision of one inch.	"
Carnochan, Am. Med. Monthly, vol. vi. p. 141.	Sup. maxillary.	One and a half inches excised.	Inflamed and indurated.
J. F. Miner, Buffalo Med. Jour., vol. vii. p. 427.	Median.	Three inches excised.	Not stated.
Gauelson, Med. and Surg. Rep., vol. xx. p. 293.	Ant. tibial.	One inch excised.	Not stated.
Nausick, New York Med. J., vol. ii. p. 174.	Median and int. cutaneous.	Three-quarter inch excision of both.	Neurilemma reddened.
W. Callender, St. Bartholomew's Hosp. Repts., 1870, p. 39. Comp'd fracture.	Median.	Exsection, one-quarter inch.	"

TRAUMATIC NEURALGIA.

IMMEDIATE RESULT.	REMOTE RESULT.	REMARKS AND RESULTS AS TO FUNCTION.
No relief.	No relief.	Amputation a few days later with entire relief. The ulnar was found to have been injured by the ball.
Entire relief.	Entire relief.	Loss of ulnar function, but nearly complete restoration in eighteen months.
Gradual relief.	No return in five years.	Not stated.
But little relief.	Little relief.	"
Total relief.	No return.	"
Entire relief	?	"
Entire relief.	No return.	Paralysis of extensors and loss of sensation of back of fore-arm.
Entire relief.	No return in three months.	Paralysis of motion in foot; return of power in a few days. (Sic.)
No relief.	No relief.	Sense of touch lost; hand felt dull and heavy. Amputation at line of upper and middle thirds. Entire relief.
Entire relief.	Continued relief.	Not stated.

I add, as examples, a history of amputation for causalgia, by Dr. T. G. Morton, the case of Corliss,* referred to on p. 202, a very interesting instance of exsection by Dr. D. Hayes Agnew, for which I have to thank Dr. W. W. Keen, who has more recently attended the man, and lastly, a remarkable case of bold and successful surgery by Dr. J. L. Stewart, of Erie.

Case 47.—Injury of median and ulnar nerves by a bullet; loss of motion; excessive causalgia; exsection of four inches of median nerve; no relief. Jos. H. Corliss, late private Company B, 14th New York State Militia, aged twenty-seven, shingle-dresser, enlisted April, 1861, in good health. At the second battle of Bull Run, August 29, 1862, he was shot in the left arm, three inches directly above the internal condyle. The ball emerged one and a quarter inches higher, through the belly of the biceps, without touching the artery, but with injury to the median and ulnar nerves. He was ramming a cartridge when hit, and " thought he was struck on the crazy-bone by some of the boys for a joke." The fingers of both hands flexed and grasped the ramrod and gun tightly. Bringing the right hand, still clutching the ramrod, to the left elbow, he felt the blood, and knew he was wounded. He then shook the ramrod from his grasp with a strong effort, and unloosened with the freed hand the tight grip of the left hand on the gun. After walking some twenty paces he fell from loss of blood, but still conscious; attempted to walk several times, and as often failed. He was finally helped to the rear, taken prisoner, lay three days on the field without food, but with enough of water to drink, and had his wounds dressed for the first time on the fourth day, at Fairfax Court House.

On the second day the pain began. It was burning and darting. He states that at this time sensation was lost or lessened in the limb, and that paralysis of motion

---

* Mitchell, Morehouse, and Keen, op. cit.

came on in the hand and forearm. Admitted to the Douglas Hospital, Washington, D. C., September 7, 1862. The
pain was so severe that a touch anywhere, or shaking the
bed, or a heavy step, caused it to increase. The suffering
was in the median and ulnar distribution, especially at the
palmar face of the knuckles and the ball of the thumb.
Motion has varied little since the wound, and as to sensation he is not clear.

Peter Pineo, surgeon, U. S. V., Medical Inspector
U. S. A., opened the wound and exsected two or three
inches of the median nerve. The man states, very positively, that the pain in the median distribution did not
cease, nor perceptibly lessen, but that he became more
sensitive, so that even the rattling of a paper caused
extreme suffering. He "thinks he was not himself" for
a day or two after the operation. It seems quite certain
that the pain afterwards gradually moderated, both in
the ulnar and the median tracts. Meanwhile the hand
lay over his chest, and the fingers, flexing, became stiffened
in this position.

About a week after he was shot, the *right* arm grew
weak, and finally so feeble that he could not feed himself.
He can now (April, 1864) use it pretty well, but it is mani-
festly less strong than the other. The left leg also was
weakened, but when this loss of power first showed itself
he cannot tell. He gives the usual account of the pain,
and of the use of water on the hands and in his boots, as
a means of easing it.

Present condition, April 21, 1864. — Wound healed.
Cicatrix of the operation two and a half inches long over
median nerve. The forearm muscles do not seem to be
greatly wasted. The interosseal muscles and hypothenar
group are much atrophied, and the hand is thin and bony.
The thenar muscles are partially wasted.

The skin of the palm is eczematous, thin, red, and

shining. The second and third phalanges of the fingers
are flexed and stiff; the first is extended. Nails extraor-
dinarily curved, laterally and longitudinally, except that
of the thumb.

Pain is stated to exist still in the median distribution,
but much less than in the ulnar tract, where it is excessively great.

He keeps his hand wrapped in a rag, wetted with cold
water, and covered with oiled silk, and even tucks the rag
carefully under the flexed finger-tips. Moisture is more
essential than cold. Friction outside of the clothes, at
any point of the entire surface, "shoots" into the hand,
increasing the burning in the median, sometimes, and
more commonly, in the ulnar distribution. Deep pressure
on the muscles has a like effect, and he will allow no one to
touch his skin, save with a wetted hand, and even then is
careful to exact tender manipulation. He keeps a bottle
of water about him, and carries a wet sponge in the right
hand. This hand he wets always before he handles anything; used dry, it hurts the other limb. At one time,
when the suffering was severe, he poured water into his
boots, he says, to lessen the pain which dry touch or friction causes in the injured hand. So cautious was he
about exposing the sore hand, that it was impossible thoroughly to examine it; but it was clear to us that there
was sensibility to touch in the ultimate median distribution, although he describes sensation as somewhat lessened in this region, and states that he has numbness on
the inner side of the palm, and in the third and fourth
fingers (ulnar tract). When the balls of the first and
second fingers were touched, he said he felt it; but, on
touching those of the third and fourth fingers, he refused
to permit us to experiment further, and insisted on wrap-
ping up and wetting the hand. He thus describes the
pain at its height: "It is as if a rough bar of iron were

thrust to and fro through the knuckles, a red-hot iron placed at the junction of the palm and thenar eminence, with a heavy weight on it, and the skin was being rasped off my finger-ends."

Case 48.—*Bullet wound of forearm ; causalgia ; relief by amputation.* Corporal I. D., admitted for gunshot wound of arm, received some days before. A minié-ball entered near the middle third of forearm while it was in a flexed position, producing a considerable flesh wound, and splintering off a fragment of the border of the radius. Passing across the forearm, it also struck the arm some distance above the elbow, inflicting a slight wound. Both wounds were open, and there were two inconsiderable hemorrhages from muscular branches in the upper wound.

The patient suffered with most extensive causalgia, locating the pain principally along the radial site of the forearm and hand. The tissues of the entire arm and hand became shrunken and shriveled.

Despite all local and constitutional treatment, including hypodermic injections of morphia sulph., very little relief could be obtained. He was unwilling to submit to amputation, which, it was feared, must eventually be done. Dr. Morton made an incision through the cicatrix in the region of the radial nerve, and removed four or five inches of the nerve. With the exception of slight contraction of the diameter of the nerve, in the vicinity of the wound, no other abnormal change was perceptible. Very little relief followed the operation. A few days after, the patient being now very anxious for the operation, the member was amputated ; and, upon dissection, it was found that the ulnar nerve was injured in the track of the wound. Entire relief followed the operation, and is said to have been lasting.

Case 49.—*Repeated fractures of the humerus ; one involving the ulnar nerve ; anchylosis of the shoulder and elbow ; ex-*

section of the ulnar nerve to the extent of two and one-half inches; recovery of motion almost perfect, of sensation very great; entire relief from pain. Charles Kelly, aged forty, examined February 13, 1869. At ten years of age, he fractured his right humerus, and since then it has been broken several times,—once with a firehorn, once with a brick, once purposely broken across his leg by a surgeon, once by a fall in a boat, etc. He is unable to specify the particular points of fracture or their number. After the first one, his elbow became anchylosed at a right angle, and subsequently to several of the fractures, he had frequent abscesses. In 1850, four inches of the humerus were resected after one of his fractures.

In 1861, he broke his arm for the last time, but at what point he cannot say,—a simple fracture. He fell into a boat, five or six feet, and struck on his elbow, probably breaking off the internal condyle. He felt the shock in the "funny-bone" at the time. It was followed by repeated abscesses, extending not only around the elbow, but also about the shoulder-joint and arm, and resulting in the discharge of various pieces of bone. The pain in the ulnar nerve at the elbow was only temporary, but repeated abscesses kept him at intervals for six years under the doctor's care.

In August, 1868, pain returned violently in the ulnar nerve at the seat of fracture, shooting into the hand, its exact locality not being now definable. It was a burning pain, and like "running a jagged piece of wood into the hand." The fingers twitched and shook violently. The pain was so severe that at each shoot "he jumped all over." He could not sleep, and finally suffered so much that he demanded amputation of the arm of several surgeons, but was refused.

Dr. D. Hayes Agnew removed two and one-half inches of the ulnar nerve, just above the elbow-joint, in September, 1868. He lost but a few hours from his business after the operation, and no time during recovery. Since then he "has never known a second's pain." For two months afterwards he had no sensation in the ulnar distribution, as he has repeatedly proved by sticking needles into it. To relieve it, he began to wear, a week after the operation, a rough glove filled with hair, the pricking of which during movements of the hand usefully irritated the integuments. In about two months sensation had begun to improve, and in three months his power to feel was as good as now. Motion began to return at the knuckles within a week, and gradually improved, till in three months it was perfectly restored. He took no medicine, and had not the use of the battery.

Present condition, February 13, 1869.—Right arm, ten and a half inches from acromion to head of radius; left arm, eleven and a half inches from acromion to head of radius; on right arm, ten cicatrices from abscesses, one of them four and a half inches long, on the outer border of the biceps, where the large piece of bone was removed; head of humerus nearly completely anchylosed to the glenoid cavity, but can be moved slightly in all directions; elbow-joint anchylosed firmly at a right angle; external and internal condyles both gone, and cicatrices over each. Over the internal condyle, and extending upward in the course of the ulnar nerve, is the incision made for its removal. The radius has three-quarters its natural rotation. The muscles are much wasted in the arm and forearm. What is left of the deltoid and biceps, say one-third, is active; the biceps acting only as a supinator. The muscles in the forearm are wasted: right forearm, three inches below olecranon, nine inches; left forearm, three inches below olecranon, ten and a half inches. He has every movement of all the joints of the fingers, and every movement is perfect in extent, but he has lost about one-

fifth or one-sixth in power. Sensation, save the softest
touches, was well recognized as to locality. As estimated
by the æsthesiometer, it is very defective, but cannot be
measured accurately, owing to want of intelligence in the
patient.

Electro-muscular sensibility lessened, probably one-
third. Electro-muscular irritability is not lost in any
muscle of the whole extremity, nor diminished, save one-
sixth in the last two ulnar interossei of the right hand and
the hypothenar muscles. His hand is normal in appearance, except that from absence of use it is more delicate
and smoother than is natural. The hypothenar muscles
are one-fifth wasted, and the nails are quite clubbed. He
has lost very much in general weight of body, and is not
so robust as before his last fracture. His memory, in
some points, is not exact, nor is it so retentive as it used
to be.

The following case I quote without change from Dr.
J. L. Stewart's printed account:

*Case 50.—Bullet injury of the median nerve ; causalgia ;
excision of three inches of the median nerve ; entire relief.*
"A. F. Swann, aged thirty-four, a native of Pennsylvania,
a stout, robust man, and then captain of C Company, 16th
Pennsylvania Cavalry, was wounded by a minié-ball at
the battle of Cold Harbor, Virginia, May 28, 1864. The
ball, fired at about ten rods distance, entered the left forearm two inches below the head of the radius, and passing
obliquely across the elbow-joint, made its exit just above
the inner condyle of the humerus. From the moment he
was struck he suffered the most intense pain in the arm
and hand, and lost a large quantity of blood.

"The wound was dressed on the field, and healed
kindly. The patient came home to Erie 'on leave' soon
after, and remained until the end of June, when, there being
no improvement in his case, he returned to Washington,

and applied to Surgeon Bliss, U. S. V., then in charge of Armory Square Hospital, for relief. He was directed to use the electrical bath, which he did for four or five days without any apparent effect. The pain at this time was constant and excruciating, and confined chiefly to the palm of the hand; while the sensation was as if grasping a ball of red-hot iron. He demanded an operation, which was performed by Surgeon Bliss (about July 5, 1864), who cut down through the wound of exit, and (*so the patient was told*) removed three inches of the median nerve.

"For two days after the operation the pain was very *slightly* less, but when the wound began to heal assumed its former intensity.

"Mr. Swann had commenced the use of morphia hypodermically, about two weeks before this operation, and resumed it two days afterwards. From the first it required from three to five grains a day to relieve pain, and he continued to increase the quantity gradually up to the time of the second operation, until he very generally injected *ten* grains a day, and has used as much as *one drachm* in *three days*. Both arms are covered with the punctures of the syringe, discolored, and the cellular tissue indurated.

"Mr. Swann consulted me in June, 1865, when I advised another operation; but he did not submit to it on account of being told by several physicians here and elsewhere, whom he consulted, that it would be unsuccessful. He again came under my care in June, 1870, six years after the receipt of the wound. His condition was most deplorable, the pain in the hand, which was intensified by any excitement, was indescribable, and he was unable to attend to any active duties, except while under the influence of morphia.

"He suffered from irregular nervous chills of two or three hours' duration, when he would be obliged, in the heat of midsummer, to lie by a hot stove with four or five blankets over him; the cold perspiration, meanwhile, streaming from him. His appetite was nearly gone; his bowels were habitually constipated; and the whole man was emaciated, feeble, and fretful. He was willing to undergo any operation which promised relief, even amputation of the arm.

"June 27, 1870.—Assisted by my friend, Surgeon Woolverton, United States Navy, I proceeded to etherize the patient, which was accomplished with great trouble and difficulty. Fourteen ounces of ether were used, and an hour passed, the patient struggling violently and under great excitement, before the muscles relaxed and he became quiet.

"An incision was made in the forearm, between the flexor carpi radialis and the palmaris longus muscles, three and one-half inches in length, terminating two inches above the wrist-joint; and three inches of the median nerve were removed. There was considerable venous hemorrhage after the operation, which ceased on the application of ice. The wound was closed by sutures and adhesive strips, and water-dressing applied.

"As soon as patient passed from under the influence of the ether, he declared that 'the pain in the hand had left him.' He slept three or four hours the first night under the influence of immense doses of bromide of potassium. He never used any opiate after the operation, and insists that he scarcely slept an hour for fourteen days, and had not a sound night's sleep for twenty-six days after it; but his appetite returned at once, and he was in exuberant spirits at his freedom from pain. During the first four days after the operation chloral hydrate in drachm doses, and hyoscyamus, Cannabis Indica, etc., in heroic doses, failed to produce sleep, when I sent him to a quiet country home, and directed the free use of ale, with a generous diet. No medicine of any kind was afterwards necessary.

"There was no return of the chills after the operation, but he was much annoyed by a peculiar feeling of the surface, which he described as 'craving of his skin for morphine,' with burning of the feet; but these gradually passed away until he experienced no unpleasant or unnatural sensations. He has not suffered a moment's pain in the hand or arm since the operation, now seven months past, and has gained forty pounds in weight, and is, in his own language, 'in perfect health without pain or ache.' He has good use of the small and ring fingers, and the paralyzed parts are well nourished.

"The operation was undertaken under the belief that there still remained near the original wound some injured portion of the nerve, and that relief might be given by severing its connection with the seat of pain, as the result has happily proved.

"What seem to me to be the important points in this case are—first, the unceasing and great severity of the pain, from the moment of receiving the wound until I severed the nerve; second, the entire freedom from pain since the operation; third, the vast amount of morphine used by the patient, estimated by him to amount to from two hundred and fifty to three hundred drachms, requiring the use of the syringe from six to twenty times every day for six years and some days; fourth, the rapidity with which he recovered from the effects of this long-continued and excessive use of morphine, suffering *no* inconvenience from its omission, in a few weeks after the operation; fifth, the fact that the operation was undertaken in opposition to the freely-expressed opinion of *all* the medical gentlemen here and elsewhere who had been consulted, after the failure of Dr. Bliss's operation."

The following cases have been selected from my notes,

or from our former essays, as illustrating the chief phenomena of nerve wounds and the modes of treatment. Some of the cases are incomplete, owing to causes which I could not control:

Case 51.—*Gunshot wound of axillary nerves; paralysis of motion; slight loss of sensation; burning on tenth day; great atrophy and contracted muscles; subluxation of fingers; nutritive changes; eczema in both palms; great improvement; discharged ;* re-examined four years later.* David Schiveley, aged seventeen, no trade, Pennsylvania, enlisted August, 1862, in Company E, 114th Pennsylvania Volunteers. Healthy before and after enlisting, except a slight attack of typhoid fever.

At Gettysburg, July 2, 1863, while aiming, a ball entered one inch to the left of the middle line, and one inch above the sternal end of the clavicle. Exit on the posterior part of the right arm, at the middle line, two inches below the axilla. The ball passed in front of the trachea, broke the inner half of the right clavicle, went in front of the vessels of the neck and the subclavian artery, in front of the axillary artery, and below the humerus,—speaking of that bone as raised and abducted at the time. When hit, he thought his arm was shot off. It dropped, the gun fell, and, screaming that he was murdered, he staggered, bleeding freely, and soon fell unconscious. When a little later he revived and raised his head, a second ball struck him in the right temporal fossa, and emerged through the right eye. He jumped up, ran a little way, and fell once more. When hit, he lost all motion in the limb, which became numbed, but felt no pain. Two weeks later, feeble power to move returned gradually in the elbow, shoulder, and arm, and after two months in the wrist and hand.

---

* Gunshot Wounds and Injuries of Nerves.

Treatment.—Cold-water dressings and means to relieve burning, but all ineffectual. The joints became swollen early, and the arm bent at a right angle. The hand, dependent, lay across his chest during a long period. He made some attempts at passive motion as he found the hand becoming stiff, but no great good was thus gained; and, as the contractions took place and the joints grew worse, the wrist became moulded to the curve of the chest, on which it lay.

About the tenth day, burning pain began in the palm and fingers, especially in the cushions of the fingers and the knuckles. It was at its worst a month later, and remained thus another month, after which it grew less. When at its height, he suffered from loud sounds, vibrations, and dry contact. The rubbing of his boots on the floor was the greatest annoyance, and this he relieved by wetting his stockings. Since October, four months after he was wounded, it has been unaltered. Sensation, little affected at the outset, has undergone no change of moment. Voluntary motion, which grew better for awhile, suffered anew and increasingly as the nutritive changes developed themselves. When they first arose we have been unable to determine.

Present state, December 17, 1863. *Nutrition.* — The wounded arm is shrunken, generally with well-marked atrophy of the supra- and infra-spinatus, deltoid, and biceps, the loss in the last two being fully one-half. Triceps, no wasting of moment. Supinator longus and radial extensors, two-thirds loss. Flexors and extensors in forearm, one-half loss. Thumb muscles almost absent. Little finger and interosseal group, no loss.

Contractions.—The flexor carpi ulnaris, palmaris longus, and flexor carpi radialis being strongly contracted, the wrist is bent at a right angle to the arm and drawn to the ulnar side; the extensor group is in like manner contracted, and the first phalanges, having thus been violently extended while the wrist was flexed, have undergone subluxation.

The color of the back of the arm and hand is natural as far as the knuckles. Thence to the finger-tips the skin is tense, shining, hairless, mottled red and blue, abraded in spots; the nails curved, and the joints swollen and very tender. Palmar surface normal to wrist. The whole palmar face of the hand and fingers is polished, deep scarlet, abraded in points, and eczematous all over to a remarkable degree. The eruption followed the burning in about six weeks. The palm of the left hand is nearly equally eczematous. If his account may be trusted, it began to be so nearly a month before any eczema appeared in the wounded member. There is slight soreness on pressure in the infra-spinatus, biceps, and flexors of the fingers.

Voluntary motion.—Entire in the shoulder, though weak. The elbow possesses the middle third of its normal range of motion, but cannot be fully flexed or extended. The wrist, lying at a right angle to the arm, has only about forty-five degrees of extension. The thumb, nearly fixed in adduction, has slight and very feeble motion in all its joints. The fingers, bent back in extension, can be flexed to make a straight line with the dorsum of the hand. The flexors move the second and third phalanges through one-fourth of their usual range. They perform abduction and adduction well.

Sensibility.—Tactility nearly normal. Localization of touch not quite perfect on the radial distribution in the hand.

Pain.—The burning in the right hand is intense and constant. It is made worse by heat, exposure, drying of the skin, and dependent positions. He has kept it wet and wrapped up since October, 1863, which we believed might have made the skin troubles worse, until we saw this and other cases improve under treatment without any cessation in the application of the water. The left hand, which, it will be remembered, was also eczematous, is painful on pressure or touch, especially in the palm. He is positive that there is pain in that hand, and that it is a burning pain. Both hands are kept covered with loose cotton gloves, which he wets at brief intervals. He is especially fearful of having the right hand touched, and is nervous and hysterical to such a degree that his relatives suppose him to be partially insane. It is difficult even to examine him properly on account of his timidity, and his whole appearance exhibits the effects of pain, want of rest, and defective hæmatosis. His treatment was constitutional and local. It answered admirably so far as gain in health and loss of pain were concerned. The after-means employed to cure the deformities and restore motion were partially successful.

Remarks.—The electric tests satisfied us that in time the muscles could be restored, and assured us that the nerve communications were entire. The sensibility was slightly imperfect. Motion, though feeble from atrophy in some parts, was present in every group of muscles. It was limited by the contracted muscles and by the nutritive lesions in the joints. These two combined have damaged the power of movement, and left worse effects than usually result from partial paralysis affecting directly the motor nerves. Had proper passive motion been early used, there can be little doubt that the hand would now be far better than it is.

January 25, 1867.—Health and strength very good; is attending the hospital school. Eyesight in right eye lost, of course; the lids are now constantly in contact, and do not look as unseemly as before; they can be somewhat separated, showing the shrunken ball, the sclerotic only being visible.

Motion.—Perfect as to range in shoulder and elbow; would be perfect in wrist, but is limited to three-eighths range by contraction of flexors. Power is somewhat diminished. Thumb perfect, but lies adducted. He can abduct it well. It is also everted so as to form the "monkey-hand." The first phalanges are constantly at an angle of forty-five degrees in extension. They can be extended to ninety degrees voluntarily, and flexed to a line with dorsum of hand. The second phalanges have about the middle third of their range of motion, but not much force. The third phalanges cannot be moved voluntarily, but can be moved passively well. The joints appear to be normal, save the subluxation of the knuckles. Abduction and adduction good.

Sensation.—Improved.

Contractions.—The flexors are contracted so as to limit extension of wrist; the extensors are not, I think, contracted, but by the constant flexion of the wrist at ninety degrees they extend the fingers as above.

Pain.—In August, 1864, he began to lose the violent pain. It was not gradual, but one day he noticed suddenly that his glove was dry, and yet he could use his hand well and without pain. It was not entirely gone, and he continued to wet his hand for some months; but it grew much better. Even now he feels dry rubbing in the palm of the hand and down to the finger-tips, and a loud noise, such as a wagon making a great noise in passing, or a sudden emotion, as seeing a person fall, etc., makes the same impression. In the left hand there is no pain.

Appearance of hands.—Left hand perfectly normal. The eczema he is pretty sure passed away before he ceased wetting the hand. Right hand: color normal; no eczema. It continued longer than on the left hand, but also disappeared before he ceased wetting it. It sweats a great deal;

gets cold very easily; has no constant pain in it. The hair has been reproduced on the back of the hand, even to that of the fingers. Nails normal. Second and third phalanges a good deal wasted. Muscles of thumb a good deal wasted (say two-thirds), except flexor brevis, which is of nearly normal size.

Nutrition.—Right biceps, eight and five-eighths inches; left, nine and one-eighth. Right forearm, three inches below olecranon, eight and five-eighths inches; left, nine and one-quarter.

His nervousness is entirely gone, and he is perfectly well mentally.

Electro-muscular sensibility is greater in right than in left arm throughout. Electro-muscular contractility very markedly diminished in right arm from shoulder down to hand. It is not more than one-half. He can use his hand so as to handle a fork. Could use a knife, but was always left-handed; holds a book well; cannot write; can touch every finger-tip with thumb.

The temperature, taken April 20, 1867, was as follows: fold between palm and thenar eminence the only place where the thermometer-bulb could be held and covered equally well by either hand. Right, paralyzed side, $97\frac{1}{2}°$ Fahr.; left, sound side, $97\frac{1}{8}°$ Fahr.

Case 52.—*Gunshot wound of right wrist; sensation entire; loss of flexor power and general motor loss from long rest on splint, adhesions, and want of proper treatment; great gain.* T. M., aged seventeen, no trade, 121st Pennsylvania Volunteers. July 1, 1863, a ball entered the right wrist, three and a half inches above the styloid process of the radius, and made exit one inch above styloid process of ulna, breaking both bones, but injuring no large vessel. The arm was on a splint for six weeks without change or passive motion, during which time many fragments of bone escaped. When admitted, the wrist was thickened by callus. The extensor tendons were tied fast by adhesions; the hand a little swollen. The fingers were rigid, the thumb level with the palm and everted, its nail looking upward, — effects chiefly of the splint. The wound of entry was open. Sensation normal: the callus had destroyed pronation and supination and wrist movements. The fingers were bound by the fixed extensor tendons, so that they merely stirred in flexion. The thumb had all motions save only flexion, which was feeble. The interosseal motions were not lost, but limited by the flexing of the digits. Every motion or effort at motion caused tremor.

The condition of the flexors seemed difficult to explain. They were extremely feeble, without their nerves having suffered by the wound. On faradisation, all the muscles responded, and, at the third sitting, they acted freely, so that the muscles could only have been suffering from long inertia and pressure. A rapid cure resulted. This case is a fair example of the mischief which too long use of the splint may occasion. It was sent to us as a case of neural injury.

Case 53.—*Gunshot wound of left popliteal space; injury of sciatic nerve; palsy of extensors; loss of sensation; causalgia; gradual recovery; nutritive phenomena; probably cicatrix pressure; recovery.* H. M., 26th Pennsylvania Volunteers, shot May 3, 1863, from without inward, through the left popliteal space, above the joint, between the tendon of the biceps and the head of the femur. At its exit the ball touched the posterior border of the inner hamstring tendon.

The wound healed in four weeks. When hit he had great pain down the leg, and at once lost all power and all feeling, probably from local contusion or "shock." Since about June 7th, both feeling and motor power began to improve. On admission, June 18, 1863, motion was good throughout, that is, complete, but feeble. Sensation was nowhere absent, so that the gain must have been remarkable.

Ever since the wound began to heal he has had great and increasing pain and numbness in the foot. These feelings seem to arise just above the wound, and to run down to the toes. The pain is darting, pricking, and in the foot burning, with redness and œdema, which are made worse by heat, dependence of foot, etc. There are slight eczematous patches on the foot; the scar is hard, and when pressed upon causes pain down the leg. Bending the leg at the knee and turning it inward, relieves the pain, which seems to have some relation to the cicatrix. There are no notable trophic changes, the calves differing by only the fourth of an inch.

This condition was treated by frequent passive movements, by kneading the scar, by hot and cold douches, and finally by faradisation, to improve the enfeebled muscles. Under these means the pain ceased, and he improved so as to be able to go on guard duty, October 29, 1863.

Case 54.— Wound of right sciatic nerve; paralysis of extensors of foot; partial paralysis of flexors of foot and toes; incomplete anæsthesia of foot; slight analgesia; intense causalgia; twitching of the toes. Peter C. K., Pennsylvania, aged twenty-four, enlisted August, 1861, Company D, 48th Pennsylvania Volunteers; health good. August 29, 1862, he was shot through the right thigh a little above its middle. The ball went behind the femur, passing from without inward, and probably wounding the sciatic nerve. He felt a sudden intense pain and numbness of the foot, and leaped in the air. He hopped to a shelter, was taken to the rear, had his wounds dressed, and was then left on the field, where he says he lay seven days without food, but with enough of water. He was then exchanged. The foot swelled within a week, and began to burn on top of the instep and toes. At first he had no power to extend the foot or toes, but could slightly flex them. The wound healed in a month, and at George-town Hospital he got on crutches,—the limb improving. In February, 1863, he could walk with a cane, and at this time the œdema disappeared. In the third week after the wounding, the toes began to twitch in a curious manner, moving laterally. This symptom still exists, although to a less degree. He thinks that touch and pain were totally lost in the foot at first, but admits that he might not have noted the sides of the foot near the mal-leoli as being normal,—if they were so then,—as they certainly were when he was admitted to our own wards, June 15, 1863. The foot is still somewhat swollen, and is worse in hot weather, when in bed, or when the limb hangs down ; cold, exercise, and water, whether cold or not, ease the intense burning pain. The foot and leg are scarred remarkably by repeated crops of papules, which break out every two weeks with unendurable itching, and then fade away, always leaving the foot much better for a time. When admitted, the muscular motions remained, as above described, and he could stand a moment on the leg, the calf of which measured two inches less than the other.

The track of the internal saphena nerve is alone fully sensitive to touch,—elsewhere it is deficient. The flexors of the foot and toes respond well to the current of Du-chenne's large coil,—the extensors have lost electro-mus-cular contractility and sensibility.

Treatment. June 15th.—Faradisation of extensors was practiced daily, and thorough rubbing of the weakened limb twice a day. The causalgia and congestion were treated by coating the foot with collodion, and hot and cold douches were used alternately to stimulate the en-feebled vessels.

June 20th.—The extensors now respond to the currents; the burning is lessened.

August 7th.—A period of great heat has increased the burning. Conium in olive oil was used by friction, but gave no relief; nor was any impermeable dressing of value, except a cover of oiled silk, with a well-applied bandage.

October 29th.—He has every motion of the limb; the burning is slight. He left the hospital on furlough, and returned November 20th, with the burning worse, and the sensibility still unaltered. Blisters by ammonia to the sole at length diminished the burning pain, and their repetition gave still greater relief.

December 1st.—Transferred to the West, greatly improved; said to have become much worse as to burning when the blistering was abandoned.

Case 55.—Gunshot wound of arm; nerve lesions; loss of motion and slight loss of sensation; relapse from neuritis, with contraction of flexors and " claw-hand;" recovery. T. B. W., aged seventeen, Pennsylvania, bronzer, 29th Pennsylvania Volunteers. Sickly before enlistment, and has scars of scrofulous ulcers on the legs. Has had bronchitis severely, but was better since enlisting. July 2d, at Gettysburg, while erect and aiming, was wounded by a ball, which entered the middle arm, behind the brachial artery, three-fourths of an inch below the uppermost part of the axillary hollow. The wound of exit was on a line drawn directly upward in the axis of the limb, half-way between the olecranon and internal condyle, six and a quarter inches above the latter. The scars are small. After falling he received a chest wound over the third rib above the left nipple, the ball emerging in the axilla one inch behind the tendon of the pectoralis major muscle, half an inch below apex of axilla. When first hit, he felt a knifelike pang in the wound, and, laying his gun down, he stuffed the freely-bleeding axilla with a handkerchief. The blood shot out in jets, and he soon fell senseless, remaining unconscious two hours. Within an hour the wound was dressed with water, the hemorrhage having ceased. No splint was used at any time. On examining the part after it was dressed, he found it absolutely motionless, even to the finger-ends. Next day he could move the digits a little, and more easily in a week. As to sensation, he is not certain. He thinks it was impaired for a long while on the outside of the arm and on the back of the forearm. July 8th, was sent to Baltimore, and thence to Philadelphia. He was then greatly exhausted, and on the afternoon of the 8th he began to have pain in the wound and down the forearm, with hyperæsthesia of the skin of the whole member, while at the same time the fingers and thumb became drawn in tight flexion, so that they could neither be moved nor extended. Rest on a splint, cold dressings, and liberal diet rapidly improved him, and within a fortnight the arm became less sensitive and the nerves less tender. In a week the hand could be passively extended, while by slow degrees volition returned. After a time faradisation was employed, but as it renewed all the symptoms, the nerve tracks near the wound were leeched, ice-water freely employed on the whole arm, and active and passive movement added. December 20, 1863, he was nearly well, and could act as orderly.

The following case is valuable as showing the remote dangers of contusion in a person of bad constitution, and as a good illustration of the manner in which disease of one of the nerves of a limb may come finally to involve others.

Case 56.—*Contusion of right ulnar nerve at bend of elbow; paralysis in ulnar distribution; general extension of paralysis to the forearm and hand; atrophy.** Charles A. P., aged forty-

---

* Gunshot Wounds and Injuries of Nerves, Case 16.

four, enlisted December, 1861, Company G, 88th Pennsylvania Volunteers. A man of good education and of refined
habits, but uncontrollably intemperate as to stimulants.
He was, with this constant exception, in good health until
injured at Cedar Mountain, July 12, 1862. He fell and
struck the right ulnar nerve, at the bend of the elbow, on
an angle of rock, causing the usual numbness and tingling
in the ultimate distribution of the nerve. The sense of
formication along the inside of the arm continued for
some months, but the limb was in full use again the day
after the accident. About December, 1862, the third and
fourth fingers became weak, and gradually the loss of
power affected all the fingers, the thumb, and the wrist.

June 24, 1863.—At this time, the date of his admission,
he still possesses all the motions natural to the limb, but
all below the elbow are singularly feeble, so that he is
now unable to write. The motor paralysis is gaining
ground. The loss of sensation is well marked in the ulnar
distribution, and is gradually increasing in the median
distribution. The localizing sense is also much confused.
The point of injury shows no scar, but the ulnar nerve is
tender to the gentlest pressure, and the median nerve is
hardly less so. The hand is as warm as usual. There is
no swelling nor burning, and the nutritive changes are
not very notable as yet. The right forearm measures nine
and a half inches; the left measures ten inches.

The electro-muscular contractility is diminished in most
of the muscles. The electro-muscular sensibility is slightly
lessened. The treatment by faradisation and douches
was used actively, but caused electric neuralgia, which is
usually a favorable sign.

July 10th.—No better. The neuralgia less, but the extensors are contracting so as to limit flexion, and the
tenderness of the nerves continues unabated.

July 11th.—Ordered passive motion. Electricity to the

flexors and leeches to ulnar nerve track, with subsequently a long blister, one inch wide and eight long. The electricity again increased the neuralgia, and accordingly it was laid aside, and the arm kept at rest, with repeated efforts to extend the fingers, and the use of a splint for this purpose at night. The leeching gave immediate ease as to pain, but as he drank incessantly, on every opportunity, the chance of useful treatment was small.

August 10th he deserted.

November 19, 1863.—He returned to the hospital drunk and materially worse. The right forearm now measured eight and three-eighths inches; the left nine and one-eighth. The flexors are greatly shrunken. The extensor group is atrophied and contracted, limiting what flexor motion is left. Everywhere below the elbow, and especially in the forearm, the power is lessened, but the electric properties are still quite good, and are nowhere lost. A sober man so situated would, without doubt, recover under the use of faradisations for a length of time. P.'s case is hopeless. Confinement injures his health, and every time he receives a pass it is used for the worst purposes. He was finally discharged on the 12th of December.

Case 57.— Wound of left chest, causing paralysis of the great pectoral muscle, probably by injury to the external anterior thoracic nerve; extension of disease from the wounded nerve to the brachial plexus, with consequent loss of sensation and motion; lesions of nutrition; intense burning pains; musculo-spiral and median principally affected. Stephen Warner, aged thirty-three, farmer, New York, enlisted August, 1862, Company B, 18th Pennsylvania Volunteers. Healthy to date of wounding. At Locust Grove, November 27, 1863, a ball entered the left chest below the first rib, half an inch beneath the clavicle, and two and a half inches from its sternal end. Passing, probably, under the arch of the subclavian artery it went backward and downward, and made exit two inches below the inferior angle of the left scapula, three and a quarter inches from the spine. The ball was fired by a skirmisher not twenty yards distant, and was received while the patient was in the act of bending forward to aim. He fell, giddy, but conscious; tried to move, but failed, and fainted from loss of blood. After several hours he revived, and discovered that the left arm and hand were sensitive throughout. On the radial side of the forearm there was slight numbness, a condition compatible with perfect tactile sensibility. Motion appears to have been lost or greatly lessened during some hours, and within a day to have become restored entirely. No doubt exists as to this point.

No dressing was used until the third day, when cold water was applied. At this date the arm motions were complete below the shoulder, and there had been no pain. Soon after the cold dressing, to which he attributed the sequent symptoms, he was seized with neuralgic pain, which was principally in the median nerve distribution, but also on the outside of the arm and shoulder, with a spot of intense pain at the deltoid insertion. The pain was darting and pricking in its nature. Coincidently with the pain, the joints of the fingers swelled and became sore, and this was especially the case with the thumb and the fore and second fingers. At the same time the shoulder muscles grew weak, flexion of the fingers feeble, and the flexion of the forearm became affected. All of these defects increased for several months, and the flexor group in the forearm wasted so much as to attract attention. The biceps, brachialis anticus and coraco-brachialis were in like manner atrophied. The pectoralis major was also thus altered at a still earlier period. The patient spat blood freely up to the eighth day, when the hemorrhage ceased, and he has had since then no pulmonary difficulties of any kind.

February 19, 1864.—Admitted.

Nutrition. — Atrophy of pectoralis major great, of shoulder muscles slight, wasting of biceps and other anterior and internal arm muscles considerable. Arm at the centre of biceps measures: left, ten inches; right, eleven and three-quarter inches. Forearm, left, ten inches; right, eleven inches. Left hand congested, dark, and cold. It grows cold easily.

Sensation perfect.—The neuralgia has nearly disappeared, except in bad weather and about the insertion of the deltoid, where there is great tenderness and a good deal of hardening and deposit in the subcuticular tissues and about the bone. The only muscle which is hyperæsthetic to any marked degree is the biceps. The course of the musculo-cutaneous and the median nerves is acutely tender upon pressure.

Motion.—None in the pectoralis major, scarcely perceptible in the biceps, the supinator longus alone flexing the forearm. Extension of forearm perfect. The fingers act in flexion feebly, but are improving. The thumb motions are also weak, but not lost. Motion is now most limited by the state of the finger-joints, which, although no longer tender, are stiff and enlarged. So much improvement has taken place very recently that we cannot be sure as to what motions were lost. Probably the principal nerves of the external cord of the plexus, namely, the musculo-cutaneous and the median, were those chiefly affected; certain filaments of the posterior strand, as the circumflex, also sharing in the diseased conditions. The remainder of the case would be irrelevant here. It was improving when admitted, and it gained ground with increased speed under a course of baths, gymnastics, and faradisation.

We have here stated two striking instances out of several to show that a nerve being injured, it is possible for other trunks of the parent plexus to become secondarily affected. Two explanations are open to us: a reflex effect, or the theory that an inflammation originating at the wound has traveled backward along the hurt nerve and fallen upon one or more stems of the main trunks. Let us examine this view in the light cast upon it by the cases before us.

M. Duchenne ("De l'Électrisation localisée," second edition, page 194) quotes a case almost precisely like number fifty-six, in which a blow on the ulnar nerve caused ultimate paralysis in other and remote nerves. Here is his explanation: "These facts seem to me to demonstrate that there exists a sort of mutual dependence [solidarité] between all the nerves of a limb, so that no one can be suddenly destroyed [supprimé] with impunity or without compromising the general innervation of the limb."

The fact was therefore a striking one to M. Duchenne. His explanation is assuredly not very happy, for although he has stated a theory which has a basis of truth, it is inapplicable here, since the simpler view which we have enunciated is amply defended by certain circumstances, which may or may not have been present in his case, but which were evident in our own. It will suffice to analyze Case 57; undoubtedly a wound of the external anterior thoracic, as was made certain by the position of the injury and the subsequent state of the pectoralis major, which this nerve supplies. On the third day, neuralgia, subacute inflammatory state of joints of fingers, and motor paralysis occurred. The phenomena affected chiefly the musculo-cutaneous and median nerves; in other words, the remaining nerve trunks of the external cord of the brachial plexus, from which the anterior external thoracic nerve arises. Add to this the long-continued and still existing tenderness in these nerve trunks in the limb itself, and we have evidence enough to make more probable that which at the start seemed a likely means of explaining all the facts.

CHAPTER XIII.

LESIONS OF SPECIAL NERVES.

WOUNDS which involve the nerves of the neck, head, and face, though rare, are yet of more than ordinary interest to the physiologist, owing to their relations with the organs of special sense and expression. I have therefore seen fit to report in this chapter the more remarkable histories of such cases which have fallen within my experience.

Injuries of the sympathetic nerve.—The only known case of direct mechanical violence to the sympathetic nerve was reported by the staff of the U. S. A. Hospital for Injuries of Nerves, etc.* My own attention was first drawn to the man by accidentally observing as he passed me in the wards that one pupil was contracted. He had been sent to us on account of an obscure affection of the brain, with headache, occasional faintness, and some loss of memory. His was the only well-marked case of direct wound of the sympathetic which I have seen. Its great physiological and clinical importance as positive proof that in man the nerve possesses the same function as it has been shown to exhibit in animals, authorizes me to quote it at length:

Case 58.— *Wound of right sympathetic nerve; wound healed in six weeks; cerebral symptoms; contracted pupil; ptosis; lachrymation, etc.* Edward Mooney,† aged twenty-four,

---

* Gunshot Wounds and other Injuries of Nerves, p. 39.
† Ibid.

(318)

enlisted July, 1861, Company C, 110th Pennsylvania
Volunteers. He was perfectly healthy before and after
enlisting, until wounded at Chancellorsville, May 3, 1863.
He was standing erect, and was looking toward the left
side, when a ball entered his right neck, one and a half
inches behind the ramus of the jaw at the anterior edge
of the sterno-cleido-mastoid muscle. The ball passed
across the neck, rising a little, and emerged immediately
below, and a half inch in front of the angle of the jaw on
the left side. He fell senseless, and, judging from the
movements of his regiment, may have so remained during
half an hour. On awaking he found his mouth full of
clotted blood, which he pulled out. The bleeding had
ceased. After a short rest he was able to walk nearly
three miles to the rear, where his wounds were dressed
with cold water. On his way he discovered that his
speech had become hoarse, difficult, and painful, and
that deglutition gave rise to great uneasiness and to
burning pains. He says the sensation of pain was felt as
though behind the pomum Adami. After five days of
great suffering and utter inability to swallow, he obtained
some relief; but for a month or more was forced to take
a little water after every mouthful of solid food. The
power to swallow gradually improved, and is now as good
as it ever was.

A week after being wounded, he was able to articulate
without pain, although hoarsely. This difficulty also lessened by slow degrees. At present, July, 1863, his voice
is still a little hoarse. During his recovery, which was
rapid, the wounds healing within six weeks, he had a
good deal of pain in the back of the neck. He says that
he had headache, whenever after the injury he attempted
to walk far, or exert himself; but he describes the headache as chiefly behind the right ear and in the back of
the head, with some frontal pain. About one month after

he was hurt, a comrade noticed the peculiar appearance of his right eye, and called his attention to it. A little later, it began to be troublesome in bright lights, and has remained so ever since, with of late some change for the better.

July 15, 1863.—The pupil of the right eye is very small, that of the left unusually large. There is slight but very distinct ptosis of the right eye, and its outer angle appears as though it were dropped a little lower than the inner angle. The ball of the right eye looks smaller than that of the left. These appearances existed whether the eye was open or closed, and gave to that organ the look of being tilted out of the usual position. The conjunctiva of the right eye is somewhat redder than that of the left, and the pupil of the right eye is a little deformed, oval rather than round. In a dark place, or in half-lights, the difference in the pupils was best seen; but in very bright light, as sunlight, the two pupils became of nearly equal size. The left eye waters a good deal, but has the better vision, the right eye having become myopic. In sunlight he sees well at first, but, after a time, observes red flashes of light in the right eye, and finally, after long exposure, sees the same appearances with the left eye also. He complains of frontal headache at present, and thinks that since the injury his memory has been failing, although recently it has improved. Has lost flesh and strength since he was wounded.

About the 30th August, the patient rode to the office of Dr. Dyer, who examined his eyes with the ophthalmoscope, but found no abnormal retinal appearances. Mooney walked from Dr. Dyer's office to the hospital, an unusual exertion, as he was weak, and avoided exercise on account of the headache it caused. An orderly who was with him on this occasion, remarked to one of the hospital staff upon the singular appearance which his face presented after walking in the heat. It became distinctly flushed on the right side, and pale on the left. This fact was afterwards observed anew by one of us. The patient had used exercise and had just come in. The right half of the face was very red. The flush extended to the middle line, but was less definite as to its limit on the chin and lips than above these points. He complained of pain over the right eye, and of red flashes in that organ.

A careful thermometric examination, made *during repose*, showed no difference in the heat of the two sides within the mouth or ear. We regret that it did not occur to us to repeat this when the face was flushed by exertion. Under a tonic course of treatment he gained ground rapidly. The eyes became less sensitive, the pupils more nearly alike, the line of the lid straighter. He had several attacks of faintness after exposure to the sun, and these, with occasional diarrhœa, retarded his recovery. He was at last able to return to duty, and left for that purpose in October, 1863, nearly all of his peculiar symptoms having disappeared, and his general health having been altogether recovered.

The case of Captain (now Commodore) Stembel, which Dr. William Ogle, in referring to one of my papers, seems to regard as a wound of the sympathetic, could not have been this.* The ball entered a little to the right of the median line, immediately above the hyoid bone, which it touched, and slightly broke, then passing across the neck directly beneath the left sterno-mastoid muscle, it emerged through the edge of the trapezius muscle three and a half inches from the middle line above and to the right of the superior angle of the scapula. He had complete but permanent reflex paralysis of the left arm, and

---

* In an admirable paper on the Symptoms of Injury of the Cervical Sympathetic, Med.-Chir. Trans., vol. lii. p. 151.

also more permanent palsy of the right arm. I cannot well conceive how the sympathetic of the right side could have been directly hurt by the missile, yet there was temporary loss of sight in the right eye, and even after two years slight ptosis, especially in the morning, contracted pupil, and imperfect vision, without unilateral flush, but with defect of secretion of sweat in the right neck, arm, and chest, and with rather excessive perspiration on the left side of the face and neck.

That there was some affection of the sympathetic in this case seems most probable, but I incline to regard it, like the other paralytic symptoms of this extraordinary case, as due to a reflected irritation.

Dr. William Ogle has reported an instance of probable destruction of the right cervical sympathetic by abscesses. In this case the eyeball was retracted, the palpebral fissure narrowed, the pupil contracted, the right side of the face redder and hotter than the left during repose, but after violent exercise or fever colder. The left side of the face alone sweated, and the right side of the mouth and tongue was complained of as being dry.

The symptoms observed in this case differed very little from those of the history first quoted. In Dr. Ogle's case there was wanting the droop in the outer angle of the eye, which in Mooney was very apparent. The defect of secretion seems to be a late symptom, and in neither was there any notable nutritive alteration; no lachrymal lesion or hypertrophy or change in the growth of the hair, such as I have occasionally seen in animals. In all other respects these cases reproduced the symptoms seen when we divide the cervical sympathetic in an animal.

The subject needs further clinical illustration, and at present nothing can be said as to prognosis or treatment, while in most instances the diagnosis must be sufficiently clear.

The cerebral symptoms which may follow sympathetic nerve lesions demand particular attention in any future records of such wounds. In Mooney's case they were loss of memory, vertigo, and headache, and were severe enough to keep him in a hospital long after the wound had healed.

Injuries of the seventh or facial nerve—Mechanical injuries of this nerve are rare, and are valuable because they set in clearer light the precise meaning of symptoms which are common to all the modes of paralysis to which it is subject.

Injury to the facial nerve causes simply palsy of the muscles of the face, excepting such as are fed by the motor branch of the fifth nerve. It is therefore easy of recognition. The features relaxed and flabby and drawn to the uninjured side, the drooping mouth angle, the unwinking eye, constantly open, occlusion of light being effected only by rolling the ball upward, the unwrinkled forehead and the motionless nostril make up a pathological sketch easy enough of recognition whatever its cause.

I have seen no case of traumatic injury to the seventh nerve at its cerebral origin, where it is sometimes compressed by pathological formations. The records of injury to the nerve in its passage through the temporal bone are more frequent, but lesions of the nerve after exit on the face are rare, on account of its deep position and the protection afforded it by the neighboring parts, so that it is not often hurt in this part of its course unless divided by the surgeon's knife during removal of the parotid gland.

Injuries of the facial, after emergence on the neck, occasion simple palsy of the face without any affection of the tongue or throat, and such lesions cause results precisely similar to those which are produced by exposure to cold, the common cause of simple facial palsy. I saw in the Filbert Street Hospital a man who had been struck just below the meatus of the ear by a fragment of shell, which cut away the lower edge of the auricular cartilage and divided the facial nerve at the same time, so injuring the carotid that on the occurrence of hemorrhage it had to be tied. This man had all the usual signs of facial palsy; but taste, speech, and deglutition were unchanged. The palsied facial muscles finally underwent contraction, which, on the whole, rather improved the appearance of the face.

The lesions of the seventh nerve (facial), which lie deeper in the ear, are diagnosticated by the addition to the palsy of certain symptoms, the occurrence of which depends upon the affection of the minor nerves related to the facial in its outward course.

These nerves are in succession from within outward, the greater and lesser superficial petrosal nerves, which arise where the canal of Fallopius turns backward, and lastly, the chorda tympani given off in the descending portion of the canal. The first of these nerves after passing through Meckel's ganglion is distributed to the levator palati and azygos uvulæ, and probably also to the palato-glossus and palato-pharyngeus muscle. The second nerve passes from the facial to the otic ganglion, and through the latter is possibly related to the tensor tympani and tensor palati muscles. The third, or chorda tympani nerve, sends filaments to the submaxillary gland, to the papillæ of the tongue, and to some of the fibres of the lingual muscles.

When the lesion lies exterior to the chorda tympani nerve, we have simple muscular palsy of the face. If the cause lies beyond the tympanic nerve, we may have added dryness of the tongue and slightly impaired sense of taste, owing to the fact that the chorda tympani has under its control the erection of the gustatory papillæ, the secretion of the submaxillary gland, and the vessels of the tongue. Its paralysis by making dry the mouth aids in lessening the acuteness of gustation.

When the injury involves also, as it commonly does, the origins of the two petrosal nerves, we have in addition partial paralysis of the palate and pharynx, with nasal voice and slight difficulty of speech and even of swallowing, all of which symptoms are more remarkably developed in cases of diplegia of the face. To these may be also added in traumatic cases more or less injury of the sense of hearing.

The palatal change consists in "a vertical relaxation or lowering of the palsied side of the velum, with diminished height, and curvature of the posterior arch." The soft palate is curved, its point turned to the paralyzed side, its base curved to the sound side,—the symmetry of the parts being totally lost.

Since the occurrence of some of these symptoms as signs of pathological lesion of the facial in the canal of Fallopius has been disputed, I have been careful to look for them in undoubted traumatic injuries of this part, so that I believe my cases will be found on this account to possess a more than common interest and value.

The following history admirably illustrates in its progress the simple palsy due to peripheral lesions, the addition of the gustatory lingual and vocal symptoms as the deeper branches became involved, and finally, the fact so often alluded to in these pages, that inflammatory affections of nerves sometimes extend in a central direction.

Case 59.—Blow from a flail, breaking the left jaw and paralyzing the left facial nerve; twitching of face muscles; gradually increasing disease of the deeper parts of the nerve, and affection of speech and deglutition. C. J., a florid, rather slightly-built man, who had in childhood scrofulous cervical glands, received a blow from a threshing-flail which fractured the angle of the left jaw and caused extensive inflammation of the face, followed by a large abscess. The jaw united, leaving him with slight neuralgia of the chin, owing no doubt to injury of the inferior maxillary branch of the fifth nerve. For a few weeks the facial muscles twitched a good deal, and as the inflammation subsided, the suspicion which existed very soon after the blow, that the left face was palsied, became distinctly justified. After two months he came to the city to consult me. I found him suffering from an uncomplicated peripheral palsy of the left seventh nerve. All the usual muscles were palsied, the eye open, and the skin singularly relaxed. The tongue had all the normal motions, the voice being unaffected, and the taste perfect on both sides of the tongue.

One year later I saw this case again. The palsy had diminished during two months, and then become worse without known cause; but his health seemed to have declined from this period, and he complained of some difficulty in speaking for any length of time. The trouble lay chiefly in uttering the linguals. His tongue could be thrust out and moved laterally, but not bent upward with the usual readiness. The left side of the tongue was tardy in recognizing all sapid substances, and he made frequent mistakes if urged to a hasty decision. The sense of touch in the tongue remained perfect, but the left half of the palate hung lower than the right, and was partially paralyzed, failing to respond to galvanism as perfectly as did the sound side. The palate was bent, the tip turned forward, and to the left, the upper portion curved towards the right, and the whole body of the palate twisted a little from left to right. These newly-acquired symptoms seem to me to have been caused by centrally progressive changes in the injured nerve. The patient died the year after of rapidly-developed tuberculosis.

The following case also amply illustrates the subject of wounds of the facial nerve:

Case 60.—*Gunshot wound involving portio dura ; loss of electric contractility in the muscles of expression ; no relief.* William S. Sylvester,* farmer, aged twenty-two, born in Norway. In this country sixteen years. Enlisted for three years, September, 1861, Company D, 7th Wisconsin. In good health up to date of wound. At Gettysburg, July 1, 1863, he was shot, while standing, with a minié-ball, which entered the face an inch below the outer angle of the left eye. It passed backward and outward across the external auditory meatus, apparently injuring the left ramus of the jaw, high up, and finally emerged behind the lower half of the mastoid process, which it fractured. He fell instantly senseless, and reviving after a few minutes, crawled away, and with aid reached the shelter of a house, where he was taken prisoner. After three days he was recaptured, and sent to the Satterlee Hospital, Philadelphia, and thence to us, August 2, 1863. The wound has never been painful, rarely more than sore ; fragments of the jaw escaped anteriorly, during the treatment, and also portions of the mastoid process at the wound of exit. The left side of his face swelled, and is still greatly enlarged. The conjunctiva of the left eye was a good deal inflamed at first, but is now free from inflammation, and the sight unaltered. Early in the case a good deal of blood escaped from his left ear, and the hearing was noticed to be, as it still is, rather dull. The inflammation about the articular portion of the lower jaw is such as to have caused great and painful difficulty in opening the mouth, which is so locked that it is impossible now to ascertain by touch, within the oral cavity, how much injury has been done to the bones. At present, August 4, the ante-

---

* Gunshot Wounds, etc., op. cit.

rior wound is healed, but the posterior is open, and an abscess, which formed below the left ear, is discharging very freely. The parts in front of the ear are confused in a mass of firm plastic deposit. There is total palsy of the muscles of expression in the face. The brow and lid hang, the cheek is flabby, the mouth pulled toward the sound side. The tongue moves, but as the jaw is locked by the inflammatory deposit about the ramus, the cheek, and the articulation of the maxilla, it cannot be closely examined. He was long annoyed by the inability to cover his eye with the lid; but has now learned to roll the eye upward, so as to cover the iris. He then supposes that he has closed the lid. This same phenomenon was noted by Sir C. Bell in several of his earlier cases.

The history of the present case is somewhat obscure, nor can we be absolutely sure as to whether the portio dura, which is paralyzed, was primarily injured by the ball, or secondarily affected by the large and firm deposit in front of the ear, which must of necessity have involved nearly all the facial branches of the nerve. The wound was dressed with water without other treatment.

October 19, 1863.—The swelling has subsided one-half, but there is still dead bone in the wound, probably a piece of the ramus of the jaw. A mass of granulations fills the outer ear, but the hearing does not seem to be utterly lost. After tearing the granulations away, it was found that the membrane was gone, that there was some inflammation of the middle ear, and that below the bony meatus, and in front of it, dead bone could be felt.

Faradisation of the face showed total loss of electric contractility in all the muscles supplied by the portio dura, and also in the posterior portion of the masseter, which had been injured by the ball and by the subsequent inflammation.

As the face was still inflamed in September, no attempt

to treat the case was made till October. From October 1st, however, to November 3d, he was faradised, although with slight hope of aiding him. At this date he was no better. On returning, December 3d, from a furlough, a cast of his face was made. The wounds were then healed, and the mouth could be opened.

At this time we noticed that taste was duller on the left side of the tongue than on the right, and that the motions and tactile sense of the tongue were healthy. Electricity was used persistently up to January 10, 1864. It gave a good deal of pain, but in no way relieved the patient's paralysis. In February he was transferred to the Veteran Reserve Corps. He had gained the power to chew his food, but suffered from all the annoyances of complete facial palsy.

It will be observed that in this man's case the injury was deep, the hearing wonderfully little affected, and the sense of taste distinctly altered. The mouth never became sufficiently open to enable us to study the palate.

Case 61.—Gunshot wound of left facial nerve; hearing lost; speech impaired; gustation affected; recovery. J. Gager,* aged forty-two, blacksmith, Company M, 14th New York Heavy Artillery, enlisted December, 1863. Health good. Wounded May 12th, at the battle of Spottsylvania Court House. The ball entered the left posterior neck one and three-quarter inches from the spine of the third cervical vertebra, and was cut out immediately behind and below the left ear, about two and a half inches beneath the meatus, and a quarter of an inch behind the jaw. The track of the bullet is unknown, except that it injured the ear, paralyzed the portio dura of the seventh nerve, and splintered the edge of the ramus of the jaw. The man's head, at the time he was shot, was bent forward and

* Gunshot Wounds, etc., op. cit.

downward. He fell, conscious, bleeding freely from the ear only. After two minutes he arose and walked away, the blood still spouting from the ear until it was checked by a bandage over that organ. He did not suffer until the next day, when he had the usual inflammatory pains. The sight of the left eye is said to have become affected on the second day,—a defect which remains unchanged. The paralysis of the muscles was immediate, and his speech was at once rendered difficult, owing, as it seemed to him, to some loss of power in the tongue and lips.* Hearing was lost at once in the left ear.

June 8, 1864.—The pains in the face, and the swelling, which was never great, are now less severe. The wounds are open, but healing.

The nutrition is unaltered. The lines of the face are lost, the tip of the nose and the lower mobile portions of the face are drawn to the right. The left eyebrow has fallen a little. The tears run over the edge of the lid.

The tongue is perfectly movable and under entire control of the will.

Speech perfect, except a slight impediment in articulating the gutturals, but there is more difficulty as to the labials.

Special Senses.—The left eye sees only one-third as well as the right.

Hearing is lost in the left ear. On washing out the pus, a mass of granulations was seen at the bottom of the ear. Possibly the bony meatus may have been fractured by the ball, but no bone escaped except pieces of the jaw, which came out with the ball.

Taste.—There seems to be slight loss of gustation on the

---

* It is to be remembered that the facial proper directly supplies several muscles more or less concerned in the motions of the tongue.

left side. Tactility is equally good on the two sides, both in the tongue and face.

June 20th.—The sight is becoming worse. Dr. Dyer, who examined the patient with care, is of opinion that it was affected before he received his wound. Induced electric currents give rise to slight movement in the left eyelid, and the elevator of the angle of the mouth. A rapid recovery was predicted, and, in fact, three days later voluntary power returned in the orbicular muscle of the eye. By July 27th, every motion had been re-acquired.

In this case the ball must have injured the auditory as well as the facial nerve by shock rather than directly. Yet, as all the nerve tissues in the temporal bone alike suffered, the result was seen in loss of power and in disturbance of speech and taste.

Case 62.—*Gunshot wound of left portia dura nerve; total paralysis of motion; taste affected; tongue movements impaired; deafness on left side.* John C. Dyre,* Pennsylvania, aged nineteen, machinist, enlisted May, 1861, Company E, 71st Pennsylvania Volunteers. Health good up to date of wound, at Gettysburg, July 3, 1863. While aiming, a ball entered just behind the left ear at the level of the meatus. It broke the mastoid process slightly, and was said to have gone forward and downward. It has not been found. He fell unconscious, and reviving within about two hours at a hospital where he had been carried, he found that he could not use the jaw, owing to pain in the ear. There was also pain in the left cheek and brow, left neck, shoulder, arm, and hand. The left arm was weak for several days. He thinks he may have fallen upon it. The pain was a neuralgic ache, not the pain of a bruise. Water-dressings were used after a vain search

---

* Gunshot Wounds, etc., op. cit.

for the ball. **Within** two days he had pain in the lower teeth and jaw on the left side. At the expiration of five weeks all pain disappeared, and the motions of the jaw returned. The ear was deaf from the first; but he does not know whether blood flowed from it or not, or when pus first came from it.

Present state, February 14, 1864, *eight months after reception of wound.*—The features are slightly drawn to the right in repose, and excessively so during laughter and speech. The left side is absolutely paralyzed. The inner canthus of the left eye is a little rounder than that of the right eye. The tears overrun the lid at times. Inability to close the lids on the left side; owing to which he has formed the habit of rolling the eyeball upward, so as to cover it with the passive lid. He then supposes that he has closed the eye. Chewing on the left side causes pain in the teeth, which continues for some time. Sensation is perfectly normal on the paralyzed side. Motion is of course utterly lost in all the muscles of expression.

Electric test.—Not the slightest contractility exists in any of the muscles of expression, on the left side, with a curious exception. The orbicularis oris in the upper and lower lips still responds to the current, but more remarkably below than above. There is, however, no voluntary control over these parts. The buccinator alone of the masticating muscles seems to have its electric contractility enfeebled, but not wholly lost.

Examination of special senses; tongue motions.—The upward and backward motion of the base of the tongue is awkwardly performed. In most of its movements the tongue inclines slightly to the right, but is capable of being drawn to the left side. The palate tip points towards the right side and acts imperfectly, so that *food is apt to enter the nose.* There is some further loss of power in the other muscles of deglutition, for he is often troubled by food entering the glottis, while at times it is thrust back again into the mouth.

Speech.—He pronounces many letters with difficulty or imperfectly, so that his speech may be said to be a little thick, and he so describes it, referring the trouble to his lips and tongue. The labials are of course affected, but the guttural sounds are also imperfectly executed.

Taste is apparently impaired over the entire left tongue.

Electric state of tongue.—No loss of its electric properties was detected. Hearing on the left side was destroyed. The back part of the bony meatus was carious, and the membrane absent, perhaps from inflammation consequent upon the wound.

Treatment.—The patient was industriously faradised for several months without the least gain in any respect.

In this case, in which there was a deep injury of the facial nerve, taste, deglutition, and speech were all alike impaired.

The following history is yet more conclusive:

Case 63.—*Ball wound of right neck destroying the ear and injuring the facial nerve; deafness; vertiginous attacks with forward impulses; facial palsy; contracted muscles; nasal voice; impaired deglutition; nutrition and functions of right side of tongue affected; sense of taste diminished.*—J., aged about thirty, was shot in 1864, the ball entering the right neck behind the mastoid process, through which it passed. Its course after entrance is unknown, except that it seemed to have traversed and destroyed the inner and middle ear. The tympanal membrane was gone, the bones of the middle ear absent, and a constant discharge occurred through the meatus and the wound of entry for many months, when finally the latter healed.

The flow from the ear, June, 1869, was slight, but the probe detected caries deep in the temporal bone. The missile was probably a small rifle-ball, not a minié. Up

to the time of examination the man was deaf in the right
ear, and was subject to attacks of vertigo, during which
he would run forward a few steps and then rotate to the
right several times, external objects seeming to move
from left to right.

The facial palsy was complete, and some of the muscles, as the levator anguli oris and zygomaticus, were contracted so as to give to his visage a most singular look.
No electrical excitation was capable of inducing movement, but, as I have often observed in these cases, the skin
of the right face was hyperæsthetic.

The voice was slightly nasal, and deglutition was awkward at times, while there was considerable difficulty in
pronouncing certain sounds, especially the letters l and p.

The right side of the tongue was of a light brown tint,
and smooth; the left rougher and covered with a moist
white fur. The recognition of tastes was slow on the
right side, and was plainly impaired, but not lost. The
chief difficulty as to the lingual movements seemed to be
in turning the tip of the tongue up and carrying it to the
right side. The right palatal arches were lower than
those of the left, and the palate, which was œdematous,
was pulled to the left, the tip looking to the right and a
little forward, but the whole organ being dragged to the
left, a little past the middle line, by the action of the
healthy opponent muscles. After a careful examination,
I was satisfied that the right palatal muscles were less
responsive to induced currents than the left. I should also
add that the right half of the tongue was distinctly less
in size than the left.

I regret that this very instructive case passed out of
my control and knowledge. It is an admirable confirmation of the opinions which Davaine, Saunders, and others
founded upon pathological and physiological data.

The treatment of these cases does not differ from that

of other traumatic palsies; but in deep injuries of the
ear by a missile, as in most nerve wounds involving
closely related bone, the prognosis is usually hopeless,
while in the external cases, even of severe wounds,
recoveries are not uncommon. We should not, however,
despair until long periods have passed and the muscles
have been often and patiently tested by the galvanic current or by faradisation.

I am indebted to Dr. Allison, resident physician at the
Pennsylvania Hospital, for the following notes of a case
of traumatic palsy of the left hypoglossal nerve, which occurred in the service of Dr. T. G. Morton. I have already
referred to it in discussing the subject of trophic nerves.

Case 64.—Pistol-ball wound of the left hypoglossal nerve.
Alonzo B. Rogers, a colored lad, aged nineteen, was
admitted into the Pennsylvania Hospital November 24,
1871, suffering from a gunshot wound of the neck. The
patient stated that the distance from which the pistol—a
Smith & Wesson revolver—was fired could not have
been more than five feet.

The ball entered the left side of the neck one and a
half inches behind and a little below the angle of the
jaw. The wound of entrance was small and sharply defined. The examining probe passed upward and inward; the ball could not be felt. No traces of the bullet
were seen in the fauces.

The tongue was found paralyzed on the left side as
regards motion, but not sensation. When protruded, it
turned toward the left or wounded side, and could not be
held against the upper lip without the aid of the under.
When the tip was pressed against the roof of the mouth,
it turned toward the left side. The patient could readily
press the tip against any point on the right side of
the mouth, but on the left the attempt was attended
with difficulty. There was no trouble in swallowing, but

the patient thought he could not articulate as distinctly as formerly.

Sensation was not at all impaired. Several tests were made at different times, but the result was always the same. No difference was discovered by means of the æsthesiometer. He could readily distinguish salt from sugar when placed upon either side. The right side of the tongue readily responded to the electric current, the wounded side did not, but seemed the more sensitive under the current. The wounded side of the tongue was notably atrophied before the patient was discharged.

Several attempts were made to find the bullet, but all were unsuccessful. The wound healed without any difficulty, and the patient left December 12, 1871, the paralysis continuing unaltered.

Lesions of the oculo-motor nerves and of the fifth nerve.— Mechanical injuries of the motor nerves of the eye which do not at once involve loss of life are rare. I have several times seen cases of injury to the base of the brain affecting these trunks, especially the sixth nerve, there being at the same time no permanent cerebral or other symptoms indicative of lesions of centres. There is at present such a case under treatment at the Hospital for Deformities and for Nervous Diseases.

The following case, which I report at length, stands alone in the history of oculo-motor-nerve lesions, and is interesting for its relation to the physiology of the iris.

Case 65.—*Pistol-ball wound involving the third, fourth, sixth, and ophthalmic branch of the fifth nerve; secondary injury of the olfactory nerve; death.*

December 31, 1870.—I saw in consultation with Dr. Morton the case of W. P., male, aged thirteen, who was accidentally shot on the 29th of December, in the afternoon. A pistol-ball entered the right temple, and, passing inward beneath the right optic nerve, lodged in the body of the ethmoid bone. The nerve was pushed upward, but suffered no other injury. In its path the ball cut the third, fourth, sixth, and ophthalmic branch of the fifth nerve where they pass across the wall of the cavernous sinus. About half an ounce of blood was effused, and found its way upward and forward so as to compress the olfactory bulb at its narrower central portion, which at the time of the post-mortem inspection was completely softened.

When I saw the lad he was slightly drowsy, but could be very easily aroused, and answered all our questions with intelligence and promptness.

The right eyeball was absolutely motionless, although the other moved readily. In the absence of better means, I placed an edge of paper across the eyelids in various directions so as to mark the edge of the cornea; but despite his utmost efforts, there was no measurable movement in any direction.

The iris was largely but not completely dilated. When I passed a light close to the eye, he was annoyed at the glare, but the pupil rested motionless, as was equally the case when the eye was alternately covered and uncovered. When directed to regard a near object, the left pupil contracted, the right iris remained motionless.

A little extract of Calabar bean was now placed on the eye, and in about fifteen or twenty minutes the iris had so contracted that the pupil was scarcely larger than a pin's head. About an hour later atropia was put upon the eye, and within an hour the pupil dilated again, so that eight hours after it was larger than before.

The eye was absolutely dry, there being no lachrymal secretion, and the ball was so completely insensible to touch that a finger rubbed on the cornea caused no annoyance. There were also anæsthesia and analgesia in the supra-orbital region and the lid. I endeavored to measure their extent; but the lad had become weary, and gave me unsatisfactory replies. I could only learn that there was sensory loss, but was unable to determine its exact area.

The lid was moveless, except when feebly stirred by extreme effort of the supra-ciliary muscles, and the eye-ball projected from its socket. When the vapor of vine-gar was allowed to enter the left nostril, he knew it at once and named it, but the right had no perception of it either as an odor or an irritant, and such was also the case as regards mustard. I inferred from this that probably the nasal ophthalmic branch of the fifth had been injured; but the sectio cadaveris proved that both this nerve and the olfactory had been destroyed, so that neither irritations nor odors were readily felt.

The patient became comatose by degrees, and died on the third day, when the conditions above described were found to exist. The symptoms presented by the eye cor-responded to the lesions demonstrated after death. The dull, insensible, and slightly-clouded cornea, the supra-orbital and nasal anæsthesia were due to the lesion of the fifth nerve; the motionless eye and fallen lid, with the non-secretion of tears and the projection of the eyeball, depended on the section of the oculo-motor and the fourth and sixth nerves; and the absence of smell was owing to the injury to the fifth nerve and the subsequent pressure upon the olfactory bulb.

The lenticular ganglion being undisturbed, our experi-ments on the effects of Calabar bean and atropia have but a limited physiological value, and only prove that ex-treme contraction and dilatation of the pupil are possible after total section of the fifth and third nerves, posterior to that body.

Case 66.—*Gunshot wound of the inferior dental branch of*

the fifth pair. John Schultze,* aged twenty-three, German, enlisted August, 1862, Company G, 26th Wisconsin
Volunteers. His previous health was good. At Gettysburg, July 3, 1863, while marching at a long distance
from the enemy, a single shot, from some remote picket,
took effect on his left cheek, over the lower edge of the
malar prominence. It was probably fired from an elevation, since it passed across the ramus of the jaw and
entered the anterior margin of the trapezius muscle,
whence, two weeks later, it was removed by Dr. Keen.
The ball, a minié, was very much deformed. It somewhat injured the ear in its passage, but although it
crossed the ramus of the jaw obliquely, and probably
broke off some splinters, it did not fracture the bone so
as to affect mastication. The patient fell senseless when
hit, and remained thus for at least half an hour. He had
no pain. The whole left side of the face was devoid of
feeling, and so continued until the second day, when sensation came back rather suddenly, except in a space,
which included a large part of the ultimate distribution
of the left mental nerve.

The first and larger loss of sensory appreciation was
probably a result of the local shock. When he recovered
his senses, he found that the left arm was almost useless
from loss of power. The fingers could be moved well
enough, but the arm could not be flexed at the elbow.
Sensation was but slightly altered. The arm was merely
numbed. The right arm was also weakened, though to
a less degree, but in it the sense of touch was defective
to a remarkable extent, so that when he sought to undo
his belt he could not feel the buckle. This was not
merely a general shock or weakness, for his legs were as
strong as usual, and he was able to walk to the rear un-

* Gunshot Wounds, etc., op. cit.

assisted. Motion and feeling returned within four days
to the right arm, but the left recovered more gradually,
and was still weak as late as August 10, 1863.

During the first week there was great swelling of the
neck, which was relieved when the ball was cut out.
During September two or more small spiculæ of bone
escaped from the neck, below the chin. They were probably fragments from the injured jaw.

When Schultze entered our wards, August 10, 1863,
his wounds were healed. The mouth could be but slightly
opened, owing to the amount of deposit on the cheek and
over the articulation. Early in his case, before swelling
occurred, he could open and shut the mouth easily. Motion gradually returned.

August 12, 1863.—The skin of the left lower lip and
chin is perfectly insensitive to pain and touch from the
middle line to the left angle of the mouth, and, within a
space between the middle line of the chin and a line drawn
obliquely downward and outward, from the left angle of
the mouth to the lower edge of the inferior maxillary
bone. The curve of the lip within the mouth is dead to
touch, and so also are the gums in this region. The teeth
and gums of the left lower jaw are generally less sensitive to touch and pain than is natural, but they are not
altogether deprived of sensation. The external region,
defined above, has no appreciation of touch or pain, but
the point of exit of the nerve is the seat of neuralgic
pain, and pressure on this point is felt by the patient, so
that even here the deeper tissues are less affected than
the skin. The most intense applications of the electric
brush to the dried and powdered chin caused no pain.
Wet conductors, which threw the subjacent muscles into
contraction, seemed to cause deep-seated pain. Under
the use of dry conductors, Schultze improved, but not

until the thirtieth application of the battery, which was used daily.

November 19th.—He returned to duty as orderly.

November 27th.—The anæsthetic region has gradually narrowed, and is now within a triangle, the base of which is the border of the lip, and the apex of which lies at the edge of the chin, immediately below the left angle of the mouth. Electricity was steadily used during four months, when, the anæsthetic space being one-third of its original size, the teeth and gums more sensitive, and the jaw motions good, treatment was abandoned. Within twenty days the anæsthetic space again enlarged. It was more speedily lessened in size by twenty electrizations. As he could now chew well and was in other respects healthy, and desirous of being in the field, he was sent to duty at the close of February, 1864. Whether or not the area of insensibility increased afterward, we cannot state, since the patient finally passed from under our observation.

CHAPTER XIV.

NEURAL MALADIES OF STUMPS.

THE nervous affections of stumps are chorea, neuralgia, neuritis, and sclerosis. They have received but little notice at the hands of neuro-pathologists, and, indeed, the physiology of stumps, a comprehension of which is necessary before studying their diseases, may be said to have been almost entirely neglected.

I have therefore thought it fitting to introduce here an original study of the vital conditions of stumps before speaking of their diseases.

Functional and other changes after amputation.—The amputation of limbs gives rise to certain functional and other conditions which have never as yet been fully studied. According to my own experience, removal of large limbs tends to cause plethora, more rapid pulse, and in very many cases greater tendency to sweat. The tissue changes in the stumps which follow amputation have been pretty fully described by surgeons, and need not be considered here, save as to certain practical points. In many cases the stumps, after wasting for a time, seem to gain in bulk, although this is not always the case, for it occasionally happens that both muscles and bone undergo remarkable and permanent atrophy. Perhaps in chosing a line of amputation, more attention should be paid to the points at which the nerves enter the muscles or the bones, since, if these can be respected, wasting will be less

(342)

likely to occur, and the mobility and nutrition of the stumps will benefit by the precaution.

Neuromata of stumps. — At the ends of the severed nerves, tumors of various size form. They are chiefly masses of connective tissue, over which the nerve filaments spread, and are finally lost to view. In most thin stumps these enlargements can be easily felt, and very often a thickened nerve trunk running from them is also readily perceptible. Perhaps no stump is altogether without these tumors, which are far too apt to be regarded by surgeons as the cause of neuralgia, a disease usually due in stumps to neuritis or the sclerotic state which it is apt to occasion. In all the stumps I have studied, these neuromata existed, and are, I think, to be looked upon as inevitable appendages.

In very many stumps, the neuromatous tumors in which the nerves end are united to one another, or are adherent to the bone and the cicatricial tissue of the muscles and skin. Owing to this fact, and to sclerotic conditions of the nerves which lessen their natural elasticity, they fail to yield readily when stretched, and for this reason are apt to suffer when the limb is suddenly and violently moved, as in spasm or by the will. Only in this manner can I explain the occurrence of pain and inflammation due to such motion. A man previously well has an unusually violent and abrupt spasm of the deltoid, such as has often before occurred to him in a lighter form, and always with painful results; but on this occasion the pain is excessive and continuous; the nerves then become tender, neuralgia follows, and we have at last a well-marked case of neuritis. Although these are rare cases, they are not to be overlooked in seeking for causes of inflammation, and seem to me to be explained by the facts I have mentioned.

Neuro-physiology of stumps. — When a limb has been

removed, the stump which forms is liable to certain nervous disorders, which are often intractable. The part which they affect exists under physiological conditions so new and peculiar that it is desirable to comprehend them as fully as possible before proceeding to study these maladies. So far as I am aware, there is but one essay on the physiology of stumps, and this by no means covers all the ground. My own information on the subject is derived from the careful study of ninety stumps, and from the statements of fourteen persons who have consulted me on account of neuralgia or choreiform movements of their stumps, as well as from dissections of such parts.

Sensibility.—The sense of touch, which soon after amputation is oftentimes dull or deficient in limited areas of stumps, becomes in time more acute, but is rarely perfect. In cases of arm amputations remote from the date of operations, I have often found portions of the skin of the stump almost devoid of tactile feeling, while the rest of the stump showed as distinct an appreciation of the distance of two compass points as regions similarly placed in the corresponding limb.

Sense of pain.—A large proportion of stumps, especially those of the arm, are hyperæsthetic, or have some unpleasing sensation as a consequence of any, and especially of rough contacts. Lateral pressure is very annoying to many, and if long continued is apt to cause aching neuralgia; complete anæsthesia is much more rare. I have seen one case in which the entire end of the limb was insensible to a needle, but this was the remote, and, I may say, the fortunate consequence of a severe attack of painful neuritis.

The sensitiveness of stumps varies greatly with the season of the year, with the weather, and with constitutional conditions, while of course there are many instances of well-cushioned stumps which are no more sensitive than other parts. As a rule, great heat or imperfect ventilation of the stump where artificial limbs are worn occasions increased sensibility, with excessive cutaneous congestion; so that in our July weather many persons are unable to endure their false limbs.

Cold has usually the effect of causing pain in the part with referred sensations, and both cold and heat are apt, in rare cases, to occasion twitching or even choreic movements of the stump. So well are these facts known to many patients that they pay extreme attention to the temperature of the part, and prefer to guard it in winter by some unusual amount of covering, knowing perfectly well that it is singularly sensitive to thermal changes. I have found this to be more remarkably true of the arm than the leg, and especially so of thin stumps, perhaps because of the insufficient protection they afford to the nerves and of the defective circulation produced by want of exercise.

But besides the influence of palpable changes in temperature, stumps are subject to a variety of unpleasant or painful sensations whenever a change of weather is about to occur, from dry to wet, or rather when we are about to have an easterly storm. The certainty with which some persons who have had limbs amputated can predict such a change is curious and puzzling, and renders likely the existence of peculiarities in these storms which our instruments have as yet failed to discover.

After questioning closely fifty persons, the following are the conclusions reached:

Less than half the number feel no nerve sensation upon the coming or during the continuance of an east wind; of the remainder, two-thirds insist upon their power to foretell such a change of weather, and are positive that they are unaffected by the onset of a thunderstorm, or of southerly rains, although as to the latter point some of them feel doubtful.

I have never had the chance of absolutely testing the power of any such patients to predict a storm, but the intelligence and character of a few of my witnesses lend force to statements like their own coming from less responsible persons.

Aching pains and twitching of the stump muscles, with sensations of various kinds, motor or sensory, referred to the lost part, are the symptoms which are described as preceding an east wind,* and in many cases as persisting until their sudden cessation foretells an impending change of weather.

Many stumps are liable to slight pain during the performance of certain normal reflex actions. I have seen one person who has a sharp pang in the arm-stump (left) when he yawns, and others who always suffer more or less in leg-stumps (thigh) during defecation. The most common of such referred sensations is the pain which is felt in thigh-stumps during micturition. A highly intelligent gentleman first mentioned this to me, and assured me that it was quite frequent among the amputated, with numbers of whom his business had brought him into relation. Since then I have had repeated evidence of the truth of his statement. The pain comes on at the beginning of the act of passing water, and is felt in the stump, and sometimes down the lost leg. Professor Gross, in his Surgery, speaks of incontinence of urine as apt to follow for a time thigh amputations. I have only seen two persons in whom there was any such symptom at a later date. Both were high amputations.

---

* As every physician knows, these feelings are common to many sufferers from rheumatic disease or maladies of the bones.

Guéniot* speaks of the same symptom in a woman who lost her arm at the shoulder.

Motor phenomena.—The ease and dexterity with which many persons use their stumps evince how little the muscles may suffer. Excepting near to their attachment to the divided bone or to the tissues of the cicatrix, the muscles I have examined were sound. In most mobile stumps they react with electricity as well as those of the entire limb, and in patients afflicted with twitching or choreoid movements, so called, they are often over-excitable, and very sensitive to the pain caused by induced currents.

The motility of muscular stumps is very apt to be disturbed by mental emotions, and even the most healthy are liable, when excited, to sudden and annoying discharges of motor nerve power. These are sometimes only fibrillar spasms, in others they are cramp-like, and in some are productive of sudden and violent motion in one direction. They are apt to cause pain, even severe pain, and are most common in the arm and in patients who suffer constantly with twitching of the stump. I have attended one gentleman who has a very useful arm-stump, but who at times is compelled to seize and confine it at the side in order to terminate a spasm of the deltoid, which gives great pain in the nerve tracks, and which has once at least been the starting-point of a sharp attack of neuritis. While emotion may cause involuntary movement, it may also check choreiform spasms, as in the case of Colonel Parr, whose arm-stump was never at repose a moment, except when, at Cedar Mountain, his regiment being cut off for a time, and in danger of being taken,—the restless limb was seen for some hours to hang motionless at his

---

* D'une Hallucination du Toucher, Journal de la Physiologie, 1861, p. 418.

side. In another instance of remarkable and constant
motions of an arm-stump, they ceased for some hours
after the patient had emerged unhurt from the wreck of
a railway accident.

Sensory hallucinations.—No history of the physiology of
stumps would be complete without some account of the
sensorial delusions to which persons are subject in connection with their lost limbs. These hallucinations are
so vivid, so strange, and so little dwelt upon by authors,
as to be well worthy of study, while some of them seem
to me especially valuable, owing to the light which
they cast upon the subject of the long-disputed muscular
sense.

Nearly every man who loses a limb carries about with
him a constant or inconstant phantom of the missing
member, a sensory ghost of that much of himself, and
sometimes a most inconvenient presence, faintly felt at
times, but ready to be called up to his perception by a
blow, a touch, or a change of wind.

Ambrose Paré* remarked upon the curious fact that
the absent limb is felt as if existing, and in some of the
earlier treatises on amputation the same symptom is ex-
pressly noticed. Among ninety cases, including a great
variety of amputations, I have found but four cases—two
of an arm, the others of legs—in which there never had
been delusion as to the presence of the absent member.
None of these cases were in any way singular as to
the state of the stump or other symptoms, but three of the
four were persons of inferior intellect, laborers by occupation. In one of the arm cases, I carefully faradised the
brachial plexus without obtaining from the patient any
indication of subjective feelings referred to the lost parts.
Nor was he ever conscious, under any circumstances, of

---

* Œuvres Complètes, edit. Malgaigne, t. ii. pp. 221 and 231, Paris.

such phenomena. I confess myself unable to explain these exceptions.

The sensation of the presence of the part removed exists in many persons as soon as they come from under the influence of the anæsthetic used at the time of the amputation, but in others it only arises after they cease to suffer pain, being rarely delayed beyond three weeks. The more healthy the stump, the less perfect after a time becomes the sense of the existence of the limb removed, while it is liable to be recalled by a blow or anything which causes a return of subjective sensations. In one case the foot was scarcely felt as present, when a second amputation above the knee restored permanently the faded consciousness of the part below the first point of operation. Even in those who are least conscious of the missing part, I have amazed them by suddenly recalling it with the aid of a faradaic current applied to the nerves of the stump. It is not easy to forget the astonishment with which some of these persons reawaken to a perception of the long-lost leg or arm.

I recently faradised a case of disarticulated shoulder without warning my patient of the possible result. For two years he had altogether ceased to feel the limb. As the current affected the brachial plexus of nerves, he suddenly cried aloud, "Oh, the hand, the hand!" and attempted to seize the missing member. The phantom I had conjured up swiftly disappeared, but no spirit could have more amazed the man, so real did it seem. Very many have a constant sense of the existence of the limb, a consciousness even more intense than exists for the remaining member. "If," says one, "I should say I am more sure of the leg which aint than the one which are, I guess I should be about correct." Where there is subjective pain, or itching, or sense of cramp, and the like, the limb is unceasingly felt, but in nearly all cases the

most absurd mishaps occasionally remind a man at once
of his loss, and of the obstinacy of the consciousness of
the limb's existence. The sufferer who has lost a leg gets
up in the night to walk, or he tries to rub or scratch it.
One of my cases attempted, when riding, to pick up his
bridle with the lost hand, while he struck his horse with the
other, and was reminded of his mistake by being thrown.
Another person, for nearly a year, tried at every meal to
pick up his fork, and was so disturbed emotionally at the
result as frequently to be nauseated, or even to vomit.

The site of the amputation does not seem to exercise
any influence upon the consciousness of the existence of
the limb, but in time, if not reminded by pain or other
subjective symptom, the patient is apt to lose sense of the
presence of the part, and this, I think, is most liable to
occur as regards the leg.

The limb is rarely felt as a whole; nearly always the
foot or the hand is the part more distinctly recognized,
and, on careful questioning, we learn that the fingers and
toes are readily perceived; next to these the thumb; then
more rarely the ankle or wrist; and, still less frequently,
the elbow and knee. Very often some fingers are best
felt, especially the forefinger. On the other hand, there
is, in but few cases, any consciousness of the parts which
intervene between the stump and the extremity of the
limb. The patients describe themselves as knowing that
they have a hand which is connected to the stump, and
feel able to move it, but of the rest of the limb they are
unconscious, and the subjective sensations which are so
common are always referred to the hand or foot, and
rarely to the continuity of the member.*

---

* These facts are not confined to lost limbs or parts of limbs. The
amputated breast is often felt as if present, and the lost penis is subject to
erections, of which Dr. Ruschenberger, U. S. N., has related to me a
remarkable example.

Closely related to these facts is a curious symptom, which M. Guéniot (op. cit.) was the first to describe. In about one-third of the leg cases, and in one-half of the arm amputations, the patient asserts that the foot or hand, as the case may be, is felt to be nearer to the trunk than is the extremity of the other limb. The lost limb seems to be shortened. This is a sensation which, in many cases, is first felt within a week of the amputation, and goes on progressively, the hand, for instance, slowly approaching the stump. Very often the change is not noticed until attention is called to it, although usually the gradual alteration is recognized during its occurrence. The phantom hand at last reaches a point where it ceases to move, and this may be at almost any part of the intervening distance which once separated it from the seat of operation. Sometimes it continues to approach the trunk until it touches the stump, or lies seemingly in its interior,—the shadow within the substance.

We are competent in health, even with closed eyes, to know where and how far removed the hand may be at any moment, and this knowledge is the result of long-continued and complicated sensory impressions, ocular, muscular, and tactile. Should we lose these by amputation, we cease to have consciousness of the extremity of a limb as set at any fixed distance. Such is very nearly the explanation which M. Guéniot offers in his interesting account of the delusion in question, but we fail to learn from him why, after losing sense of the distance of the hand or foot, these should seem to approach the stump. Wherefore, indeed, should they not appear to recede? Perhaps the following explanation may assist us to answer this question. To the lost hand alone are sensations referred. There are none in the intervening portions of the lost limb, and the stump is the lowest visible point where pain or touch is felt; and therefore it is that the sensorium learns by degrees to associate in place the lost hand, which seems to feel, with the stump, the latter being the lowest existent point impressions on which are referred to the hand.   Now, we may conceive that if, for motor purposes, we substitute for the lost limb an artificial member which does not possess feeling, the sense of sight will soon refer, in our consciousness, the hand or foot to its old position.   Exactly this is described as occurring by two observant and acute persons who have lost legs.   One of them, who sees in his business capacity hundreds of the amputated every year, assures me that his experience is a common one.   He lost his leg at the age of eleven, and remembers that the foot by degrees approached, and at last reached, the knee.   When he began to wear an artificial leg it reassumed, in time, its old position, and he is never, at present, aware of the leg as shortened, unless for some time he talks and thinks of the stump and of the missing leg, when, as happens in many who have submitted to amputation, the direction of attention to the part causes a feeling of discomfort, and the subjective sensation of active and unpleasant movement of the toes.   With these feelings returns at once the delusion of the foot as being placed at the knee.

Guéniot is of opinion that the hallucination as to the shortening of the limb is most apt to occur in cases of amputation which heal most kindly and offer the most healthy stumps.   I have been unable to make out any such relation.

Subjective sensations referred to the absent limb.—In a few cases there is no distinct subjective symptom to remind the patient of his limb, but in nearly all there is some feeling, such as pain, itching, or other sensation.

I have found no one who ever had the subjective delusion of the lost part being touched; but itching is quite common, and is referred usually to the backs of the fingers, very rarely to the elbow, or, in the leg, to the arch of the foot. Many persons relieve this feeling by rubbing the stump; but others derive no benefit from this procedure.

I have elsewhere spoken of the sensitiveness of stumps to heat and cold. Some men have no subjective sensation due to thermal changes in the stump; but about one-third complain of coldness in the lost part when the stump is chilled, and of heat in it when the stump is warm. I tested this by dipping arm-stumps in iced-water or water at one hundred degrees Fahrenheit, and found that a few men experience a subjective sensation of heat and cold, but of the rest more feel a sensation of referred cold than of heat, and there is often some confusion as to whether the missing part experiences cold or heat, or is merely painful. Perhaps in these cases, the knowledge of the fact that cold or heat is being used on the stump inclines the patient, in whom there is thus produced any subjective impression, to consider it as heat or cold. I see no way of escape from this possible fallacy; but some of my best witnesses are confident as to the fact that a cold or hot stump makes a cold or hot limb; and if so, it is interesting in a physiological point of view to know that thermal impressions on the ends of nerves or on their continuity may occasion like sensations referred to the ultimate distributions. I have known persons who suffered in hot weather from sense of heat in the lost hand, and were able to ease it by using cold to the stump.

Subjective sensations as to motor phenomena in the lost limb.— The facts connected with subjective sensations of movement and as to delusions in regard to the position of the part are extremely curious.

Position.—Impressions regarding the leg are far less vivid than those connected with the arm. The former limb when lost seems to hang straight, and there is usu-

ally some difficulty in determining whether or not it
swings with the motions of the body in walking. In only
one case did it appear to be bent at the knee.

In fourteen arm amputations at divers points, the arm
seemed in two to hang at the side, and in seven to be
bent, the hand lying in air a little way from the left breast
or straight in front, and the hallucination as to position
being insisted on even by those who declared themselves
unconscious of the limb's continuity. The remaining five
felt the hand to be in the air, somewhere in front of the
chest, but had no consciousness of flexion at the elbow.
The posture of the lost hand may best be described by
simply quoting a few of the descriptions given me by
patients. In many it seems to be at rest, extended, the
fingers in a like posture; and these cases have usually, or
seem to themselves to have, the best power of voluntary
movements. Others carry with them a hand in a state of
more or less violent flexion, and possess but slight control over it. Another class has the hand constantly in
some painful position which it occupied before the operation, so that the last real sensation is so stamped upon the
sensorium as to forbid its erasure by any future impression. We have realized here, in regard to common sensation, the fable which describes the retina as retaining after
death the last picture which fell upon its living concavity.
These cases suffer horribly both from volitional efforts
and from such faradisation of the nerves as causes subjective motor sensations.

Mr. T. lost his arm five inches below the elbow at the
age of six years, eighteen years ago. The arm appears to
lie out from the side, the wrist flexed, the fingers semi-
flexed; every voluntary effort causes intense pain in the
stump; the hand seems to be at the elbow.

J. H., aged forty-two, lost his right arm four inches
above the elbow, twenty-four years ago. He feels the

presence of the whole limb more plainly than ever. The hand is described as half shut, the thumb standing out from the palm, the elbow and wrist half flexed.

W. S: lost his right arm at the upper fourth, and the left at the lower third, eleven years ago. Is conscious of the left arm throughout, less of the right, but neither seems shortened. Both hang at the sides extended, but at night, after being in bed some time, both arms are felt as if lying over the head, and as if bent at the elbows. The hands are tightly clinched, the wrists violently flexed at times, while occasionally the hands open of themselves.

E. C., aged thirty-two, lost his left arm five inches below the shoulder, nine years ago. When shot, the thumb turned into the palm, and continued in this state of spasm, so that when, six hours later, the limb was removed, the nail of the thumb had cut into the palm. He several times lifted the thumb, but it always returned to the same place. For nine years the absent thumb still remains cutting into the palm. The coming of a storm makes the spasm more severe and causes the fingers to close over it. The limb seems shortened six inches.

L. B., on account of a gunshot wound of the wrist, lost his forearm at the middle. He wears an artificial arm. He realizes the presence of the hand only. It is half flexed, hangs at his side, and is under full control of the will. The hand appears to be on the stump.

C. T., aged sixty, lost his right arm twenty years ago. It was crushed between two car buffers, and was taken off ten hours later. He wears no artificial arm. He feels the arm rather less distinctly than at first, but is more conscious of it than of the left arm. At present only the hand is perceived. It seems to lie in front of the chest pointing to the left, and is semi-flexed and capable of limited movement.

H. N., aged twenty-seven. Three years ago the hand was

crushed by rollers and removed at the middle of the fore-arm on the fourth day. He has no artificial limb. The hand is on the stump and tightly closed, the thumb over the fingers.

R. R., aged fifty-two. The right hand was caught be-tween two hot rollers and dreadfully burned, but not severely crushed. It rested in rigid extension on a pillow for two weeks, and was then taken off five inches below the elbow; does not use an artificial arm. The hand is felt as lying in extension; the fingers rigid, just as they were before the amputation. He can slightly stir them, the muscles in the forearm acting visibly, and the attempt causing pain. Efforts to move the intrinsic muscles of the hand also occasion pain, but he has very little con-sciousness of motion in the lost part, although the muscles of the stump act freely.

J. K., aged forty-four, has had his leg amputated thrice: once below the knee, once above it, and finally at the upper third of the thigh,—all fourteen years ago. The sensation of the presence of the toes, and rarely of the heel, continued throughout, but has of late lessened, so that unless the stump has been hurt he does not feel fully conscious of the lost parts.

A. M., aged twenty-four, had his right hand injured by the discharge of a cannon. Has no artificial limb. Am-putation was performed two inches below the elbow; the stump is very tender, the hand seems half way up the arm, the fingers are shut, the thumb lying over them. Can stir the thumb, but not the fingers.

J. C., aged thirty-one, received a wound in the elbow, for which amputation at the lower third of the arm was performed four hours later. The stump is healthy; it has no artificial arm. The lost hand lies seemingly in the stump. He is most conscious of the index and medius fingers, which are always painful and intensely cramped; there is no perception of the wrist or elbow.

The lost limb, and especially the arm, is usually found to follow the movements of the stump, whether these be passive or active, while in some instances it never leaves its place, or else there is only a vague sense of its common position having been disturbed.

Involuntary movements of the absent toes or fingers are frequent, and in very many persons are unfailing precursors of an east wind. Sometimes only one finger is thus active, or the digits flex one after another, and then slowly extend, while wrist movements are exceptionally rare, and the elbow and knee are never felt to change place at all.

Leaving out of the question cases which have no sense of the presence of a lost limb, we find that in a very small number there is no consciousness of power to stir any part of the absent members by force of will. All others are able to will a movement, and apparently to themselves to execute it more or less effectively, although in most of the amputated such phantom motions are confined to the fingers or toes, which rarely seem to possess the normal range either of flexion or extension. Yet the certainty with which these patients describe the limitations of motion, and their confidence as to the place assumed by the parts moved, are truly remarkable; while these restricted movements are pretty surely painful, and the effort is apt to excite twitching in the stump.

A small number have entire and painless freedom of motion as regards all parts of the hand. "My hand is now open, or it is shut," they say. "I touch the thumb with the little finger." "The hand is now in the writing position," etc. Between these cases and such as are conscious of an immobile member, every grade of difference as to motion is to be found, with equally wide varieties as to the associated pain, which perhaps is most acute in such as will with vigor a motion that they seem to fail of executing.

In some of these cases, as in forearm amputations low down, the muscles which chiefly move the fingers are present, wholly or in part, and move readily under volitional impulses, so that whatever knowledge of movements comes to the sensorium through the muscles moved is here not wanting.

In others, as in shoulder-joint cases or amputations through the humerus, the muscles which act on the hand are absent altogether; yet in these there is fully as clear and definite a consciousness of the movement of the fingers and of their change of positions as in the former cases.   In other words, the volition to move certain parts is accompanied by a mental condition which represents to the consciousness the amount of motion, its force and ideas of the change of place in the parts so willed to move.

The physiology of the day accepts the belief that all of our accurate notions as to the amount of power put forth, and as to the parts thus stirred, reach the sensorium from the muscles acted on and the parts moved.   It would appear, however, from the statements here made, as if coevally with the willing of a motion there came to the consciousness, perhaps from the spinal ganglia acted upon, some information as to these points.   If, in reply to this, I be told that the constancy of long habit may have associated memorially with certain ganglionic activities the ideas of local movements, I should hardly feel that this was an answer, because in some of my cases the amputations took place so early in life that there was no remembrance of the lost limb, and yet twenty years after, a volition directed to the hand seemed to cause movement which appeared to be as capable of definite regulation, and was as plainly felt to occur as if it had been the other arm which was moved.   Probably, then, a part of those ideas which we are presumed to obtain through the muscular sense are really coincident with, and necessitated by, the originative act of will, or else are messages sent to the sensorium from the spinal ganglia which every act of motor volition excites.

The influence of electrical currents on the nerves of the stump introduces into our calculations certain novel and puzzling considerations.

If we faradise the track of the nerves in or above the stump, we may cause the lost fingers and thumb to seem to be flexed or extended, and, what is most remarkable, parts of which the man is conscious, but which he has not tried to stir for years, may thus be made to appear to move to his utter amazement. In one case I thus acted on the nerves, so as to cause a thumb which for years was constantly and violently bent in on the palm to straighten out completely. On breaking the circuit, without warning, the patient exclaimed that his thumb was cutting the palm again, and the same result was obtained by shifting the conductors so as to put the nerves out of the circuit.

In a case of amputation at the shoulder-joint, in which all consciousness of the limb had long since vanished, I suddenly faradised the brachial plexus, when the patient said at once, " My hand is there again. It is bent all up and hurts me." These impressions are correctly referred by the patient, so that faradisation of the musculo-spiral or the ulnar gives sensation of movement in the related parts. It is of course impossible that the motor nerves stimulated should convey any impression centrally, and we must therefore conclude that irritation of sensory trunks may occasion impressions of muscular motion in the sensorium.

It would appear, then, that when we will a movement, there arises coincidently, or from the spinal ganglia through which it is carried out, impressions as to the force of the act and the position of the parts which we

will to move; so that given the volition, there springs up
in the mind a consciousness as to the act and its qualities,
which is too generally believed to originate altogether
from the external parts disturbed. On the other hand,
the second series of experiments proves, or makes probable, that certain nerves carry centrally, during motion,
impressions which, with those nascent in the centres
when the act is willed, go to complete the general knowledge as to motor activities. The subject admits of much
further study and of other inferences, which, however,
are scarcely entitled to a place here, but are related in an
interesting way to the group of ataxial diseases.

Neuralgia of stumps.—I have elsewhere said that many
stumps are extremely sensitive, and this is especially true
of the arm. In these cases it will almost always be found,
upon careful examination, that certain nerves are enlarged,
hardened, and tender. I have relieved a number of such
cases by cold, by repeated leeching, and by general irritation of the surface of the stump.

Acute neuralgia of stumps is happily more rare. It
sometimes follows the operation closely, or is brought on
by a blow or by more occult causes. In one case it came
on during an attack of acute rheumatism; in another
from an influenza; and I have seen two instances where a
sudden spasmodic motion of the arm-stump was followed
at once by intense pain, and seemed to be the starting-
point of an attack of neuritis. One of these cases I saw
with Dr. Packard. It yielded to leeches and hot fomentations after much torment. So far, indeed, as my own
experience goes, old stump neuralgias never exist without
a sclerotic state of the nerve,—originating, I presume,
in neuritis, and tending without fail to progress centrally.

The rules for treating neuritis of course apply here, and
every care should be taken to deal early and boldly with
indications of neural pain in stumps.

The torture endured in some of these cases must be extreme. The pain is often unceasing, and is usually referred to the lost limb, or, as the case progresses, to the stump itself; while in some curious instances, as in Nott's case, it is never felt or referred below this point. The aching and shooting pains are finally complicated by excessive hyperæsthesia of the stump, with all the mental and moral consequences which prolonged and constant pain engenders. Opiates in excess become at last the only comfort, and even these may fail to give entire relief.

I have treated several of the moderately severe forms of this disease. All of them were removed by months or years from the date of operation. In four, which were arm cases, one below and three above the elbow, the nerves were exquisitely tender and enlarged for some distance above the stump. In another patient, they were tender but not perceptibly larger. One case I failed to relieve, and he declined an operation. Three others were successfully treated by leeches at intervals, with hypodermic injections of morphia and atropia, and large, warm poultices, applied constantly. One proved obstinate, yet was relieved, but not quite completely, by a short mercurial course, mercurial ointment being used over the arm-stump and axilla until slight salivation took place. The gain was permanent, but was not so great as in the other instances. I have seen no example of the terrible forms of this disease which some authors describe, and which require section of nerves or reamputation for their relief. The history of such operations is by no means encouraging, and too often one operation follows another without permanent help to the patient. The reason for these failures lies in the fact that the disease of the nerve passes gradually upward, and that an operation, being unfortunately looked upon as a last resort, is put off until by degrees the whole nerve trunk is so completely involved that there remains no healthy portion of nerve in which to perform neurotomy; while to leave any of the sclerotic nerve above the line of section is only to make probable future suffering.

Whatever hesitation as to nerve section may be reasonable in other cases, there should be but little as regards stumps: first, because delay is apt to make useless any operation; and secondly, because division of nerves in stumps is productive of so little loss of valuable function. When, then, the pain is intense and lasting, and does not readily yield, and the nerve trunks are tender, I should strongly advise an early resection of the nerve as high up the limb as possible.

The operation should be such as to provide against re-union, by means already described;* and if on microscopic examination of the exsected portion of nerve it prove to be diseased, it would be advisable at once to divide it still higher; or if this be impossible, the central part of the nerve should be actively treated by leeching, by counter-irritants, and, perhaps, by cold.

Large numbers of operations for the relief of stump neuralgia have failed because of attempts to remove only the button-like enlargements at the ends of the nerves, under the impression, not always erroneous, that in these growths lies the cause of mischief. I fancy these, however, to be but rarely the cause of trouble, and the opinion is mischievous, because it postpones a more radical operation.

Dr. Nott's case, which I have elsewhere related,† is a good example of progressive neuritis extending toward the centres, consequent neuralgia, and mischievous delay

---

* See Neurotomy, p. 282.
† See p. 240, Treatment.

in performing the operation for relief early enough and far enough up the limb.

Chorea of stumps.—I find nowhere any detailed account of the disease which, for lack of a better name, I have called chorea of the stump. The muscles of stumps, of arm-stumps especially, are constantly in what I might call a condition of unstable equilibrium, liable to act irregularly under volition, or to contract spasmodically from emotion or from changes in the weather. The mere act of thinking of the lost limb, or the concentration of attention upon the stump, will, in many, suffice to excite tremor, irregular brief contractions, or cramp; while in some persons quite violent spasms occur without any assignable cause.

The stump muscles or nerves are in the condition of those of a person fully charged with strychnia, ready to respond excessively and without regularity to every excitation, and this is especially true of irritable stumps on which no artificial limb can be worn. Owing to this state of excitability, it is easy in many stumps to cause twitching, or still freer movement, by rolling the nerves under the compressing finger, or by pushing them aside, and then suddenly releasing them, vibrating them, so to speak. These nerves are in just such a state as may be brought about artificially in a healthy nerve by chilling it with ice, when the least tap will occasion sudden spasm. No wonder, then, that more permanent spastic affections of stumps are occasionally met with.

I have myself seen and treated but two instances of well-marked choreoid disease, although through other physicians I have had partial experience of a number of cases.

Case 67.—I. C. suffered amputation of the left arm, in Georgia, in 1863, for a wound of the forearm. I examined him once, a year later, and have not heard of him since. While the stump was yet unhealed, in the fifth week, the biceps began to twitch, and finally union was only attained by bandaging the limb firmly. From that time the arm was constantly subject to spasms, which jerked it forward with clocklike regularity and with great force. When an effort was made to secure the stump to his side, the movements attacked the shoulder, but ceased when the stump was set free. There was also slight twitching of the left facial muscles, and occasionally some irregularity in the vocal muscles, causing him to speak with difficulty. The general health was good, but memory was defective, and the man, who was a mendicant, was unwilling to take the chance of relief which division of the neural supply of the biceps seemed to offer. The motions ceased at night. I understood that he had had a great variety of fruitless treatment, and his arm showed signs of some of it. The following case was more satisfactory as a history. I have already had occasion to allude to it.

Case 68.—*Gunshot wound of right wrist; immediate amputation; choreal affection of muscles of the stump of the right forearm and of the shoulder.* Colonel J. G. P., aged forty-one, 139th Pennsylvania Volunteers, an officer of high character, in good health up to the date of wound, was shot, June 3, 1864, through the right wrist with a slug. He became at once singularly excited, and felt as if he were crazed. Under the sudden influence of these sensations, he ran along the line of his regiment, only half conscious, until he fell senseless, having gone about fifty feet. Within a few minutes he revived, and was assisted to a hospital near by, where Dr. Chapin, surgeon of the regiment, amputated his forearm at the junction of the lower and middle thirds.

Colonel P. never remained in bed, but continued in active service while the wound healed. This process was over about September 20, 1864. At this date some one

remarked to him that his stump shook a good deal, thus
first attracting his attention to the spasmodic motions.
Within a month the quivering extended to all the muscles
of the forearm, except the extensor group, and at the
close of the second month it attacked the biceps, triceps,
and deltoid. In November, a seton was carried through
the skin of the stump. For a day or two the limb was
much more quiet, but again became worse. Tincture of
aconite was used locally without relief. A firm bandage
applied to the whole limb produced no good result, the
movements getting constantly worse. At length a large
part of the cicatrix of the stump was dissected out. For
a few days he did better, and then relapsed, as happened
after the use of other remedies.

March 1, 1865.—The forearm is incessantly in motion,
the muscles quivering in a singular manner, night and
day, whether asleep or awake. Every twenty seconds, or
oftener, the forearm is suddenly flexed, and more rarely
the arm is thrown across the chest by the pectoral group,
or upward and outward by the deltoid. These movements are beginning to involve the trunk and neck muscles of the right side. They are increased if attention
be drawn to them, but they still allow him to make
regular voluntary movements, and do not seem to interfere with or disturb this volitional control, as happens in the chorea of children. The moment his will
ceases to act, the spasms recur, but he does not feel
any fatigue from this endless muscular action. All
the muscles move readily under induced electric currents. The stump is not unusually tender, and there is
no soreness in the nerve tracks when tested by heat or
pressure. Colonel P.'s general health is suffering somewhat, but at no time, except during the few days of leave
which he sought in order to consult me, has he failed to
do duty in the field. On one occasion only is he aware

that the arm ceased to move. This occurred at the battle
of Cedar Mountain, when, his regiment having been cut
off, he was in grave danger of capture. He fought his
way out and saved his command. During the two or
three hours of suspense, and while constantly under fire,
his men observed that his arm ceased to move, and hung
motionless at his side.

I felt strongly disposed to consider these movements as
caused by some nerve lesion originally confined to the
stump, and occasioning in the centres an excitation which
gave rise reflectively to the spasms. To test this, I proposed to inject a paralyzing agent into the neighborhood
of the main nerve trunks, and failing thus to check the
conveyance of irritations to the centres, I should have
wished to divide the chief nerves in the arm. This, of
course, would have paralyzed the lower muscles concerned. If, then, it were found that the deltoid and
pectoralis still twitched, I should have concluded that the
nerves were diseased above the point of section; and as to
this, some judgment could have been formed by examining with the microscope the portion of nerve removed by
the knife. After this there would have been no surgical
remedy, excepting section of the brachial plexus in the
neck,—an operation which, I presume, might offer some
embarrassments.

As Colonel P. was obliged to return to duty at once, I
contented myself with ordering him to have two setons
carried through the stump, and to take increasing doses
of bromide of potassium thrice daily.

He was severely wounded in the left side, March 25th,
1865, and lay insensible for some time, although the limb
all the while twitched as usual. He recovered readily, and,
under date of April 17th, wrote that the limb had ceased
to jump as freely as it had done, but was never quite still.
I saw Colonel P. again, September 29. The arm, at this

time, rarely executed any violent or wide movements; but the forearm was much the same as his letter described it to have been in April. A greater gain was visible in the chest, neck, and trunk, the muscles of which no longer twitched. His general health was better, and he had become quite robust. I desired him to renew the treatment as soon as he was at rest in any one place, and hoped to persuade him at a future period to allow of some such operation as I have alluded to above.

I have heard of Colonel P. very recently, and learned that he has still the same movements, but is otherwise in perfect health.

I alluded in the medical volume of "Sanitary Reports" to a case of chorea following amputation of the thumb, but have, unfortunately, no notes of it. The choreoid motions extended from the intrinsic thumb muscles to the arm and shoulder, and after a year or more became limited again to the forearm. The patient was cauterized, blistered, treated by setons, and by an endless variety of drugs, without avail.

Full doses of the bromides seemed to be of some use in Colonel P.'s case. In the localized chorea of adults, I cannot boast of success with these drugs, with any form of electricity, or with other means of treatment, and there seems to me to be much resemblance between these cases and the no less persistent form of chorea in stumps.

To this obstinacy in the face of all therapeutic interference I can make but one exception. An officer had incessant movement of the biceps muscle of an arm-stump. The spasm was annoying, but rarely violent, and was limited to the upper two-thirds of the muscle, the line of amputation having passed through it. In this case, daily injections of atropia ($\frac{1}{30}$ to $\frac{1}{50}$ grain) into the mass of the muscle, entirely relieved him after nearly twenty such applications.

I think that it would be justifiable in these cases to divide the nerves concerned in the motions; but I should feel cautious and anxious about any such operation, having seen two instances in which operations for other causes proved fatal in adult chorea. ,

Choreal spasms with neuralgia.—There are also examples of chorea in stumps associated with intense pain, and it is not uncommon to find that in certain persons the rare spasmodic movements of stump muscles are accompanied by neuralgic paroxysms, just as happens in certain facial tics, and more rarely in such instances of general neuralgia as I have described elsewhere.*

A distressing example of this combination is related by Mr. Langstaff.† The forearm of a woman was removed on account of neuralgia from injury, and, healing with difficulty, there ensued a constant state of convulsive action in the stump muscles with agonizing pain. A great variety of treatment failed to relieve her. The skin over the bones was red and sore, the arteries beat with extreme violence, frequent convulsive fits followed, and her general health gave way. The limb was finally reamputated above the elbow, when the nerves were found to be greatly enlarged and to end in the stump in the usual button-like growths. Entire and continued relief was obtained by the operation.

---

* Reports of Philadelphia College of Physicians, 1869.
† Med.-Chir. Trans., v. xvi. p. 140.

INDEX.

25   (369)

Sensation, reference of, 48.
  why less injured than motion, 188.
Sense of locality, 185.
  muscular acts, 358.
  of pain, 187.
  of shortening in lost limbs, 351, 352.
Sensibility, how examined, 84, 182.
  of stumps, 344.
  prognosis as to, 227.
Sensitive nerves, terminations of in skin, 18.
Sensory hallucination after amputation, 348.
  lesions, 179.
  counter-irritation in, 266.
Shock, 138.
  cases of, 144.
  effects of, on motility, 140.
  proportion of cases feeling, 139.
  theory of, 139, 142, 144.
Skin, change of, in partial nerve lesions, 152.
  nutrition of, how altered by nerve wounds, 151.
Spasm, atropia in, 258.
  from rheumatism, 257.
  immediate, from nerve wound, 138.
  of muscles, causing neuritis, 343.
  local, 202.
  muscular, 203.
  treatment of, 257.
Spinal palsy, diagnosis of, 223.
Stewart, J. L., exsection of median, 298.
Stich, diagnosis of local paralyses, 224.
Stimulants, neural, 49.
Stöhrer, battery of, 248.
Stricker, structure of nerves, 17.
Strychnia, hypodermic injections of, 251.
  in nerve lesions, 251.
Stumps, chorea of, 363.
  influence on, of weather, 345.
  motility of, 347.
  motor phenomena in, 347.
  neuralgia of, 360.
  neuralgia of, treatment, 361.
  neural maladies of, 343.
  neuromata of, 343.
  neuro-physiology of, 343.

Stumps, sensibility of, 344.
Sutures in nerve wounds, 235.
  of nerves, 237, 238, 242.
  how to make, 242.
  Vulpian on, 242, 243.
Swan, callus, pressure from, 118.
  on intermittent traumatic pain 195.
  on lancet wounds of nerves, 89.
  on contusion, 96.
  wounds of small nerves, 89.
Sweat, changes of, in nerve wounds, 173.
Sympathetic nerve, wound of, 318.
  pressure on, in labor, 124.

Tactile corpuscles, 19.
Temperature, after physiological sections of nerves, 176.
  Bernard on, 176.
  changes of, in nerve wounds, cause of, 175.
  fall of, in compression of nerves, 178.
  in causalgia, 175.
  in nerve wounds, 255.
  range of, in nerve lesions, 174.
  rise of, after massage, 250.
Tension, loss of muscular, in nerve sections, 150.
Tetanus, 147.
Theories of shock, Brown-Sequard, 142.
Thermal delusions as to lost limbs, 353.
Thermometer, how to use, 174.
Tillaux, 236, 238.
  on diagnosis, 221.
  strength of nerves, 22, 23.
Traumatic neuralgia, statistics of operations for, 288.
Treatment, 229.
  of causalgia, 272.
  of chorea, 367.
  of contusion, 229, 230.
  of hyperæsthetic states, 266.
  of incised wounds, 234.
  of joint diseases, 258, 259.
  of lancet wounds, 233.
  of neuralgia, 267.
  of pain, 270.
  of sensory lesions, 265.
Tremor of muscles, 203.
Trophic centres, 74.

CATALOGUE OF DOVER BOOKS

Medicine

CLASSICS OF MEDICINE AND SURGERY, edited by C. N. B. Camac. 12 greatest papers in medical history, 11 in full: Lister's "Antiseptic Principle;" Harvey's "Motion in the Heart and Blood;" Auenbrugger's "Percussion of the Chest;" Laënnec's "Auscultation and the Stethoscope;" Jenner's "Inquiry into Smallpox Vaccine," 2 related papers; Morton's "Administering Sulphuric Ether," letters to Warren, "Physiology of Ether;" Simpson's "A New Anaesthetic Agent;" Holmes' "Puerperal Fever." Biographies, portraits of authors, bibliographies. Formerly "Epoch-making Contributions to Medicine, Surgery, and the Allied Sciences." Introduction. 14 illus. 445pp. 5⅜ x 8. S539 Paperbound **$2.25**

A WAY OF LIFE, Sir William Osler. The complete essay, stating his philosophy of life, as given at Yale University by this great physician and teacher. 30 pages. Copies limited, no more than 1 to a customer. Free.

SOURCE BOOK OF MEDICAL HISTORY, compiled, annotated by Logan Clendening, M.D. Unequalled collection of 139 greatest papers in medical history, by 120 authors, covers almost every area: pathology, asepsis, preventive medicine, bacteriology, physiology, etc. Hippocrates, Gain, Vesalius, Malpighi, Morgagni, Boerhave, Pasteur, Walter Reed, Florence Nightingale, Lavoisier, Claude Bernard, 109 others, give view of medicine unequalled for immediacy. Careful selections give heart of each paper save you reading time. Selections from non-medical literature show lay-views of medicine: Aristophanes, Plato, Arabian Nights, Chaucer, Molière, Dickens, Thackeray, others. "Notable . . . useful to teacher and student alike," Amer. Historical Review. Bibliography. Index. 699pp. 5⅜ x 8. T621 Paperbound **$2.75**

EXPERIMENTS AND OBSERVATIONS ON THE GASTRIC JUICE AND THE PHYSIOLOGY OF DIGESTION, William Beaumont. A gunshot wound which left a man with a 2½ inch hole through his abdomen into his stomach (1822) enabled Beaumont to perform the remarkable experiments set down here. The first comprehensive, thorough study of motions and processes of the stomach, "his work remains a model of patient, persevering investigation. . . . Beaumont is the pioneer physiologist of this country." (Sir William Osler, in his introduction.) 4 illustrations. xi + 280pp. 5⅜ x 8. S527 Paperbound **$1.50**

AN INTRODUCTION TO THE STUDY OF EXPERIMENTAL MEDICINE, Claude Bernard. 90-year-old classic of medical science, only major work of Bernard available in English, records his efforts to transform physiology into exact science. Principles of scientific research illustrated by specific case histories from his work; roles of chance, error, preliminary false conclusions, in leading eventually to scientific truth; use of hypothesis. Much of modern application of mathematics to biology rests on the foundation set down here. New foreword by Professor I. B. Cohen, Harvard Univ. xxv + 266pp. 5⅜ x 8. T400 Paperbound **$1.50**

A WAY OF LIFE, AND OTHER SELECTED WRITINGS, Sir William Osler, Physician and humanist, Osler discourses brilliantly in thought provoking essays and on the history of medicine. He discusses Thomas Browne, Gui Patin, Robert Burton, Michael Servetus, William Beaumont, Laënnec. Includes such favorite writings as the title essay, "The Old Humanities and the New Science," "Creators, Transmitters, and Transmuters," "Books and Men," "The Student Life," and five more of his best discussions of philosophy, religion and literature. 5 photographs. Introduction by G. L. Keynes, M.D., F.R.C.S. Index. xx + 278pp. 5⅜ x 8. T488 Paperbound **$1.50**

THE HISTORY OF SURGICAL ANESTHESIA, Thomas E. Keys. Concise, but thorough and always engrossing account of the long struggle to find effective methods of eliminating pain during surgery, tracing the remarkable story through the centuries to the eventual successes by dedicated researchers, the acceptance of ether, the work of men such as Priestley, Morton, Lundy, and many, many others. Discussions of the developments in local, regional, and spinal anesthesia, etc. "The general reader as well as the medical historian will find material to interest him in this fascinating story," U.S. QUARTERLY BOOKLIST. Revised, enlarged publication of original edition. Introductory essay by C. D. Leake. Concluding chapter by N. A. Gillespie. Appendix by J. F. Fulton. 46 illustrations. New preface by the author. Chronology of events. Extensive bibliographies. Index. xxx + 193pp. 5⅜ x 8½. T1122 Paperbound **$2.00**

A SHORT HISTORY OF ANATOMY AND PHYSIOLOGY FROM THE GREEKS TO HARVEY, Charles Singer. Corrected edition of THE EVOLUTION OF ANATOMY, classic work tracing evolution of anatomy and physiology from prescientific times through Greek & Roman periods, Dark Ages, Renaissance, to age of Harvey and beginning of modern concepts. Centered on individuals, movements, periods that definitely advanced anatomical knowledge: Plato, Diocles, Aristotle, Theophrastus, Herophilus, Erasistratus, the Alexandrians, Galen, Mondino, da Vinci, Linacre, Sylvius, others. Special section on Vesalius; Vesalian atlas of nudes, skeletons, muscle tabulae. Index of names, 20 plates. 270 extremely interesting illustrations of ancient, medieval, Renaissance, Oriental origin. xii + 209pp. 5⅜ x 8. T389 Paperbound **$1.75**

Biological Sciences

AN INTRODUCTION TO GENETICS, A. H. Sturtevant and G. W. Beadle. A very thorough exposition of genetic analysis and the chromosome mechanics of higher organisms by two of the world's most renowned biologists, A. H. Sturtevant, one of the founders of modern genetics, and George Beadle, Nobel laureate in 1958. Does not concentrate on the biochemical approach, but rather more on observed data from experimental evidence and results . . . from Drosophila and other life forms. Some chapter titles: Sex chromosomes; Sex-Linkage; Autosomal Inheritance;; Chromosome Maps; Intra-Chromosomal Rearrangements; Inversions—and Incomplete Chromosomes; Translocations; Lethals; Mutations; Heterogeneous Populations; Genes and Phenotypes; The Determination and Differentiation of Sex; etc. Slightly corrected reprint of 1939 edition. New preface by Drs. Sturtevant and Beadle. 1 color plate. 126 figures. Bibliographies. Index. 391pp. 5⅜ x 8½. S306 Paperbound **$2.00**

THE GENETICAL THEORY OF NATURAL SELECTION, R. A. Fisher. 2nd revised edition of a vital reviewing of Darwin's Selection Theory in terms of particulate inheritance, by one of the great authorities on experimental and theoretical genetics. Theory is stated in mathematical form. Special features of particulate inheritance are examined: evolution of dominance, maintenance of specific variability, mimicry and sexual selection, etc. 5 chapters on man and his special circumstances as a social animal. 16 photographs. Bibliography. Index. x + 310pp. 5⅜ x 8. S466 Paperbound **$2.00**

THE ORIENTATION OF ANIMALS: KINESES, TAXES AND COMPASS REACTIONS, Gottfried S. Fraenkel and Donald L. Gunn. A basic work in the field of animal orientations. Complete, detailed survey of everything known in the subject up to 1940s, enlarged and revised to cover major developments to 1960. Analyses of simpler types of orientation are presented in Part I: kinesis, klinotaxis, tropotaxis, telotaxis, etc. Part II covers more complex reactions originating from temperature changes, gravity, chemical stimulation, etc. The two-light experiment and unilateral blinding are dealt with, as is the problem of determinism or volition in lower animals. The book has become the universally-accepted guide to all who deal with the subject—zoologists, biologists, psychologists, and the like. Second, enlarged edition, revised to 1960. Bibliography of over 500 items. 135 illustrations. Indices. xiii + 376pp. 5⅜ x 8½. T786 Paperbound **$2.25**

THE BEHAVIOUR AND SOCIAL LIFE OF HONEYBEES, C. R. Ribbands. Definitive survey of all aspects of honeybee life and behavior; completely scientific in approach, but written in interesting, everyday language that both professionals and laymen will appreciate. Basic coverage of physiology, anatomy, sensory equipment; thorough account of honeybee behavior in the field (foraging activities, nectar and pollen gathering, how individuals find their way home and back to food areas, mating habits, etc.); details of communication in various field and hive situations. An extensive treatment of activities within the hive community—food sharing, wax production, comb building, swarming, the queen, her life and relationship with the workers, etc. A must for the beekeeper, natural historian, biologist, entomologist, social scientist, et al. "An indispensable reference," J. Hambleton, BEES. "Recommended in the strongest of terms," AMERICAN SCIENTIST. 9 plates. 66 figures. Indices. 693-item bibliography. 252pp. 5⅜ x 8½. T1137 Paperbound **$2.00**

BIRD DISPLAY: AN INTRODUCTION TO THE STUDY OF BIRD PSYCHOLOGY, E. A. Armstrong. The standard work on bird display, based on extensive observation by the author and reports of other observers. This important contribution to comparative psychology covers the behavior and ceremonial rituals of hundreds of birds from gannet and heron to birds of paradise and king penguins. Chapters discuss such topics as the ceremonial of the gannet, ceremonial gaping, disablement reactions, the expression of emotions, the evolution and function of social ceremonies, social hierarchy in bird life, dances of birds and men, songs, etc. Free of technical terminology, this work will be equally interesting to psychologists and zoologists as well as bird lovers of all backgrounds. 32 photographic plates. New introduction by the author. List of scientific names of birds. Bibliography. 3-part index. 431pp. 5⅜ x 8½. T1128 Paperbound **$2.00**

THE SPECIFICITY OF SEROLOGICAL REACTIONS, Karl Landsteiner. With a Chapter on Molecular Structure and Intermolecular Forces by Linus Pauling. Dr. Landsteiner, winner of the Nobel Prize in 1930 for the discovery of the human blood groups, devoted his life to fundamental research and played a leading role in the development of immunology. This authoritative study is an account of the experiments he and his colleagues carried out on antigens and serological reactions with simple compounds. Comprehensive coverage of the basic concepts of immunolgy includes such topics as: The Serological Specificity of Proteins, Antigens, Antibodies, Artificially Conjugated Antigens, Non-Protein Cell Substances such as polysaccharides, etc., Antigen-Antibody Reactions (Toxin Neutralization, Precipitin Reactions, Agglutination, etc.). Discussions of toxins, bacterial proteins, viruses, hormones, enzymes, etc. in the context of immunological phenomena. New introduction by Dr. Merrill Chase of the Rockefeller Institute. Extensive bibliography and bibliography of author's writings. Index. xviii + 330pp. 5⅜ x 8½. S299 Paperbound **$2.00**

CATALOGUE OF DOVER BOOKS

CULTURE METHODS FOR INVERTEBRATE ANIMALS, P. S. Galtsoff, F. E. Lutz, P. S. Welch, J. G. Needham, eds. A compendium of practical experience of hundreds of scientists and technicians, covering invertebrates from protozoa to chordata, in 313 articles on 17 phyla. Explains in great detail food, protection, environment, reproduction conditions, rearing methods, embryology, breeding seasons, schedule of development, much more. Includes at least one species of each considerable group. Half the articles are on class insecta. Introduction. 97 illustrations. Bibliography. Index. xxix + 590pp. 5⅜ x 8.
S526 Paperbound **$2.75**

THE BIOLOGY OF THE LABORATORY MOUSE, edited by G. D. Snell. 1st prepared in 1941 by the staff of the Roscoe B. Jackson Memorial Laboratory, this is still the standard treatise on the mouse, assembling an enormous amount of material for which otherwise you spend hours of research. Embryology, reproduction, histology, spontaneous tumor formation, genetics of tumor transplantation, endocrine secretion & tumor formation, milk, influence & tumor formation, inbred, hybrid animals, parasites, infectious diseases, care & recording. Classified bibliography of 1122 items. 172 figures, including 128 photos. ix + 497pp. 6⅛ x 9¼.
S248 Clothbound **$6.00**

MATHEMATICAL BIOPHYSICS: PHYSICO-MATHEMATICAL FOUNDATIONS OF BIOLOGY, N. Rashevsky. One of most important books in modern biology, now revised, expanded with new chapters, to include most significant recent contributions. Vol. 1: Diffusion phenomena, particularly diffusion drag forces, their effects. Old theory of cell division based on diffusion drag forces, other theoretical approaches, more exhaustively treated than ever. Theories of excitation, conduction in nerves, with formal theories plus physico-chemical theory. Vol. 2: Mathematical theories of various phenomena in central nervous system. New chapters on theory of color vision, of random nets. Principle of optimal design, extended from earlier edition. Principle of relational mapping of organisms, numerous applications. Introduces into mathematical biology such branches of math as topology, theory of sets. Index. 236 illustrations. Total of 988pp. 5⅜ x 8.
S574 Vol. 1 (Books 1, 2) Paperbound **$2.50**
S575 Vol. 2 (Books 3, 4) Paperbound **$2.50**
2 vol. set **$5.00**

ELEMENTS OF MATHEMATICAL BIOLOGY, A. J. Lotka. A pioneer classic, the first major attempt to apply modern mathematical techniques on a large scale to phenomena of biology, biochemistry, psychology, ecology, similar life sciences. Partial Contents: Statistical meaning of irreversibility; Evolution as redistribution; Equations of kinetics of evolving systems; Chemical, inter-species equilibrium; parameters of state; Energy transformers of nature, etc. Can be read with profit even by those having no advanced math; unsurpassed as study-reference. Formerly titled ELEMENTS OF PHYSICAL BIOLOGY. 72 figures. xxx + 460pp. 5⅜ x 8.
S346 Paperbound **$2.45**

THE BIOLOGY OF THE AMPHIBIA, G. K. Noble, Late Curator of Herpetology at the Am. Mus. of Nat. Hist. Probably the most used text on amphibia, unmatched in comprehensiveness, clarity, detail. 19 chapters plus 85-page supplement cover development; heredity; life history; speciation; adaptation; sex, integument, respiratory, circulatory, digestive, muscular, nervous systems; instinct, intelligence, habits, environment, economic value, relationships, classification, etc. "Nothing comparable to it," C. H. Pope, Curator of Amphibia, Chicago Mus. of Nat. Hist. 1047 bibliographic references. 174 illustrations. 600pp. 5⅜ x 8.
S206 Paperbound **$2.98**

STUDIES ON THE STRUCTURE AND DEVELOPMENT OF VERTEBRATES, E. S. Goodrich. A definitive study by the greatest modern comparative anatomist. Exceptional in its accounts of the ossicles of the ear, the separate divisions of the coelom and mammalian diaphragm, and the 5 chapters devoted to the head region. Also exhaustive morphological and phylogenetic expositions of skeleton, fins and limbs, skeletal visceral arches and labial cartilages, visceral clefts and gills, vacular, respiratory, excretory, and peripheral nervous systems, etc., from fish to the higher mammals. 754 illustrations. 69 page biographical study by C. C. Hardy. Bibliography of 1186 references. "What an undertaking . . . to write a textbook which will summarize adequately and succinctly all that has been done in the realm of Vertebrate Morphology these recent years," Journal of Anatomy. Index. Two volumes. Total 906pp. 5⅜ x 8.
Two vol. set S449-50 Paperbound **$5.00**

A TREATISE ON PHYSIOLOGICAL OPTICS, H. von Helmholtz, Ed. by J. P. C. Southall. Unmatched for thoroughness, soundness, and comprehensiveness, this is still the most important work ever produced in the field of physiological optics. Revised and annotated, it contains everything known about the subject up to 1925. Beginning with a careful anatomical description of the eye, the main body of the text is divided into three general categories: The Dioptrics of the Eye (covering optical imagery, blur circles on the retina, the mechanism of accommodation, chromatic aberration, etc.); The Sensations of Vision (including stimulation of the organ of vision, simple and compound colors, the intensity and duration of light, variations of sensitivity, contrast, etc.); and The Perceptions of Vision (containing movements of the eyes, the monocular field of vision, direction, perception of depth, binocular double vision, etc.). Appendices cover later findings on optical imagery, refraction, ophthalmoscopy, and many other matters. Unabridged, corrected republication of the original English translation of the third German edition. 3 volumes bound as 2. Complete bibliography, 1911-1925. Indices. 312 illustrations. 6 full-page plates, 3 in color. Total of 1,749pp. 5⅜ x 8.
Two-volume set S15, 16 Clothbound **$15.00**

CATALOGUE OF DOVER BOOKS

INTRODUCTION TO PHYSIOLOGICAL OPTICS, James P. C. Southall, former Professor of Physics in Columbia University. Readable, top-flight introduction, not only for beginning students of optics, but also for other readers—physicists, biochemists, illuminating engineers, optometrists, psychologists, etc. Comprehensive coverage of such matters as the Organ of Vision (structure of the eyeball, the retina, the dioptric system, monocular and binocular vision, adaptation, etc.); The Optical System of the Eye (reflex images in the cornea and crystalline lens, Emmetropia and Ametropia, accommodation, blur circles on retina); Eye-Glasses; Eye Defects; Movements of the Eyeball in its Socket; Rod and Cone Vision; Color Vision; and other similar topics. Index. 134 figures. x +426pp. 5⅜ x 8.   S924 Paperbound **$2.25**

LIGHT, COLOUR AND VISION, Yves LeGrand. A thorough examination of the eye as a receptor of radiant energy and as a mechanism (the retina) consisting of light-sensitive cells which absorb light of various wave lengths—probably the most complete and authoritative treatment of this subject in print. Originally prepared as a series of lectures given at the Institute of Optics in Paris, subsequently enlarged for book publication. Partial contents: Radiant Energy—concept, nature, theories, etc., Sources of Radiation—artificial and natural, the Visual Receptor, Photometric Quantities, Units, Calculations, Retinal Illumination, Trivariance of Vision, Colorimetry, Luminance Difference Thresholds, Anatomy of the Retina, Theories of Vision, Photochemistry and Electro-physiology of the Retina, etc. Appendices, Exercises, with solutions. 500-item bibliography. Authorized translation by R. Hunt, J. Walsh, F. Hunt. Index. 173 illustrations. xiii + 512pp. 5⅜ x 8½.   S979 Clothbound **$10.00**

FINGER PRINTS, PALMS AND SOLES: AN INTRODUCTION TO DERMATOGLYPHICS, Harold Cummins and Charles Midlo. An introduction in non-technical language designed to acquaint the reader with a long-neglected aspect of human biology. Although a chapter dealing with fingerprint identification and the systems of classification used by the FBI, etc. has been added especially for this edition, the main concern of the book is to show how the intricate pattern of ridges and wrinkles on our fingers have a broader significance, applicable in many areas of science and life. Some topics are: the identification of two types of twins; the resolution of doubtful cases of paternity; racial variation; inheritance; the relation of fingerprints to body measurements, blood groups, criminality, character, etc. Classification and recognition of fundamental patterns and pattern types discussed fully. 149 figures. 49 tables. 361-item bibliography. Index. xii + 319pp. 5⅝ x 8⅜.   T778 Paperbound **$1.95**

Classics and histories

ANTONY VAN LEEUWENHOEK AND HIS "LITTLE ANIMALS," edited by Clifford Dobell. First book to treat extensively, accurately, life and works (relating to protozoology, bacteriology) of first microbiologist, bacteriologist, micrologist. Includes founding papers of protozoology, bacteriology; history of Leeuwenhoek's life; discussions of his microscopes, methods, language. His writing conveys sense of an enthusiastic, naive genius, as he looks at rainwater, pepper water, vinegar, frog's skin, rotifers, etc. Extremely readable, even for non-specialists. "One of the most interesting and enlightening books I have ever read," Dr. C. C. Bass, former Dean, Tulane U. School of Medicine. Only authorized edition. 400-item bibliography. Index. 32 illust. 442pp. 5⅜ x 8.   S594 Paperbound **$2.25**

THE GROWTH OF SCIENTIFIC PHYSIOLOGY, G. J. Goodfield. A compact, superbly written account of how certain scientific investigations brought about the emergence of the distinct science of physiology. Centers principally around the mechanist-vitalist controversy prior to the development of physiology as an independent science, using the arguments which raged around the problem of animal heat as its chief illustration. Covers thoroughly the efforts of clinicians and naturalists and workers in chemistry and physics to solve these problems—from which the new discipline arose. Includes the theories and contributions of: Aristotle, Galen, Harvey, Boyle, Bernard, Benjamin Franklin, Palmer, Gay-Lussac, Priestley, Spallanzani, and many others. 1960 publication. Biographical bibliography. 174pp. 5 x 7½.   T1066 Clothbound **$3.00**

MICROGRAPHIA, Robert Hooke. Hooke, 17th century British universal scientific genius, was a major pioneer in celestial mechanics, optics, gravity, and many other fields, but his greatest contribution was this book, now reprinted entirely from the original 1665 edition, which gave microscopy its first great impetus. With all the freshness of discovery, he describes fully his microscope, and his observations of cork, the edge of a razor, insects' eyes, fabrics, and dozens of other different objects. 38 plates, full-size or larger, contain all the original illustrations. This book is also a fundamental classic in the fields of combustion and heat theory, light and color theory, botany and zoology, hygrometry, and many other fields. It contains such farsighted predictions as the famous anticipation of artificial silk. The final section is concerned with Hooke's telescopic observations of the moon and stars. 323pp. 5⅜ x 8.   T8 Paperbound **$2.00**

Nature

AN INTRODUCTION TO BIRD LIFE FOR BIRD WATCHERS, Aretas A. Saunders. Fine, readable introduction to birdwatching. Includes a great deal of basic information on about 160 different varieties of wild birds—elementary facts not easily found elsewhere. Complete guide to identification procedures, methods of observation, important habits of birds, finding nests, food, etc. "Could make bird watchers of readers who never suspected they were vulnerable to that particular virus," CHICAGO SUNDAY TRIBUNE. Unabridged, corrected edition. Bibliography. Index. 22 line drawings by D. D'Ostilio. Formerly "The Lives of Wild Birds." 256pp. 5⅜ x 8½. T1139 Paperbound **$1.00**

LIFE HISTORIES OF NORTH AMERICAN BIRDS, Arthur Cleveland Bent. Bent's historic, all-encompassing series on North American birds, originally produced under the auspices of the Smithsonian Institution, now being republished in its entirety by Dover Publications. The twenty-volume collection forms the most comprehensive, most complete, most-used source of information in existence. Each study describes in detail the characteristics, range, distribution, habits, migratory patterns, courtship procedures, plumage, eggs, voice, enemies, etc. of the different species and subspecies of the birds that inhabit our continent, utilizing reports of hundreds of contemporary observers as well as the writings of the great naturalists of the past. Invaluable to the ornithologist, conservationist, amateur naturalist, and birdwatcher. All books in the series contain numerous photographs to provide handy guides for identification and study.

LIFE HISTORIES OF NORTH AMERICAN BIRDS OF PREY. Including hawks, eagles, falcons, buzzards, condors, owls, etc. Index. Bibliographies of 923 items. 197 full-page plates containing close to 400 photographs. Total of 907pp. 5⅜ x 8½.
Vol. I: T931 Paperbound **$2.50**
Vol. II: T932 Paperbound **$2.50**
The set Paperbound **$5.00**

LIFE HISTORIES OF NORTH AMERICAN SHORE BIRDS. Including 81 varieties of such birds as sandpipers, woodcocks, snipes, phalaropes, oyster catchers, and many others. Index for each volume. Bibliographies of 449 entries. 121 full-page plates including over 200 photographs. Total of 860 pp. 5⅜ x 8½.
Vol. I: T933 Paperbound **$2.35**
Vol. II: T934 Paperbound **$2.35**
The set Paperbound **$4.70**

LIFE HISTORIES OF NORTH AMERICAN WILD FOWL. Including 73 varieties of ducks, geese, mergansers, swans, etc. Index for each volume. Bibliographies of 268 items. 106 full-page plates containing close to 200 photographs. Total of 685pp. 5⅜ x 8½.
Vol. I: T285 Paperbound **$2.50**
Vol. II: T286 Paperbound **$2.50**
The set Paperbound **$5.00**

LIFE HISTORIES OF NORTH AMERICAN GULLS AND TERNS. 50 different varieties of gulls and terns. Index. Bibliography. 93 plates including 149 photographs. xii + 337pp. 5⅜ x 8½.
T1029 Paperbound **$2.75**

LIFE HISTORIES OF NORTH AMERICAN GALLINACEOUS BIRDS. Including partridge, quail, grouse, pheasant, pigeons, doves, and others. Index. Bibliography. 93 full-page plates including 170 photographs. xiii + 490pp. 5⅜ x 8½.
T1028 Paperbound **$2.75**

THE MALAY ARCHIPELAGO, Alfred Russel Wallace. The record of the explorations (8 years, 14,000 miles) of the Malay Archipelago by a great scientific observer. A contemporary of Darwin, Wallace independently arrived at the concept of evolution by natural selection, applied the new theories of evolution to later genetic discoveries, and made significant contributions to biology, zoology, and botany. This work is still one of the classics of natural history and travel. It contains the author's reports of the different native peoples of the islands, descriptions of the island groupings, his accounts of the animals, birds, and insects that flourished in this area. The reader is carried through strange lands, alien cultures, and new theories, and will share in an exciting, unrivalled travel experience. Unabridged reprint of the 1922 edition, with 62 drawings and maps. 3 appendices, one on cranial measurements. xvii + 515pp. 5⅜ x 8. T187 Paperbound **$2.00**

THE TRAVELS OF WILLIAM BARTRAM, edited by Mark Van Doren. This famous source-book of American anthropology, natural history, geography is the record kept by Bartram in the 1770's, on travels through the wilderness of Florida, Georgia, the Carolinas. Containing accurate and beautiful descriptions of Indians, settlers, fauna, flora, it is one of the finest pieces of Americana ever written. Introduction by Mark Van Doren. 13 original illustrations. Index. 448pp. 5⅜ x 8. T13 Paperbound **$2.00**

COMMON SPIDERS OF THE UNITED STATES, J. H. Emerton. Only non-technical, but thorough, reliable guide to spiders for the layman. Over 200 spiders from all parts of the country, arranged by scientific classification, are identified by shape and color, number of eyes, habitat and range, habits, etc. Full text, 501 line drawings and photographs, and valuable introduction explain webs, poisons, threads, capturing and preserving spiders, etc. Index. New synoptic key by S. W. Frost. xxiv + 225pp. 5⅜ x 8. T223 Paperbound **$1.45**

CATALOGUE OF DOVER BOOKS

LIFE HISTORIES OF NORTH AMERICAN MARSH BIRDS. A wealth of data on 54 different kinds of marsh bird (flamingo, ibis, bittern, heron, egret, crane, crake, rail, coot, etc.). Index. Bibliography. 98 full-page plates containing 179 black-and-white photographs. xiv + 392pp. 5⅜ x 8½.
T1082 Paperbound **$2.75**

LIFE HISTORIES OF NORTH AMERICAN DIVING BIRDS. Thirty-six different diving birds including grebe, loon, auk, murre, puffin, and the like. Index. Bibliography. 55 full-page plates (92 photographs). xiv + 239pp. 5⅜ x 8½.
T1091 Paperbound **$2.75**

LIFE HISTORIES OF NORTH AMERICAN WOOD WARBLERS. Covers about 58 types. Index. Bibliography. 83 full-page plates containing 125 black-and-white photographs. xi + 734pp. of text. 5⅜ x 8½.
Vol. I: T1153 Paperbound **$2.50**
Vol. II: T1154 Paperbound **$2.50**
The set Paperbound **$5.00**

LIFE HISTORIES OF NORTH AMERICAN FLYCATCHERS, LARKS, SWALLOWS, AND THEIR ALLIES. Complete information on about 78 different varieties. Index. Bibliography. 70 full-page plates (117 photographs). xi + 555pp. of text. 5⅜ x 8½.
T1090 Paperbound **$2.75**

AMERICAN WILDLIFE, AND PLANTS: A GUIDE TO WILDLIFE FOOD HABITS, A. C. Martin, H. S. Zim, A. L. Nelson. Result of 75 years of research by U. S. Fish and Wildlife Service into food and feeding habits of more than 1,000 species of birds and mammals, their distribution in America, migratory habits, and the most important plant-animal relationships. Treats over 300 common species of birds, fur and game animals, small mammals, hoofed browsers, fish, amphibians, reptiles by group, giving data on their food, ranges, habits and economies. Also focuses on the different genera of plants that furnish food for our wildlife, animals that use them, and their value. Only thorough study of its kind in existence. "Of immense value to sportsmen, naturalists, bird students, foresters, landscape architects, botanists," NATURE. "Undoubtedly an essential handbook," SCIENTIFIC MONTHLY. Unabridged republication of 1951 edition. Over 600 illustrations, maps, etc. Classified bibliography. Index. x + 500pp. 5⅜ x 8.
T793 Paperbound **$2.25**

HOW TO KNOW THE WILD FLOWERS, Mrs. Wm. Starr Dana. A Guide to the names, haunts, and habits of wild flowers. Well-known classic of nature lore. Informative and delightful. Plants classified by color and season of their typical flowers for easy identification. Thorough coverage of more than 1,000 important flowering, berry-bearing and foliage plants of Eastern and Central United States and Canada. Complete botanical information about each important plant. Also history, uses, folklore, habitat, etc. Nomenclature modernized by C. J. Hylander. 174 full-page illustrations by Marion Satterlee. xii + 481pp. 5⅜ x 8½.
T332 Paperbound **$1.85**

HOW PLANTS GET THEIR NAMES, L. H. Bailey. Introduction to botanical nomenclature for the horticulturist and garden-lover. Discussions of Carl Linnaeus, "father of botany," and analysis of his definitions of genus and species, a brief history of the science before Linnaean systematization, a chapter on plant identification, a mine of information on the rules of nomenclature and Latin stems and word-endings used in botanical nomenclature, with pronunciation guides. An important section contains a full list of generic terms of horticultural literature and common Latin words and their English botanical applications and meanings. "Written with knowledge and authority, charm and eloquence and poetic imagination on the varied aspects of the author's specialty," New York Times. 11 illustrations. vi + 181pp. 5⅜ x 8½.
T796 Paperbound **$1.25**

THE CACTACEAE: DESCRIPTIONS AND ILLUSTRATIONS OF PLANTS OF THE CACTUS FAMILY, N. L. Britton and J. N. Rose. Definitive study of plants of the Cactus Family. The authors devoted more than 15 years of research to this monumental task and produced an exhaustive, rigorously scientific account never likely to be superseded. 3 major classifications, or tribes, are recognized, under which they arrange and describe in full detail 124 genera and 1,235 species of cactus from all over the world. Complete data on each species: leaves, flowers, seeds, fruit, distribution, growth, spines, stem structure, economic uses, etc. In addition, 125 keys facilitate identification of genera and species. For teachers and students of botany and forestry, naturalists, conservationists, and nature lovers, this is an indispensable work. Unabridged republication of second (1937) edition. First edition originally published under the auspices of the Carnegie Institution, Washington, D.C. 4 vols. bound as 2. 1279 illustrations, photographs, sketches, etc. 137 plates. Total of xxvii + 1039pp. 8 x 10¼.
T771 Clothbound, 2-volume set **$20.00**

GUIDE TO SOUTHERN TREES, Elwood S. and J. George Harrar. A handy, comprehensive 700-page manual with numerous illustrations and information on more than 350 different kinds of trees, covering the entire area south of the Mason-Dixon line from the Atlantic Ocean to the Florida Keys and western Texas. Descriptions range from the common pine, cypress, walnut, beech, and elm to such rare species as Franklinia, etc. A mine of information on leaves, flowers, twigs, bark, fruit, distribution etc. of each kind of tree. Eminently readable, written in non-technical language, it is an indispensable handbook for all lovers of the outdoors. Revised edition. Index. 81-item bibliography. Glossary. 200 full-page illustrations. ix + 709pp. 4⅝ x 6⅜.
T945 Paperbound **$2.25**

CATALOGUE OF DOVER BOOKS

WESTERN FOREST TREES, James B. Berry. For years a standard guide to the trees of the Western United States. Covers over 70 different subspecies, ranging from the Pacific shores to western South Dakota, New Mexico, etc. Much information on range and distribution, growth habits, appearance, leaves, bark, fruit, twigs, etc. for each tree discussed, plus material on wood of the trees and its uses. Basic division (Trees with needle-like leaves, scale-like leaves, and compound, lobed or divided, and simple broadleaf trees), along with almost 100 illustrations (mostly full-size) of buds, leaves, etc., aids in easy identification of just about any tree of the area. Many subsidiary keys. Revised edition. Introduction. 12 photos. 85 illustrations by Mary E. Eaton. Index. xii + 212pp. 5⅜ x 8.

T1138 Paperbound **$1.35**

MANUAL OF THE TREES OF NORTH AMERICA (EXCLUSIVE OF MEXICO), Charles Sprague Sargent. The magnum opus of the greatest American dendrologist. Based on 44 years of original research, this monumental work is still the most comprehensive and reliable sourcebook on the subject. Includes 185 genera and 717 species of trees (and many shrubs) found in the U.S., Canada, and Alaska. 783 illustrative drawings by C. E. Faxon and Mary W. Gill. An all-encompassing lifetime reference book for students, teachers of botany and forestry, naturalists, conservationists, and all nature lovers. Includes an 11-page analytical key to genera to help the beginner locate any tree by its leaf characteristics. Within the text over 100 further keys aid in easy identification. Synopsis of families. Glossary. Index. 783 illustrations, 1 map. Total of 1 + 891pp. 5⅜ x 8.

T277 Vol. I Paperbound **$2.25**
T278 Vol. II Paperbound **$2.25**
The set **$4.50**

TREES OF THE EASTERN AND CENTRAL UNITED STATES AND CANADA, W. M. Harlow, Professor of Wood Technology, College of Forestry, State University of N. Y., Syracuse, N. Y. This middle-level text is a serious work covering more than 140 native trees and important escapes, with information on general appearance, growth habit, leaf forms, flowers, fruit, bark, and other features. Commercial use, distribution, habitat, and woodlore are also given. Keys within the text enable you to locate various species with ease. With this book you can identify at sight almost any tree you are likely to encounter; you will know which trees have edible fruit, which are suitable for house planting, and much other useful and interesting information. More than 600 photographs and figures. xiii + 288pp. 4⅝ x 6½.

T395 Paperbound **$1.35**

FRUIT KEY AND TWIG KEY TO TREES AND SHRUBS (FRUIT KEY TO NORTHEASTERN TREES, TWIG TREE TO DECIDUOUS WOODY PLANTS OF EASTERN NORTH AMERICA), W. M. Harlow. The only guides with photographs of every twig and fruit described—especially valuable to the novice. The fruit key (both deciduous trees and evergreens) has an introduction explaining seeding, organs involved, fruit types and habits. The twig key introduction treats growth and morphology. In the keys proper, identification is easy and almost automatic. This exceptional work, widely used in university courses, is especially useful for identification in winter, or from the fruit or seed only. Over 350 photos, up to 3 times natural size. Bibliography, glossary, index of common and scientific names, in each key. xvii + 125pp. 5⅝ x 8⅜.

T511 Paperbound **$1.25**

HOW TO KNOW THE FERNS, F. T. Parsons. Ferns, among our most lovely native plants, are all too little known. This modern classic of nature lore will enable the layman to identify any American fern he is likely to come across. After an introduction on the structure and life of ferns, the 57 most important ferns are fully pictured and described (arranged upon a simple identification key). Index of Latin and English names. 61 illustrations and 42 full-page plates. xiv + 215pp. 5⅜ x 8.

T740 Paperbound **$1.35**

OUR SMALL NATIVE ANIMALS: THEIR HABITS AND CARE, R. Snedigar, Curator of Reptiles, Chicago Zoological Park. An unusual nature handbook containing all the vital facts of habitat, distribution, foods, and special habits in brief life histories of 114 different species of squirrels, chipmunks, rodents, larger mammals, birds, amphibians, lizards and snakes. Liberally sprinkled with first-hand anecdotes. A wealth of information on capturing and caring for these animals: proper pens and cages, correct diet, curing diseases, special equipment required, etc. Addressed to the teacher interested in classroom demonstrations, the camp director, and to anyone who ever wanted a small animal for a pet. Revised edition, New preface. Index. 62 halftones. 14 line drawings. xviii + 296pp. 5⅜ x 8⅛.

T1022 Paperbound **$1.75**

INSECT LIFE AND INSECT NATURAL HISTORY, S. W. Frost. Unusual for emphasizing habits, social life, and ecological relations of insects, rather than more academic aspects of classification and morphology. Prof. Frost's enthusiasm and knowledge are everywhere evident as he discusses insect associations, and specialized habits like leaf-mining, leaf-rolling, and case-making, the gall insects, the boring insects, aquatic insects, etc. He examines all sorts of matters not usually covered in general works, such as: insects as human food; insect music and musicians; insect response to electric and radio waves; use of insects in art and literature. The admirably executed purpose of this book, which covers the middle ground between elementary treatment and scholarly monographs, is to excite the reader to observe for himself. Over 700 illustrations. Extensive bibliography. x + 524pp. 5⅜ x 8.

T517 Paperbound **$2.25**

Dover Classical Records

Now available directly to the public exclusively from Dover: top-quality recordings of fine classical music for only $2 per record! Almost all were released by major record companies to sell for $5 and $6. These recordings were issued under our imprint only after they had passed a severe critical test. We insisted upon:

First-rate music that is enjoyable, musically important and culturally significant.

First-rate performances, where the artists have carried out the composer's intentions, in which the music is alive, vigorous, played with understanding and sensitivity.

First-rate sound—clear, sonorous, fully balanced, crackle-free, whir-free.

Have in your home music by major composers, performed by such gifted musicians as Elsner, Gitlis, Wührer, Beveridge Webster, the Barchet Quartet, Gimpel, etc. Enthusiastically received when first released, many of these performances are definitive. The records are not seconds or remainders, but brand new pressings made on pure vinyl from carefully chosen master tapes. "All purpose" 12″ monaural 33⅓ rpm records, they play equally well on hi-fi and stereo equipment. Fine music for discriminating music lovers, superlatively played, flawlessly recorded: there is no better way to build your library of recorded classical music at remarkable savings. There are no strings; this is not a come-on, not a club, forcing you to buy records you may not want in order to get a few at a lower price. Buy whatever records you want in any quantity, and never pay more than $2 each. Your obligation ends with your first purchase. And that's when ours begins. Dover's money-back guarantee allows you to return any record for any reason, even if you don't like the music, for a full, immediate refund—no questions asked.

MOZART: STRING QUARTETS: IN A (K. 464) AND C ("DISSONANT") (K. 465), Barchet Quartet. The final two of the famous Haydn Quartets, high-points in the history of music. The A Major was accepted with delight by Mozart's contemporaries, but the C Major, with its dissonant opening, aroused strong protest. Today, of course, the remarkable resolutions of the dissonances are recognized as major musical achievements. "Beautiful warm playing," MUSICAL AMERICA. "Two of Mozart's loveliest quartets in a distinguished performance," REV. OF RECORDED MUSIC. (Playing time 58 mins.)   HCR 5200 **$2.00**

MOZART: STRING QUARTETS: IN G (K. 80), D (K. 156), and C (K. 157), Barchet Quartet. The early chamber music of Mozart receives unfortunately little attention. First-rate music of the Italian school, it contains all the lightness and charm that belongs only to the youthful Mozart. This is currently the only separate source for the composer's work of this period. "Excellent," HIGH FIDELITY. "Filled with sunshine and youthful joy; played with verve, recorded sound live and brilliant," CHRISTIAN SCI. MONITOR. (playing time 51 mins.)
                                                                HCR 5201 **$2.00**

MOZART: SERENADES: #9 IN D ("POSTHORN") (K. 320), #6 IN D ("SERENATA NOTTURNA") (K. 239), Pro Musica Orch. of Stuttgart, under Edouard van Remoortel. For Mozart, the serenade was a highly effective form, since he could bring to it the immediacy and intimacy of chamber music as well as the free fantasy of larger group music. Both these serenades are distinguished by a playful, mischievous quality, a spirit perfectly captured in this fine performance. "A triumph, polished playing from the orchestra," HI FI MUSIC AT HOME. "Sound is rich and resonant, fidelity is wonderful," REV. OF RECORDED MUSIC. (Playing time 51 mins.)   HCR 5202 **$2.00**

MOZART: DIVERTIMENTO FOR VIOLIN, VIOLA AND CELLO IN E FLAT (K. 563); ADAGIO AND FUGUE IN F MINOR (K. 404a), Kehr Trio. The divertimento is one of Mozart's most beloved pieces, called by Einstein "the finest and most perfect trio ever heard." It is difficult to imagine a music lover who will not be delighted by it. This is the only recording of the lesser known Adagio and Fugue, written in 1782 and influenced by Bach's Well-Tempered Clavichord. "Extremely beautiful recording, strongly recommended," THE OBSERVER. "Superior to rival editions," HIGH FIDELITY. (Playing time 51 mins.)   HCR 5203 **$2.00**

SCHUMANN: KREISLERIANA (OPUS 16) AND FANTASIA IN C (OPUS 17), Vlado Perlemuter, Piano. The vigorous Romantic imagination and the remarkable emotional qualities of Schumann's piano music raise it to a special eminence in 19th-century creativity. Both these pieces are rooted to the composer's tortuous romance with his future wife, Clara, and both receive brilliant treatment at the hands of Vlado Perlemuter, Paris Conservatory, proclaimed by Alfred Cortot "not only a great virtuoso but also a great musician." "The best Kreisleriana to date," BILLBOARD. (Playing time 55 mins.)   HCR 5204 **$2.00**

CATALOGUE OF DOVER BOOKS

SCHUMANN: TRIOS #1 IN D MINOR (OPUS 63) AND #3 IN G MINOR (OPUS 110), Trio di Bolzano. The fiery, romantic, melodic Trio #1 and the dramatic, seldom heard Trio #3 are both movingly played by a fine chamber ensemble. No one personified Romanticism to the general public of the 1840's more than did Robert Schumann, and among his most romantic works are these trios for cello, violin and piano. "Ensemble and overall interpretation leave little to be desired," HIGH FIDELITY. "An especially understanding performance," REV. OF RECORDED MUSIC. (Playing time 54 mins.)   **HCR 5205 $2.00**

SCHUBERT: QUINTET IN A ("TROUT") (OPUS 114), AND NOCTURNE IN E FLAT (OPUS 148), Friedrich Wührer, Piano and Barchet Quartet. If there is a single piece of chamber music that is a universal favorite, it is probably Schubert's "Trout" Quintet. Delightful melody, harmonic resources, musical exuberance are its characteristics. The Nocturne (played by Wührer, Barchet, and Reimann) is an exquisite piece with a deceptively simple theme and harmony. "The best Trout on the market—Wührer is a fine Viennese-style Schubertian, and his spirit infects the Barchets," ATLANTIC MONTHLY. "Exquisitely recorded," ETUDE. (Playing time 44 mins.)   **HCR 5206 $2.00**

SCHUBERT: PIANO SONATAS IN C MINOR AND B (OPUS 147), Friedrich Wührer. Schubert's sonatas retain the structure of the classical form, but delight listeners with romantic freedom and a special melodic richness. The C Minor, one of the Three Grand Sonatas, is a product of the composer's maturity. The B Major was not published until 15 years after his death. "Remarkable interpretation, reproduction of the first rank," DISQUES. "A superb pianist for music like this, musicianship, sweep, power, and an ability to integrate Schubert's measures such as few pianists have had since Schnabel," Harold Schonberg. (Playing time 49 mins.)   **HCR 5207 $2.00**

STRAVINSKY: VIOLIN CONCERTO IN D, Ivry Gitlis, Cologne Orchestra; DUO CONCERTANTE, Ivry Gitlis, Violin, Charlotte Zelka, Piano, Cologne Orchestra; JEU DE CARTES, Bamberg Symphony, under Hollreiser. Igor Stravinsky is probably the most important composer of this century, and these three works are among the most significant of his neoclassical period of the 30's. The Violin Concerto is one of the few modern classics. Jeu de Cartes, a ballet score, bubbles with gaiety, color and melodiousness. "Imaginatively played and beautifully recorded," E. T. Canby, HARPERS MAGAZINE. "Gitlis is excellent, Hollreiser beautifully worked out," HIGH FIDELITY. (Playing time 55 mins.)   **HCR 5208 $2.00**

GEMINIANI: SIX CONCERTI GROSSI, OPUS 3, Helma Elsner, Harpsichord, Barchet Quartet, Pro Musica Orch. of Stuttgart, under Reinhardt. Francesco Geminiani (1687-1762) has been rediscovered in the same musical exploration that revealed Scarlatti, Vivaldi, and Corelli. In form he is more sophisticated than the earlier Italians, but his music delights modern listeners with its combination of contrapuntal techniques and the full harmonies and rich melodies charcteristic of Italian music. This is the only recording of the six 1733 concerti: D Major, B Flat Minor, E Minor, G Minor, E Minor (bis), and D Minor. "I warmly recommend it, spacious, magnificent, I enjoyed every bar," C. Cudworth, RECORD NEWS. "Works of real charm, recorded with understanding and style," ETUDE. (Playing time 52 mins.)   **HCR 5209 $2.00**

MODERN PIANO SONATAS: BARTOK: SONATA FOR PIANO; BLOCH: SONATA FOR PIANO (1935); PROKOFIEV, PIANO SONATA #7 IN B FLAT ("STALINGRAD"); STRAVINSKY: PIANO SONATA (1924), István Nádas, Piano. Shows some of the major forces and directions in modern piano music: Stravinsky's crisp austerity; Bartok's fusion of Hungarian folk motives; incisive diverse rhythms, and driving power; Bloch's distinctive emotional vigor; Prokofiev's brilliance and melodic beauty couched in pre-Romantic forms. "A most interesting documentation of the contemporary piano sonata. Nadas is a very good pianist." HIGH FIDELITY. (Playing time 59 mins.)   **HCR 5215 $2.00**

VIVALDI: CONCERTI FOR FLUTE, VIOLIN, BASSOON, AND HARPSICHORD: #8 IN G MINOR, #21 IN F, #27 IN D, #7 IN D; SONATA #1 IN A MINOR, Gastone Tassinari, Renato Giangrandi, Giorgio Semprini, Arlette Eggmann. More than any other Baroque composer, Vivaldi moved the concerto grosso closer to the solo concert we deem standard today. In these concerti he wrote virtuosi music for the solo instruments, allowing each to introduce new material or expand on musical ideas, creating tone colors unusual even for Vivaldi. As a result, this record displays a new area of his genius, offering some of his most brilliant music. Performed by a top-rank European group. (Playing time 45 mins.)   **HCR 5216 $2.00**

LÜBECK: CANTATAS: HILF DEINEM VOLK; GOTT, WIE DEIN NAME, Stuttgart Choral Society, Swabian Symphony Orch.; PRELUDES AND FUGUES IN C MINOR AND IN E, Eva Hölderlin, Organ. Vincent Lübeck (1654-1740), contemporary of Bach and Buxtehude, was one of the great figures of the 18th-century North German school. These examples of Lübeck's few surviving works indicate his power and brilliance. Voice and instrument lines in the cantatas are strongly reminiscent of the organ: the preludes and fugues show the influence of Bach and Buxtehude. This is the only recording of the superb cantatas. Text and translation included. "Outstanding record," E. T. Canby, SAT. REVIEW. "Hölderlin's playing is exceptional," AM. RECORD REVIEW. "Will make [Lübeck] many new friends," Philip Miller. (Playing time 37 mins.)   **HCR 5217 $2.00**

CATALOGUE OF DOVER BOOKS

DONIZETTI, BETLY (LA CAPANNA SVIZZERA), Soloists of Compagnia del Teatro dell'Opera Comica di Roma, Societa del Quartetto, Rome, Chorus and Orch. Betly, a delightful one-act opera written in 1836, is similar in style and story to one of Donizetti's better-known operas, L'Elisir. Betly is lighthearted and farcical, with bright melodies and a freshness character-istic of the best of Donizetti. Libretto (English and Italian) included. "The chief honors go to Angela Tuccari who sings the title role, and the record is worth having for her alone," M. Rayment, GRAMOPHONE REC. REVIEW. "The interpretation . . . is excellent . . . This is a charming record which we recommend to lovers of little-known works," DISQUES.
HCR 5218 **$2.00**

ROSSINI: L'OCCASIONE FA IL LADRO (IL CAMBIO DELLA VALIGIA), Soloists of Compagnia del Teatro dell'Opera Comica di Roma, Societa del Quartetto, Rome, Chorus and Orch. A charm-ing one-act opera buffa, this is one of the first works of Rossini's maturity, and it is filled with the wit, gaiety and sparkle that make his comic operas second only to Mozart's. Like other Rossini works, L'Occasione makes use of the theme of impersonation and attendant amusing confusions. This is the only recording of this important buffa. Full libretto (English and Italian) included. "A major rebirth, a stylish performance . . . the Roman recording engineers have outdone themselves," H. Weinstock, SAT. REVIEW. (Playing time 53 mins.)
HCR 5219 **$2.00**

DOWLAND: "FIRST BOOKE OF AYRES," Pro Musica Antiqua of Brussels, Safford Cape, Director. This is the first recording to include all 22 of the songs of this great collection, written by John Dowland, one of the most important writers of songs of 16th and 17th century Eng-land. The participation of the Brussels Pro Musica under Safford Cape insures scholarly ac-curacy and musical artistry. "Powerfully expressive and very beautiful," B. Haggin. "The musicianly singers . . . never fall below an impressive standard," Philip Miller. Text included. (Playing time 51 mins.)
HCR 5220 **$2.00**

FRENCH CHANSONS AND DANCES OF THE 16TH CENTURY, Pro Musica Antiqua of Brussels, Safford Cape, Director. A remarkable selection of 26 three- or four-part chansons and de-lightful dances from the French Golden Age—by such composers as Orlando Lasso, Crecquil-lon, Claude Gervaise, etc. Text and translation included. "Delightful, well-varied with respect to mood and to vocal and instrumental color," HIGH FIDELITY. "Performed with . . . dis-crimination and musical taste, full of melodic distinction and harmonic resource," Irving Kolodin. (Playing time 39 mins.)
HCR 5221 **$2.00**

GALUPPI: CONCERTI A QUATRO: #1 IN G MINOR, #2 IN G, #3 IN D, #4 IN C MINOR, #5 IN E FLAT, AND #6 IN B FLAT, Biffoli Quartet. During Baldassare Galuppi's lifetime, his instru-mental music was widely renowned, and his contemporaries Mozart and Haydn thought highly of his work. These 6 concerti reflect his great ability; and they are among the most interesting compositions of the period. They are remarkable for their unusual combinations of timbres and for emotional elements that were only then beginning to be introduced into music. Performed by the well-known Biffoli Quartet, this is the only record devoted exclu-sively to Galuppi. (Playing time 47 mins.)
HCR 5222 **$2.00**

HAYDN: DIVERTIMENTI FOR WIND BAND, IN C; IN F; DIVERTIMENTO A NOVE STROMENTI IN C FOR STRINGS AND WIND INSTRUMENTS, reconstructed by H. C. Robbins Landon, performed by members of Vienna State Opera Orch.; **MOZART DIVERTIMENTI IN C, III (K. 187) AND IV (K. 188), Salzburg Wind Ensemble.** Robbins Landon discovered Haydn manuscripts in a Bene-dictine monastery in Lower Austria, edited them and restored their original instrumentation The result is this magnificent record. Two little-known divertimenti by Mozart—of great charm and appeal—are also included. None of this music is available elsewhere (Playing time 58 mins.)
HCR 5223 **$2.00**

PURCELL: TRIO SONATAS FROM "SONATAS OF FOUR PARTS" (1697): #9 IN F ("GOLDEN"), #7 IN C, #1 IN B MINOR, #10 IN D, #4 IN D MINOR, #2 IN E FLAT, AND #8 IN G MINOR, Giorgio Ciompi, and Werner Torkanowsky, Violins, Geo. Koutzen, Cello, and Herman Chessid, Harpsichord. These posthumously-published sonatas show Purcell at his most advanced and mature. They are certainly among the finest musical examples of pre-modern chamber music. Those not familiar with his instrumental music are well-advised to hear these outstanding pieces. "Performance sounds excellent," Harold Schonberg. "Some of the most noble and touching music known to anyone," AMERICAN RECORD GUIDE. (Playing time 58 mins.)
HCR 5224 **$2.00**

BARTOK: VIOLIN CONCERTO; SONATA FOR UNACCOMPANIED VIOLIN, Ivry Gitlis, Pro Musica of Vienna, under Hornstein. Both these works are outstanding examples of Bartok's final period, and they show his powers at their fullest. The Violin Concerto is, in the opinion of many authorities, Bartok's finest work, and the Sonata, his last work, is "a masterpiece" (F. Sackville West). "Wonderful, finest performance of both Bartok works I have ever heard," GRAMOPHONE. "Gitlis makes such potent and musical sense out of these works that I suspect many general music lovers (not otherwise in sympathy with modern music) will discover to their amazement that they like it. Exceptionally good sound," AUDITOR. (Playing time 54 mins.)
HCR 5211 **$2.00**

Social Sciences

SOCIAL THOUGHT FROM LORE TO SCIENCE, H. E. Barnes and H. Becker. An immense survey of sociological thought and ways of viewing, studying, planning, and reforming society from earliest times to the present. Includes thought on society of preliterate peoples, ancient non-Western cultures, and every great movement in Europe, America, and modern Japan. Analyzes hundreds of great thinkers: Plato, Augustine, Bodin, Vico, Montesquieu, Herder, Comte, Marx, etc. Weighs the contributions of utopians, sophists, fascists and communists; economists, jurists, philosophers, ecclesiastics, and every 19th and 20th century school of scientific sociology, anthropology, and social psychology throughout the world. Combines topical, chronological, and regional approaches, treating the evolution of social thought as a process rather than as a series of mere topics. "Impressive accuracy, competence, and discrimination . . . easily the best single survey," Nation. Thoroughly revised, with new material up to 1960. 2 indexes. Over 2200 bibliographical notes. Three volume set. Total of 1586pp. 5⅜ x 8.

T901 Vol I Paperbound **$2.50**
T902 Vol II Paperbound **$2.50**
T903 Vol III Paperbound **$2.35**
The set **$7.35**

FOLKWAYS, William Graham Sumner. A classic of sociology, a searching and thorough examination of patterns of behaviour from primitive, ancient Greek and Judaic, Medieval Christian, African, Oriental, Melanesian, Australian, Islamic, to modern Western societies. Thousands of illustrations of social, sexual, and religious customs, mores, laws, and institutions. Hundreds of categories: Labor, Wealth, Abortion, Primitive Justice, Life Policy, Slavery, Cannibalism, Uncleanness and the Evil Eye, etc. Will extend the horizon of every reader by showing the relativism of his own culture. Prefatory note by A. G. Keller. Introduction by William Lyon Phelps. Bibliography. Index. xiii + 692pp. 5⅜ x 8. T508 Paperbound **$2.49**

PRIMITIVE RELIGION, P. Radin. A thorough treatment by a noted anthropologist of the nature and origin of man's belief in the supernatural and the influences that have shaped religious expression in primitive societies. Ranging from the Arunta, Ashanti, Aztec, Bushman, Crow, Fijian, etc., of Africa, Australia, Pacific Islands, the Arctic, North and South America, Prof. Radin integrates modern psychology, comparative religion, and economic thought with first-hand accounts gathered by himself and other scholars of primitive initiations, training of the shaman, and other fascinating topics. "Excellent," NATURE (London). Unabridged reissue of 1st edition. New author's preface. Bibliographic notes. Index. x + 322pp. 5⅜ x 8.
T393 Paperbound **$1.85**

PRIMITIVE MAN AS PHILOSOPHER, P. Radin. A standard anthropological work covering primitive thought on such topics as the purpose of life, marital relations, freedom of thought, symbolism, death, resignation, the nature of reality, personality, gods, and many others. Drawn from factual material gathered from the Winnebago, Oglala Sioux, Maori, Baganda, Batak, Zuni, among others, it does not distort ideas by removing them from context but interprets strictly within the original framework. Extensive selections of original primitive documents. Bibliography. Index. xviii + 402pp. 5⅜ x 8. T392 Paperbound **$2.25**

A TREATISE ON SOCIOLOGY, THE MIND AND SOCIETY, Vilfredo Pareto. This treatise on human society is one of the great classics of modern sociology. First published in 1916, its careful catalogue of the innumerable manifestations of non-logical human conduct (Book One); the theory of "residues," leading to the premise that sentiment not logic determines human behavior (Book Two), and of "derivations," beliefs derived from desires (Book Three); and the general description of society made up of non-elite and elite, consisting of "foxes" who live by cunning and "lions" who live by force, stirred great controversy. But Pareto's passion for isolation and classification of elements and factors, and his allegiance to scientific method as the key tool for scrutinizing the human situation made his a truly twentieth-century mind and his work a catalytic influence on certain later social commentators. These four volumes (bound as two) require no special training to be appreciated and any reader who wishes to gain a complete understanding of modern sociological theory, regardless of special field of interest, will find them a must. Reprint of revised (corrected) printing of original edition. Translated by Andrew Bongiorno and Arthur Livingston. Index. Bibliography. Appendix containing index-summary of theorems. 48 diagrams. Four volumes bound as two. Total of 2063pp. 5⅜ x 8½. The set Clothbound **$15.00**

THE POLISH PEASANT IN EUROPE AND AMERICA, William I. Thomas, Florian Znaniecki. A seminal sociological study of peasant primary groups (family and community) and the disruptions produced by a new industrial system and immigration to America. The peasant's family, class system, religious and aesthetic attitudes, and economic life are minutely examined and analyzed in hundreds of pages of primary documentation, particularly letters between family members. The disorientation caused by new environments is scrutinized in detail (a 312-page autobiography of an immigrant is especially valuable and revealing) in an attempt to find common experiences and reactions. The famous "Methodological Note" sets forth the principles which guided the authors. When out of print this set has sold for as much as $50. 2nd revised edition. 2 vols. Vol. 1: xv + 1115pp. Vol. 2: 1135pp. Index. 6 x 9.
T478 Clothbound 2 vol. set **$12.50**

New Books

101 PATCHWORK PATTERNS, Ruby Short McKim. With no more ability than the fundamentals of ordinary sewing, you will learn to make over 100 beautiful quilts: flowers, rainbows, Irish chains, fish and bird designs, leaf designs, unusual geometric patterns, many others. Cutting designs carefully diagrammed and described, suggestions for materials, yardage estimates, step-by-step instructions, plus entertaining stories of origins of quilt names, other folklore. Revised 1962. 101 full-sized patterns. 140 illustrations. Index. 128pp. 7⅞ x 10¾.
T773 Paperbound **$1.85**

ESSENTIAL GRAMMAR SERIES
By concentrating on the essential core of material that constitutes the semantically most important forms and areas of a language and by stressing explanation (often bringing parallel English forms into the discussion) rather than rote memory, this new series of grammar books is among the handiest language aids ever devised. Designed by linguists and teachers for adults with limited learning objectives and learning time, these books omit nothing important, yet they teach more usable language material and do it more quickly and permanently than any other self-study material. Clear and rigidly economical, they concentrate upon immediately usable language material, logically organized so that related material is always presented together. Any reader of typical capability can use them to refresh his grasp of language, to supplement self-study language records or conventional grammars used in schools, or to begin language study on his own. Now available:

ESSENTIAL GERMAN GRAMMAR, Dr. Guy Stern & E. F. Bleiler. Index. Glossary of terms. 128pp. 5⅜ x 8.
T422 Paperbound **$1.00**

ESSENTIAL FRENCH GRAMMAR, Dr. Seymour Resnick. Index. Cognate list. Glossary. 159pp. 5⅜ x 8.
T419 Paperbound **$1.00**

ESSENTIAL ITALIAN GRAMMAR, Dr. Olga Ragusa. Index. Glossary. 111pp. 5⅜ x 8.
T779 Paperbound **$1.00**

ESSENTIAL SPANISH GRAMMAR, Dr. Seymour Resnick. Index. 50-page cognate list. Glossary. 138pp. 5⅜ x 8.
T780 Paperbound **$1.00**

PHILOSOPHIES OF MUSIC HISTORY: A Study of General Histories of Music, 1600-1960, Warren D. Allen. Unquestionably one of the most significant documents yet to appear in musicology, this thorough survey covers the entire field of historical research in music. An influential masterpiece of scholarship, it includes early music histories; theories on the ethos of music; lexicons, dictionaries and encyclopedias of music; musical historiography through the centuries; philosophies of music history; scores of related topics. Copiously documented. New preface brings work up to 1960. Index. 317-item bibliography. 9 illustrations; 3 full-page plates. 5⅜ x 8½. xxxiv + 382pp.
T282 Paperbound **$2.00**

MR. DOOLEY ON IVRYTHING AND IVRYBODY, Finley Peter Dunne. The largest collection in print of hilarious utterances by the irrepressible Irishman of Archey Street, one of the most vital characters in American fiction. Gathered from the half dozen books that appeared during the height of Mr. Dooley's popularity, these 102 pieces are all unaltered and uncut, and they are all remarkably fresh and pertinent even today. Selected and edited by Robert Hutchinson. 5⅜ x 8½. xii + 244p.
T626 Paperbound **$1.00**

TREATISE ON PHYSIOLOGICAL OPTICS, Hermann von Helmholtz. Despite new investigations, this important work will probably remain preeminent. Contains everything known about physiological optics up to 1925, covering scores of topics under the general headings of dioptrics of the eye, sensations of vision, and perecptions of vision. Von Helmholtz's voluminous data are all included, as are extensive supplementary matter incorporated into the third German edition, new material prepared for 1925 English edition, and copious textual annotations by J. P. C. Southall. The most exhaustive treatise ever prepared on the subject, it has behind it a list of contributors that will never again be duplicated. Translated and edited by J. P. C. Southall. Bibliography. Indexes. 312 illustrations. 3 volumes bound as 2. Total of 1749pp. 5⅜ x 8.
S15-16 Two volume set, Clothbound **$15.00**

THE ARTISTIC ANATOMY OF TREES, Rex Vicat Cole. Even the novice with but an elementary knowledge of drawing and none of the structure of trees can learn to draw, paint trees from this systematic, lucid instruction book. Copiously illustrated with the author's own sketches, diagrams, and 50 paintings from the early Renaissance to today, it covers composition; structure of twigs, boughs, buds, branch systems; outline forms of major species; how leaf is set on twig; flowers and fruit and their arrangement; etc. 500 illustrations. Bibliography. Indexes. 347pp. 5⅜ x 8.
T1016 Clothbound **$4.50**

HOW PLANTS GET THEIR NAMES, L. H. Bailey. In this basic introduction to botanical nomenclature, a famed expert on plants and plant life reveals the confusion that can result from misleading common names of plants and points out the fun and advantage of using a sound, scientific approach. Covers every aspect of the subject, including an historical survey beginning before Linnaeus systematized nomenclature, the literal meaning of scores of Latin names, their English equivalents, etc. Enthusiastically written and easy to follow, this handbook for gardeners, amateur horticulturalists, and beginning botany students is knowledgeable, accurate and useful. 11 illustrations. Lists of Latin, English botanical names. 192pp. 5⅜ x 8½.
T796 Paperbound **$1.15**

PIERRE CURIE, Marie Curie. Nobel Prize winner creates a memorable portrait of her equally famous husband in a fine scientific biography. Recounting his childhood, his haphazard education, and his experimental research (with his brother) in the physics of crystals, Mme. Curie brings to life the strong, determined personality of a great scientist at work and discusses, in clear, straightforward terms, her husband's and her own work with radium and radioactivity. A great book about two very great founders of modern science. Includes Mme. Curie's autobiographical notes. Translated by Charlotte and Vernon Kellogg. viii + 120pp. 5⅜ x 8½.
T199 Paperbound **$1.00**

STYLES IN PAINTING: A Comparative Study, Paul Zucker. Professor of Art History at Cooper Union presents an important work of art-understanding that will guide you to a fuller, deeper appreciation of masterpieces of art and at the same time add to your understanding of how they fit into the evolution of style from the earliest times to this century. Discusses general principles of historical method and aesthetics, history of styles, then illustrates with more than 230 great paintings organized by subject matter so you can see at a glance how styles have changed through the centuries. 236 beautiful halftones. xiv + 338pp. 5⅝ x 8½.
T760 Paperbound **$2.00**

NEW VARIORUM EDITION OF SHAKESPEARE
One of the monumental feats of Shakespeare scholarship is the famous New Variorum edition, containing full texts of the plays together with an entire reference library worth of historical and critical information: all the variant readings that appear in the quartos and folios; annotations by leading scholars from the earliest days of Shakespeare criticism to the date of publication; essays on meaning, background, productions by Johnson, Addison, Fielding, Lessing, Hazlitt, Coleridge, Ulrici, Swinburne, and other major Shakespeare critics; original sources of Shakespeare's inspiration. For the first time, this definitive edition of Shakespeare's plays, each printed in a separate volume, will be available in inexpensive editions to scholars, to teachers and students, and to every lover of Shakespeare and fine literature. Now ready:

KING LEAR, edited by Horace Howard Furness. Bibliography. List of editions collated in notes. viii + 503pp. 5⅜ x 8½.
T1000 Paperbound **$2.25**

MACBETH, edited by Horace Howard Furness Jr. Bibliography. List of editions collated in notes. xvi + 562pp. 5⅜ x 8½.
T1001 Paperbound **$2.25**

ROMEO AND JULIET, edited by Horace Howard Furness. Bibliography. List of editions collated in notes. xxvi + 480pp. 5⅜ x 8½.
T1002 Paperbound **$2.25**

OTHELLO, edited by Horace Howard Furness. Bibliography. List of editions collated in notes. x + 471pp. 5⅜ x 8½.
T1003 Paperbound **$2.25**

HAMLET, edited by Horace Howard Furness. Bibliography. List of editions collated in notes. Total of 926pp. 5⅜ x 8½.
T1004-1005 Two volume set, Paperbound **$4.50**

THE GARDENER'S YEAR, Karel Capek. The author of this refreshingly funny book is probably best known in U. S. as the author of "R. U. R.," a biting satire on the machine age. Here, his satiric genius finds expression in a wholly different vein: a warm, witty chronicle of the joys and trials of the amateur gardener as he watches over his plants, his soil and the weather from January to December. 59 drawings by Joseph Capek add an important second dimension to the fun. "Mr. Capek writes with sympathy, understanding and humor," NEW YORK TIMES. "Will delight the amateur gardener, and indeed everyone else," SATURDAY REVIEW. Translated by M. and R. Weatherall. 59 illustrations. 159pp. 4½ x 6½.
T1014 Paperbound **$1.00**

THE ADVANCE OF THE FUNGI, E. C. Large. The dramatic story of the battle against fungi, from the year the potato blight hit Europe (1845) to 1940, and of men who fought and won it: Pasteur, Anton de Bary, Tulasne, Berkeley, Woronin, Jensen, many others. Combines remarkable grasp of facts and their significance with skill to write dramatic, exciting prose. "Philosophically witty, fundamentally thoughtful, always mature," NEW YORK HERALD TRIBUNE. "Highly entertaining, intelligent, penetrating," NEW YORKER. Bibliography. 64 illustrations. 6 full-page plates. 488pp. 5⅜ x 8½.
T437 Paperbound **$2.25**

THE PAINTER'S METHODS AND MATERIALS, A. P. Laurie. Adviser to the British Royal Academy discusses the ills that paint is heir to and the methods most likely to counteract them. Examining 48 masterpieces by Fra Lippo Lippi, Millais, Boucher, Rembrandt, Romney, Van Eyck, Velazquez, Michaelangelo, Botticelli, Frans Hals, Turner, and others, he tries to discover how special and unique effects were achieved. Not conjectural information, but certain and authoritative. Beautiful, sharp reproductions, plus textual illustrations of apparatus and the results of experiments with pigments and media. 63 illustrations and diagrams. Index. 250pp. 5⅜ x 8.
T1019 Clothbound **$3.75**

CATALOGUE OF DOVER BOOKS

GEOMETRY OF FOUR DIMENSIONS, H. P. Manning. Unique in English as a clear, concise introduction to this fascinating subject. Treatment is primarily synthetic and Euclidean, although
hyperplanes and hyperspheres at infinity are considered by non-Euclidean forms. Historical
introduction and foundations of 4-dimensional geometry; perpendicularity; simple angles;
angles of planes; higher order; symmetry; order, motion; hyperpyramids, hypercones, hyperspheres; figures with parallel elements; volume, hypervolume in space; regular polyhedroids.
Glossary of terms. 74 illustrations. ix + 348pp. 5⅜ x 8.   S182 Paperbound **$2.00**

PAPER FOLDING FOR BEGINNERS, W. D. Murray and F. J. Rigney. A delightful introduction to
the varied and entertaining Japanese art of origami (paper folding), with a full, crystal-clear
text that anticipates every difficulty; over 275 clearly labeled diagrams of all important stages
in creation. You get results at each stage, since complex figures are logically developed from
simpler ones. 43 different pieces are explained: sailboats, frogs, roosters, etc. 6 photographic
plates. 279 diagrams. 95pp. 5⅝ x 8⅜.   T713 Paperbound **$1.00**

SATELLITES AND SCIENTIFIC RESEARCH, D. King-Hele. An up-to-the-minute non-technical account of the man-made satellites and the discoveries they have yielded up to September of
1961. Brings together information hitherto published only in hard-to-get scientific journals. Includes the life history of a typical satellite, methods of tracking, new information on the
shape of the earth, zones of radiation, etc. Over 60 diagrams and 6 photographs. Mathematical appendix. Bibliography of over 100 items. Index. xii + 180pp. 5⅜ x 8½.
                                                              T703 Paperbound **$2.00**

LOUIS PASTEUR, S. J. Holmes. A brief, very clear, and warmly understanding biography of the
great French scientist by a former Professor of Zoology in the University of California. Traces
his home life, the fortunate effects of his education, his early researches and first theses, and
his constant struggle with superstition and institutionalism in his work on microorganisms,
fermentation, anthrax, rabies, etc. New preface by the author. 159pp. 5⅜ x 8.
                                                              T197 Paperbound **$1.00**

THE ENJOYMENT OF CHESS PROBLEMS, K. S. Howard. A classic treatise on this minor art by
an internationally recognized authority that gives a basic knowledge of terms and themes for
the everyday chess player as well as the problem fan: 7 chapters on the two-mover; 7 more
on 3- and 4-move problems; a chapter on selfmates; and much more. "The most important
one-volume contribution originating solely in the U.S.A.," Alain White. 200 diagrams. Index.
Solutions, viii + 212pp. 5⅜ x 8.   T742 Paperbound **$1.25**

SAM LOYD AND HIS CHESS PROBLEMS, Alain C. White. Loyd was (for all practical purposes)
the father of the American chess problem and his protégé and successor presents here the
diamonds of his production, chess problems embodying a whimsy and bizarre fancy entirely
unique. More than 725 in all, ranging from two-move to extremely elaborate five-movers,
including Loyd's contributions to chess oddities—problems in which pieces are arranged to
form initials, figures, other by-paths of chess problem found nowhere else. Classified according to major concept, with full text analyzing problems, containing selections from Loyd's
own writings. A classic to challenge your ingenuity, increase your skill. Corrected republication of 1913 edition. Over 750 diagrams and illustrations. 744 problems with solutions.
471pp. 5⅜ x 8½.   T928 Paperbound **$2.25**

FABLES IN SLANG & MORE FABLES IN SLANG, George Ade. 2 complete books of major
American humorist in pungent colloquial tradition of Twain, Billings. 1st reprinting in over
30 years includes "The Two Mandolin Players and the Willing Performer," "The Base Ball
Fan Who Took the Only Known Cure," "The Slim Girl Who Tried to Keep a Date that was
Never Made," 42 other tales of eccentric, perverse, but always funny characters. "Touch
of genius," H. L. Mencken. New introduction by E. F. Bleiler. 86 illus. 208pp. 5⅜ x 8.
                                                              T533 Paperbound **$1.00**

Prices subject to change without notice.

*Dover publishes books on art, music, philosophy, literature, languages, history, social
sciences, psychology, handcrafts, orientalia, puzzles and entertainments, chess, pets
and gardens, books explaining science, intermediate and higher mathematics, mathematical physics, engineering, biological sciences, earth sciences; classics of science, etc.
Write to:*

                                        Dept. catrr.
                                        Dover Publications, Inc.
                                        180 Varick Street, N. Y. 14, N. Y.